## Also by Meyer Levin

# EVA

by

## Meyer Levin

SIMON AND SCHUSTER · NEW YORK · 1959

LIBRARY OF CONGRESS CATALOG CARD NUMBER: 59-11198
MANUFACTURED IN THE UNITED STATES OF AMERICA
BY AMERICAN BOOK-STRATFORD PRESS, NEW YORK, N. Y.

*To I., who lived this story.*

P ERHAPS YOU WILL be the one to live," my mother said. "Then, Eva, if you live, you must write it all down, how you lived, and what happened to all of us, so it will be known. You must write down everything exactly as it was."

It seems to me now that she is still saying those words to me, and I am still standing by the door, but I am already not myself. I am some strange, clumsy Ukrainian peasant girl named Katarina. Katarina can walk away from this house, but I, Eva, cannot leave. Katarina has the same bright cheeks that Eva always had, the firm bright-red cheeks bursting with life, the cheeks everyone had to stop and pinch—they just couldn't help themselves, they said— when she was a little girl. Grown men would bend down to pinch them, and, of course, every mama in the town. Whether Eva was marching to school, or running errands, or bossing her band of playmates, nobody could resist stopping her. Even the town notary, Mr. Novick, who wore a pince-nez, would stoop down, exclaiming, "Ah, Eva, what cheeks! What life! What health! Like a real Ukrainian peasant!" And he would give them a little pinch, and she could see his golden cuff links.

So on this day Eva, with the same red cheeks, and her black hair combed down around her face, peasant style, Eva in a broad peasant skirt, holding her handbag containing her false identity papers, Eva was now Katarina, and that was why she would be able in the next moment to turn her back and leave the house, to try to slip, alone, into the world where life was allowed.

I know that I must not feel guilt for it, that life demanded it, that my mother, who still at that moment had the strength and power of life in her, demanded it. I know that Mama sent me out. She sent me out to live. And yet that moment is frozen, as though I still might never take the decision to walk out and leave them to wait there for their fate.

And it is as though my family can be released from their eternal anxious waiting only after I have come home and told them what happened to me in that whole long adventure outside, just as on the nights when I first began going out with boys, and if I was out late, I knew that my mother and father were lying awake waiting, and only after they heard me come home would they put out their light and turn to sleep.

It is surely not there in our town of Hrebenko that they might be eternally waiting, and yet it is there that I see them in that house, as I am leaving. It is not our own house, with the candy store downstairs and the three fine flats with bathrooms upstairs, the house that Papa managed to put up right near the courthouse square, putting it up floor by floor as he paid off the debts on the first story so he could borrow money for the second. But then the Russians came, in the summer of 1939, and took over our side of Poland, and took over Papa's store.

And two summers later, just after my high-school graduation, the Germans came and drove out the Russians, and then they took over Papa's house, and drove us back to the old Jewish neighborhood behind St. Stephen's church, where I had lived as a little girl.

The Blumenfelds took us in, giving us their living room. Their house had always been a second home to me, because Alla Blumenfeld was my twin, born on the same day—on New Year's Day! And her older sister Freda was the same age as my sister Tauba. The four of us had started to school together on the same day, because we younger ones wouldn't let the two older ones go without us. We had stayed together right through, always in the same class.

So the Blumenfelds took us in. They had a piano and works of art in their living room, where we put our bedding; Mr. Blumenfeld was an "advanced" person; he had been the first to install a telephone, to own a radio. His daughters were the first two girls in town to own a bicycle, and Tauba and I were the next.

It was from the Blumenfeld's house that Tauba was taken. She was taken in the third *aktione*, the third raid on the Jews of Hrebenko, when she ran out into the street to try to help four little girls get home. She was scooped up with the four little girls.

That was when the decision was made that I must leave. For some days we were stunned, and then Mother's resoluteness returned. "We cannot all sit here and wait to die," she said. "Eva, you must go out."

The way had already been whispered about. To try to go as a Christian, as a voluntary worker, through the Arbeitsamt into Germany itself. The older people could not hope to do it. But a young girl might succeed.

At first I refused. Now, more than ever, I could not leave them. But Mother would not listen to me. "Eva, I tell you, you must go."

Then I said I would try to go if I could take along my little brother Yaacov. "It would only mean the death of both of you," said my mother. She was calm and practical. A girl might deceive them. But a boy—at the first doubt, they would see he was a Jew. No, I had to go without him.

But alone? Alone into that dark enemy land? I spoke of the plan to Alla, to Freda. They were even more frightened than I. We would be caught before we got out of Hrebenko. No, no, if it was to die, then it was better to remain with the family, to die together.

My mother kept after me. "Eva, you must be the first. If you succeed, other girls will follow, and they will be saved, too."

[ 3 ]

She knew my vanity, my pride at being the first, the leader. "Eva the Cossack!" everyone had called me as a little girl. And so finally I said I would go.

Once agreed, we worked with frantic haste. First we had to decide who and what I would be. A Polish girl? Their faces were rather longer than mine, and paler. With my round face and bright-red cheeks I might pass for Ukrainian. Yes, yes, Ukrainian, Mother said. For there was an advantage in this. To the Germans, the Poles were conquered enemies, still unruly. But in our region most of the villagers were Ukrainians who had hated being governed by the Poles. They had never really given up their fight for Ukrainian independence. And the Germans saw them as allies and treated them with favor.

Settled, then. Ukrainian.

I had to have papers, a birth certificate, an identity. It was my schoolmate, Rachel Schwartz, who helped me. We had always thought of Rachel as a girl with a pretty face but not much sense. While the Russians ruled over us, Rachel had worked in one of their offices. Now it turned out that she had saved some blank identity forms, and even a rubber stamp.

From the public register, we picked the name of a dead Ukrainian girl, Katarina Leszczyszyn, of the near-by village of Werchrata. She had been four years older than I, but I was well developed and could pass for twenty-two. And so we made up a Russian identity paper for her, with the names of her parents, their dates of birth—everything. Besides this, I managed to get a blank German work card, which we filled out in her name.

And what would be my story? It had to be a common story, plausible. I thought of another of my classmates, Rita Mayer. Before the Russians came, Rita had lived with her family in a small resort town, and she had gone to boarding school in Lwów. During the Russian occupation, the NKVD had arrested her parents, who were leading Zionists, and shipped them off to Siberia. Then

[ 4 ]

Rita had come to live with her grandmother, near us in Hrebenko.

There were many such stories of young people left alone when their parents were suddenly taken off by the Russians. Such a story, the Germans would be ready to believe. And so I would be the daughter of well-to-do peasants, kulaks, who had been deported while I was away at school. And now, alone, I found life difficult. There were no decent jobs to be had in Hrebenko. I would rather go to work in the Reich.

Now I had to transform myself into Katarina. The Ukrainian girls had their own way of dress. A wide, colorful skirt, but not a real peasant skirt because Katarina was already a girl of some education. The blouse, too, had to be "in between." Katarina would nevertheless wear a kerchief, and comb her hair down around her face. And of course she would wear a cross.

Mama hurried to some Polish friends for a cross and a prayer book. I began to change myself, as an identity picture had to be made for my papers. I told myself that this had to be a real transformation, and not a disguise. For if I went out thinking of myself as Eva, only pretending to be Katarina, I would surely, somewhere, give myself away.

Mama returned, inspected me. And she too insisted, "You must cease to be Eva altogether. You must not think of us. Who knows when the war will end and what the world will be like?"

For in the fall of 1941 the German victories were uninterrupted; it seemed certain that they would rule all of Europe, perhaps the world.

Mama hung the cross on my throat. It was a good-sized cross, yellow, and it felt solid. I had never been particularly religious. On Sabbath, Papa would put on his long black coat and his fur-rimmed hat, and go off to the synagogue, but I always had felt this was mostly habit, and he had never required any observance of us. Mama kept a kosher house, also, I thought, out of habit, and on the great holidays—Passover and Rosh Hashana—we had

[ 5 ]

feasts like all the other Jewish families. In school during the Russian occupation we had been taught, of course, that all religion is superstition. Still, this moment gave me a strange feeling. Their cross. Their Christ. It was as though, from when I was a little girl, some fear and awe of their magic talisman remained with me. It was as though some additional dreadful thing could happen to me if I were caught, even wearing their cross. But, after all, hadn't Jesus been a Jew, too?

There was a knock. It was the photographer, and at the first instant he didn't recognize me. We laughed. A good beginning. He took the picture, hurried home, and was back with it in an hour. Then Rachel and I pasted it on my Russian identity paper and stamped it, half across.

I would take with me a small wooden satchel, like the peasants used. Mama packed it. I saw her putting in one of my good dresses. "Mama! No!"

"You were at school in Lwów," she said, reminding me of Katarina's story. "So you could have a few city things. Eva, take a pair of high-heeled shoes, too. You must live openly and be like any lively young girl."

I ran out on a last errand. That evening, my closest friends were coming to say goodbye, and I hoped to find something to offer them, perhaps some fruit. And then, as I was hurrying along toward the square, I encountered a close friend of my sister's, Esther Warshawsky. In the last months of the Russian rule, Esther and Tauba had been sent to the normal school in Lwów. We talked a bit, carefully, so as not to touch on Tauba. It came out that I was "thinking of going away." Suddenly Esther said, "I too have thought of going. But, by myself, I'm afraid to try it. And my parents would never let me."

"Esther! Come with me!"

It was as though half my terror were taken from me. Not to be alone! We went directly to her house. As we walked together I kept looking at Esther, trying to see her as if I didn't know her. She was quite small, thin, and pretty, with two long braids down to her waist. If the braids were wound in a circle around her head, she would appear completely Ukrainian. But in that moment she turned to me with a question, looking right at me. With her Jewish eyes. How could anyone ever mistake her eyes? Warm and dark, with their slightly melancholy look? And the way she had of twisting her head when she asked a question.

I knew where she had got that little mannerism with her head. It was her father's way. Esther's family was deeply orthodox. Reb Warshawsky was filled with sayings from the Talmud; only his sayings were usually questions. When the victim was stumped, Reb Warshawsky, his head cocked in just that way, would himself come out with the answer.

And now the same thing happened with Esther, except that her question was not from the Talmud. "How do you plan to get out of Hrebenko?" she asked. "You can't just go to the station and get on a train. Everybody knows you."

"I'll get on the train at Huta Zielona," I said. That was a stop about six miles away. "I'll slip out from the edge of town, take off my armband, and walk to Huta Zielona." It was possible. At that time, the Jewish area was not yet closed in with barbed wire.

"You'll go through town carrying a suitcase?"

I hadn't thought of that.

So now she cocked her head and recited in singsong, exactly like her father quoting the Talmud, "First, we have to find a Pole to carry our bags to Huta Zielona—"

"Esther," I said, "if we are going together, you'll have to be careful not to talk like that, in singsong, like a *rebetsen.*"

She understood at once, without taking the slightest offense. "You too, Eva. You know, you talk with your hands."

"I know. You'll have to watch me, and I'll watch you." Oh, how much safer, to be going together.

[ 7 ]

"To carry our suitcases," Esther resumed, "I'll get Antek."

Antek, the father of a dozen children, was the porter at the post office where Esther had worked, after school, under the Russians. He would do anything for her.

We came to Esther's house. She had two small sisters and an older brother. The whole family sat around the table as we discussed our plan. It was agreed that we should go. Only, couldn't I wait a few days?

I was afraid that a change would prove unlucky. In one day, anything could happen.

But there was so much for her to do. She would have to get false papers. "It will be done," her brother said.

When my girlhood friends gathered around me that evening, it seemed that my entire life had come together there, in the Blumenfeld's living room. There was Milla Stein, with her full, womanly figure, the first of us to have worn a brassière. How envious we had all been. When there was a dance, and you danced near her, you could feel the boy who was your own partner being magnetized toward Milla. And when the flock of us, a cluster of girls, walked in the street, in the old days before the Germans came, and the boys circled around us and teased, and brushed against us and touched, Milla, instead of shrieking and slapping at them as the rest of us did, would merely say, "Boys, leave me in peace." And she would sway a little as if to shake off their touch. She was pleasant, Milla, and all of our mothers agreed that she was really a nice girl, and they never told us not to go with her, as they did with some others. And this was a triumph for Milla's mother, because Milla's father was only a barber and he never worked but lay around the house while her mother went out as a midwife. But poor Mrs. Stein somehow managed to pay for piano lessons for Milla, and tried to dress her well, and so we always invited Milla.

With her came Rachel Schwartz, who had always seemed so colorless, even though she had the most perfect features, the most beautiful face of us all. When we were just coming into girlhood, I had been so envious of Rachel, with her quiet ways and her beauty. For myself, everything I did was wrong, everything I did was talked about, I was a hooligan, a bandit, a Cossack, I would become the town scandal.

Suddenly as I greeted Rachel I recalled a time when I was twelve, and walked out with Munya Frankel, the shining light of my Hebrew class. Munya, who had been taken in the same raid as Tauba. He had played the mandolin so beautifully! And that evening long ago, when we were children, scarcely adolescents, Munya and I had come home late—after ten. It had been a soft, warm evening, and the boy had wanted to linger in front of our house. So I had asked Papa if we could stay out yet for a while. And there, in front of the boy, he had slapped my face! "You get talked about enough already!" Papa had shouted. I had rushed to my room and beat the pillows in a choked hysteria, and Mother had come up, and I had cried out, "Why? Why? I don't do any more than the other girls, and I'm not even pretty like Rachel. Why must everything I do be talked about?"

Mother had soothed me and said, "Eva, be glad for it. You have life. People will always be interested in what you do. A girl can be pretty, like Rachel Schwartz, but about Rachel people will never talk."

They would talk about me now. Though Rachel had helped me with my false papers, though they all said how brave I was, they would talk about Eva, the cruel one, leaving. Rita Mayer, whose parents were already gone, in Siberia, kept saying, "I'm the one that ought to go." But she wouldn't leave her grandmother. Already, Rita had almost gone to her death with Grandma Mayer. In the second *aktione*, a month before, they had been caught, for there had been a baby crying in their hiding place, in the roof space of their house, and Grandma Mayer had taken the baby out, so the others wouldn't be endangered by the cries. Just then the SS had come into the house and caught her, and Rita, hearing the commotion, had rushed out to her grandmother and been taken, too.

I had seen Rita and her grandmother rounded up with the others in the public square, waiting to be marched to the train. It happened that I could go about the streets fairly safely, for I had been put to work in the police headquarters itself, scrubbing, shining boots, running errands for the Germans, and the police all knew me.

When I saw Rita's red head among the doomed, something came over me—an absolute recklessness. I caught her eye, signaled to her to work her way to the edge of the crowd, and then I distracted the nearest guard, asking him some excited, nonsensical questions. While he had his head turned, Rita and her grandmother escaped into an alley.

Rita kept talking about how I had saved her, and how, with my nerve, I would be sure to succeed. But why hadn't I been able to save my own sister, why hadn't I been able to think of something, do something when Tauba was seized?

Whenever this thought came over me I felt as though I wanted to burrow in among my friends, to remain here with all my friends close, close around me, with Alla, and Freda, together as from our earliest childhood, with Rosa Gelb, who always made up such romantic stories, with Lucia, the dentist's daughter. I wanted to hold close, with them all around me, even to the moment when death came for us, and even into the moment of death. Then how could I go out by myself and be away from them?

The girls begged me to show them how I would look, so I changed my hair-do and put on the kerchief, and then hung the cross around my neck. It brought a little gasp from them; how often as children had we peeked into "their" church, or watched our *shikseh* maids at their prayers, or in moments of closeness with the *shiksehs* asked them to let us touch their things, and so fingered their crosses and their talismans.

"How does it feel?" each girl asked me. And Rosa cried, "Oh, I was just going to say something, Eva, and I didn't recognize you! Oh, you'll succeed!"

And Rita had to try on the cross. "Does it make you feel any different? It must feel strange." Each tried it, in turn, and then gave it back to me.

Mother had made tea, and she had even managed to get a bit of flour and bake some cookies. But it seemed to me, all at once, that I was out of place; I was the only one "dressed up," the way we would dress up for a Purim masquerade. I went quickly and took off the kerchief and combed back my hair, away from my forehead. Then I changed back to my own skirt and shoes. And so I would say farewell to them as myself, as Eva. It was our last time together, and which of us would live?

We always chattered in Polish, but certain Jewish words remained in our Polish, so now it was "*Mazal tov,* Eva." Each spoke the words solemnly, and the thought passed through my mind that the good-luck blessing would have been uttered with such solemnity only before my wedding. Like any group of girls, we had always wondered which of us would be the first to make that mysterious step, and now, in a strange way, with the same *mazal tov,* I was going off almost as though to my wedding, my wedding with my unknown destiny, and I would be the first among them to take this step, and I would be able to tell the secret of what it was really like, so that others could quickly follow.

Out of all my friends who came to say farewell to me and to wish me good luck that night, only three were to remain alive.

Then, the next afternoon, came the parting from my family. There I stood in my guise as Katarina. In the whole two weeks since Tauba had been taken, Father had hardly stirred. He had not gone out to each morning's labor call in the town square. Let them take him; he no longer cared. He lay on the sofa, apathetic. He would hardly eat. How he had changed from the tall, quick man, the man who loved to strike a bargain, our papa who could always find a way out of every difficulty. When the Russians had taken away his store and made him a night watchman, he had begun to shrink, to bend. And now the Germans had taken the remainder of life out of him.

But when it was time for me to go, Papa seemed for a moment restored to his old self. He arose and got the metal box in which he had kept his cash, in the old days in the store. Now he placed inside it the deed to our house, and the few valuables that remained to us—his gold watch, and two small diamond earrings of Mother's, and a few American dollars that he had hoarded—and some family papers. Then we sealed it all around with wax. We wrapped the box in cloth. Then we went down to the Blumenfelds' cellar. Papa dug a hole and placed the box there, and Yaacov covered it up, and an old wine barrel was pushed over the spot.

"Perhaps you will come back," my father said. "Then you'll know where it is."

We returned upstairs.

Then I talked with Mother until it was time for me to go. She talked of the change in my plans now that another girl was going with me. "It will perhaps be easier for you to get through together. But once you are there you must separate and not see much of each other. You will be tempted; you will be lonesome for someone who knows you, Eva, for one of your own people. But it will be dangerous for you to meet. Keep in touch with each other only occasionally, and from a distance."

How did she know, to advise me of this? She had never herself done such a thing as I was going to do, and yet it was as though she had already gone ahead of me to seek out every danger that her daughter might face. If I had been able to follow her advice much grief would have been spared me. And I knew the wisdom of it; I agreed as she spoke. How hard it would be for me to follow her words I did not know, for I had never been really alone.

And so it was four o'clock. I was dressed as Katarina. I had measured the time so as to reach Huta Zielona without having to wait too long for the train.

Antek was at the back door with his bicycle. Yaacov ran out and gave him the satchel, and Antek rode off.

Father put his hand on my head. I kissed him. A sound came from him. Yaacov was back already; I hugged him. "A good journey, Eva," he said manfully. He kissed me on the cheek, and I kept my lips for a long moment on his forehead; since his childhood I had hardly ever kissed my little brother. We had always fought. Yaacov was a wild one, wilder than I. How many times had I chased him around the kitchen, to catch him, to make him obey! And afterward, how I was to long to feel his twisting, angry muscles as he wrestled with me, even to feel the hurt of his shoe kicking against my leg as he wrenched himself free. To know he was there. "A good journey," he said.

And then Mother. It was as two women that we parted. "Go and live," she said. "Eva, we cannot know what will be. If one day the war comes to an end, and there are none of us, even none of our people, and you cannot again be a Jewish daughter, then still, do as nature asks, and if the time comes, marry, and have children, and do not regret. You have been a good daughter, even if you were such a wild one." She wiped a tear and repeated, sniffing, her habitual, joking "curse," the "curse" she bestowed on me whenever I was at my worst. "May your own children be as wild as you are, and pay you back!" And then she whispered, "Live, my daughter. Live."

I stepped out the back door, resolved not to turn around.


I walked with my head down and yet I knew each house, each stone, that I passed. Here in these streets I had spent my childhood, here we had lived before Papa built the house near the town square. Yesterday, I couldn't walk through these streets without everyone's calling to me, stopping me, asking for news, because, working in the police station, I heard things. Eva, are they preparing another *aktione?* Eva, is it true that seven thousand Jews have been taken to the sports stadium in Lwów and shot down? Eva, is it true that the train that goes to Belzec—when it gets there . . .

But even in the police headquarters no one had ever spoken about what happened when the train, filled with Jews picked up in the sudden raids, arrived in Belzec. Belzec was a town several hours distant, and it had an ancient jail. Surely the jail could not possibly hold so many as had been taken there. What happened to them all? From a Polish locomotive engineer we had learned that the trains pulled into a walled yard. But no prisoners were seen. And only empty trains pulled out.

There were tales. Some said there was a floor that opened, and people were spilled into a vast pit. No, no, these were only imaginings from horror pictures, I told myself. This had not happened to Tauba. And I walked faster.

There were only a few people on the street. But I passed

Mr. Tishler, of the Judenrat itself. He had seen me every day when I had run errands to the Jewish committee from the police. Didn't he really know me? Or was he pretending not to know? Half the street must be aware of my attempt. Perhaps the Jews were watching, from behind windows, from behind doors, watching to see whether Eva would be caught even on the first steps of her journey. They were wishing me well, they were hoping the best for me.

And what was to be seen? Only a Ukrainian girl going through the street. But what was she doing here in the Jewish part of Hrebenko? Even the one Ukrainian friend I had made in school, Lucia, no longer dared come to us. We had become close friends during the Russian time, when Jews and Christians sang together in the choral society. And when the Germans came, in the first weeks, she would slip around through the back ways, always bringing something with her—half a bread, or even a few eggs. Then, later, she didn't dare come any more.

But suddenly I saw myself as even more of an obvious fraud: a Ukrainian girl wearing a Jewish armband! Quickly, quickly, I must reach the edge of the town, the fields. But I must not walk too quickly and attract attention. It was not far. Five minutes more.

I passed our old house, the house I had been born in. The front part had been Papa's old store, where he had sold things to the peasants—salt, and kerosene, and cloth—while their wagons stood in our yard. All through my childhood I had clambered over those wagons.

I could not help slowing my steps. I looked up and saw the little room on the roof of the house that Papa had built for my big brother Nahum when he was growing up and was like a young man already, needing a place for himself. And I remembered the day when I had led my whole flock of little girls up the stairway, Alla Blumenfeld, and Milla, and Rachel, one day when we knew my big brother would be away all afternoon, and we had peeped into all of his things, opened every drawer, even opened his desk. And there we had found a number of letters—from girls! And we had read them out to each other, laughing over them until we choked. Then we had replaced each thing exactly as we had found it, and fled. Did Nahum know? Did he know to this day? And a warm feeling, a feeling even of courage, swept through me. If I found Nahum, I would tell him. And we would laugh. Oh, it was so good that he was away from Hrebenko, in Palestine. So good that he had gone away in time, just before it all started with the Russians and the Germans. So good that he had not been able to get into a Polish university to study law, and had gone to Palestine. Now even if I failed, there would still be one of us, one of our family, living.

I had come to the last house. I crossed a field. On this very field, Tauba must have walked with the four little girls when she took them on an outing, just before she was caught. At the edge of the field was the woods where I was to meet Tauba's friend Esther—no, Anya. Anya Ozymok.

I stepped in among the trees and saw a girl there—braids around her head, rouge on her cheeks, a different girl, a girl at whose sight I would not say "Esther." The name Anya would always come.

With scarcely a word, we began to walk. A distance ahead of us we saw Antek walking his bicycle, on which our two satchels were tied.

At one moment, Anya stopped. She took off her armband. Then I did the same. "What'll we do with them?" I asked. Should we drop them, throw them among the trees? And if for some reason we had at once to return to Hrebenko?

I dropped mine to the earth, ground it in, and kicked leaves over it. Then Anya did the same with hers.

And so we walked. The little station came into sight. We saw

Antek set the satchels down against the wall and leave. We were in luck; there was no one on the platform.

But now we had to step up and buy tickets. For the first time, we had to face someone, we had to speak out, in our new identities. And though it was the most ordinary thing, to buy a ticket for a short journey on a train, there was still something official about a man behind a ticket window; he could scrutinize you, and even in so small a place as Huta Zielona, he might be on the look-out for Jews, as they were forbidden to travel.

We stood at the window together, like excited farm girls on an adventure, and I asked for two tickets to Przemyśl. This was the nearest city to the west. In Przemyśl we would find an Arbeitsamt headquarters for volunteers for jobs outside Poland. Of course we should properly have Arbeitsamt identity cards from our own district, but we could say that we were home girls and hadn't been registered for labor.

The ticket seller hadn't really looked at us. I had held my hands still, and Esther—Anya—hadn't asked a single question. Our calculation had been perfect: the train was just arriving. And then a distressing thought came to us both, at the same instant. I saw the sudden worry in Anya's eyes. The train came, of course, from the direction we had come. Its last stop had been Hrebenko. Suppose people who knew us had mounted the train there? Any Pole, any Ukrainian from Hrebenko would know us. Hadn't Anya once worked in the post office? And I was known to the whole town, to everyone who had stopped in for a glass of soda, or a schnapps, when Papa had his new store. Anyone could see at once through our disguise! Two stupid little Jewish girls trying to outwit the Nazis!

I pushed Anya up the steps and followed her. We entered the car, and in one swallowing look, I tried to see every single passenger. No one from Hrebenko. We took the nearest seats. The train started.

[ 17 ]

We didn't talk to each other but sat quietly. Most of the car was empty; the train was not crowded, as it had been in Russian times. There was little movement now. For months I had longed to get outside Hrebenko, to go somewhere, anywhere, but now I sat as though encased in my fear, and there was another impulse in me, against which I struggled. I wanted to jump off, to go back, to stay with them. How could I desert them? I looked at Anya. I wanted to ask her whether she felt the same thing. But I didn't dare talk of anything that belonged to that other life, our real life. Our hands squeezed together, on the seat.

The last time I had gone outside Hrebenko had been in a Gestapo car—the car of Meister Klein himself, the chief. I had gone with his chauffeur, Freitag, all the way to Lwów and back. That was the time I had brought back Tauba. That was when everybody had said, "Eva is such a one! She can manage anything. Even with the Nazis!" And perhaps it had made me so conceited that I was doing a foolish thing now.

When the Germans had come into Hrebenko, Tauba had been living in Lwów, studying and giving lessons to some children in the family where she roomed. But from the first days we had heard tales of pogroms, of massacres in Lwów. We were terrified for Tauba. Though raids and deportations were beginning in Hrebenko, too, we talked only of getting Tauba home. In such times, the first thought is to be together.

Almost from the first day, I had been sent to scrub at the police station, and there, even there, a few of the Germans showed a regret and a friendliness to us. Meister Klein's chauffeur, Freitag, was one of these. He would even pass a cigarette, occasionally, to some Jews who worked in the yard. When he sat around waiting for his orders, he would talk to us. And so one day, hearing of an *aktione* in Lwów, I told him of my agony for Tauba. "We'll bring her back," he whispered.

And, a few days later, he had actually managed it. He had an errand in Lwów, and he smuggled me into the car. The big official car passed the check posts with only a wave. When I knocked at Tauba's door, she was aghast. "Only you could do it! Eva, Evaleh, our Cossack!" We hugged and hugged, quickly packed her few things, and hurried out. Within a few hours, Freitag had smuggled us back to Hrebenko.

And now, in the train, it came to me—if I had never brought Tauba from Lwów, she might never have been caught.

I forced myself not to think of such things. Better to occupy myself, to look around the train. My eyes met those of a large, elderly woman across the aisle. She had been staring at us. Did I know her? Could she possibly know me? I whispered to Anya, "Do you know her?"

Anya turned her head as though she were looking around for the conductor. "No," she whispered back.

The woman kept staring at me. On trains, I told myself, it often happened that a person would fix his eyes on some other person, a stranger, and remain that way for hours. On trains, you even passed your time that way, talking about the other passengers, guessing what their lives were like. Two girls. Where were we going? And I tried to make up the story she might be telling herself. Girls—young girls. Going to meet men. Even soldiers. Or going to visit relatives.

And yet I was certain that she saw right through Katarina, that she saw the terrified Jewish girl sitting there, and that everyone in the whole car saw it, that it was plain, ridiculously plain, and they were all having a game of it, and when we were arrested they would all stand up and laugh.

Stop! I told myself.

The conductor came. He punched our tickets, hardly looking at us. He turned toward that woman. What if she said something, asked something? He punched her ticket and passed on.

[ 19 ]

I was an idiot. If I let myself become excited like this, I would never pass beyond the Polish frontier.

No, it was too much, too much for a girl to try to do. And all at once I felt that it was in the other direction that I must be carried. I would be taken off this train and put on a train to Belzec. Where they had taken Tauba.

And the whole thing came over me, that whole day came back to me, the day from which I was fleeing. As I arrived to work at the police station, Freitag pulled me aside. "Eva, today be careful. The Gestapo is coming from Tomaszhow for this one."

An *aktione!* For nearly a month things had been quiet. I tried to run out, to run to the Judenrat and give warning so that Jews might hide. It was for this that I had been put in the station. In the very first days after the Germans came, they had ordered the Jews to select a Judenrat, and though in other towns, we knew, the best people had avoided working with the Germans, in Hrebenko the finest Jews had accepted becoming part of the committee, hoping that somehow something could be done. Our druggist, Dr. Wattenberg, was the head of the committee, and our dentist, Dr. Lippet, turned over the downstairs of his house for its offices. There I was called, with five other girls, two of them the daughters of our Hebrew teacher, the brightest girls in Hrebenko. Dr. Wattenberg himself received us. He had selected us to fill the command for six girls to work for the Germans in the police station, he said, because there, if we were quick, if we worked hard for them but still kept our eyes and ears open, we might be of great help to our people.

And in the very first *aktione*, and in the second, we had been able to give enough warning for people to hide, to be off the streets at least, but now, the third time, as I tried to run out, Meister Klein himself blocked the way. "Eva, stay inside! Don't go buzzing in the streets!"

Cars began arriving, load after load of Gestapo in full uniform.

[ 20 ]

Doors slammed. They formed up, our local police behind the Gestapo from Tomaszhow. The entire building was soon empty except for the telegraph operator, an Austrian, from Linz. He was the other friendly one. He sat alone in his little room, with pictures of naked girls on the walls, and when we cleaned the room he sometimes gave us bread to take home, and he would say, "I'm glad I don't have to go out and do the dirty work." On this day he came into the hallway. "'Girls, go upstairs, on the roof. You're not safe today, even here. Go on, all of you!"

We climbed to the roof. We watched the cars roll out. Hours later a Polish girl from the kitchen came up and said, "It's finished."

On the stairs I met Klein himself. In a strangely quiet voice he said, "Eva, your sister is in the lot." He stood there looking at me, it might even have been thought like a friend.

I said, "Can you help me, Meister Klein?"

"No, there is nothing I can do."

I ran toward the door.

"Eva, if you want to stay alive, stay here!" he roared.

I ran out. I would save Tauba. I would pull her right out of their hands, as I had done with Rita and her grandmother. I ran to the square. It was empty. A few Poles were already in the street, and one of them said, "They're on the train."

I ran to the railway station. The train was gone. And so I went home. I found Mother on the sofa, Father sitting at the table, silent. Yaacov too was silent.

"But how was she taken?" I cried.

"It was her own fault!" my little brother shrieked. And then Mama spoke. Tauba had been out in the morning with four little girls—neighbors' children—taking them for a walk in the fields, just as on other mornings. When she heard the noise of the raid she had run back with the little girls, as far as St. Stephen's church, and there she had pleaded for shelter. Refused, she had managed to reach the house, pulling the four children into our basement hiding place.

The little girls were terrified, hysterical. "Mama! Mama!" they screamed. "I want to go home!"

Tauba couldn't bear to see them so frightened. All of them lived just near by. She would take them home. Yaacov seized her by the arm and pulled her back with all his strength. But the little girls had opened the door, and Tauba yanked herself free and ran into the street with them. A few steps away, they were all taken.

Two days later, a Pole came to us, the locomotive engineer of the Belzec train. "Your daughter gave me this note on the train," he said.

It was Tauba's farewell. "Dear ones, I am taken from you forever. There is no hope of remaining alive. You must accept my fate bravely. My one hope is that I may be the only sacrifice in our family, and the last for all the Jews. May you live in peace. Your Tauba."

I had to go back every day among the Germans and make their beds and shine their boots and try to let nothing show in my eyes when I looked at them.

Did it show in my eyes now? I had always been open with everybody; it was hard for me to hide my feelings. I must find other thoughts. I must turn my mind away from Hrebenko.

I tried to talk to Anya. But what should we talk about? If we whispered about our plans, our fears, then something might show in our faces. We should rather try to talk like two young Ukrainian farm girls, excited, laughing. We would be talking about our villages and about our families, about things in the lives of Katarina and Anya. Then I began to babble, making things up. "You know, Anya, a strange thing happened to my sister, the one whose husband fell from a horse just when she was going to have her second baby." For a moment she stared at me, and then she caught on, and added to my story with a story of her own, and together we made up brothers and sisters and marriages and a feud over a piece of land, we made up a whole village, we told tales of our girl friends who had misbehaved with the Russian soldiers, and of an old crone who was surely a witch, and we laughed over her love potions, but each of us suspected the other of having tried them out! So we regaled each other, we argued, we laughed, and we began to feel we were truly Katarina and Anya. And suddenly we were in Przemyśl.

When we alighted, twilight still hung over the city. Through the haze over the station square, we saw a few yellowish electric signs. We had planned to go directly to the Arbeitsamt, but we didn't know where it was, and we were afraid to approach anyone and ask.

We circled around and went back into the station. In the way that happens soon after a train arrives, the station was suddenly empty. We were conspicuous.

A man came up to us. He spoke in Polish. "What are you looking for, girls?" I clutched Anya's hand. In a railway station—a Gestapo man might loiter.

"We're waiting for a friend, coming to meet us," I said.

"Ah? A friend?" He pulled his face into a smile. "And if he doesn't come, won't I do?"

"No, no, thank you," I gasped, even before I realized it was only a man trying to pick up a pair of country girls. But then, perhaps that was indeed what we looked like. It was as simple as that. People still moved about, went on trips, and girls came from the country to the city. This gave me heart to go to the ticket window and ask, "Please, where is the Arbeitsamt?"

It was just beyond the station square. It had a large neon sign; we couldn't miss it.

And so we stood before the Arbeitsamt. This was the dividing point between life and death. Should we go in together? Separately? If one failed, the other might still try to flee home.

[ 23 ]

Who should go in first? Anya was the older. But my papers were better; she had only an old work card. It bore her picture, it was true, and the name of a real Ukrainian girl, but if there was the slightest checkup, the real girl would be found, still working in Hrebenko.

As I went in, Anya whispered, "Remember, not with the hands."

A hall, a reception desk, a clerk. "What do you want, Miss?"

"To register for work outside Poland," I said boldly, with the kind of half giggle that the Ukrainian girls produced with everything they said. "Is this the right place?"

"This is the right place." He motioned me to a chair. I sat down. I was suddenly completely calm.

My prepared story came out easily. Name, village. Occupation? I told how I had been away at school, and how the Russians had arrested my parents and sent them to Siberia, and how I had been left alone to take care of myself, and how there were no decent jobs to be had in Poland. Besides, I wanted to see the world. I giggled.

He had pulled out some forms. What languages did I speak? Ukrainian, Polish, Russian, good. And a little German, I said, and when he tried me out I answered only haltingly. For where would a Ukrainian girl have learned fluent German?

He was filling in the forms. Date of birth?

I had memorized all the vital dates and had been repeating them over and over, in my head, on the train. I had even written them down in tiny numerals on my wrist. Only last May, in my high-school finals, I had written down the date of the Tartar conquest on the same spot.

But I didn't have to look. I rattled off all the particulars about Katarina Leszczyszyn. And presently—the whole thing had taken only a few moments—he handed me a card. My Arbeitsamt application, stamped, accepted. Like an admission to life.

[ 24 ]

I could remain overnight in the transit camp, he explained, and the next day I would go on to a big assembly center in Kraków. From there, I would be sent to my actual area of employment.

He looked at me appreciatively. "So you want to travel, Katarina?" He chuckled. "Germany? France? Belgium?"

"Everywhere!" I laughed boldly. "I want to see the world."

He called to someone to escort me to the transit camp. And just then I thought that it might seem strange if Anya were to walk right in and tell a story similar to mine. "I have a comrade," I said. "My best friend. The same thing happened to her family as to mine. She came with me, but she's shy, so she made me go in first." And I laughed again.

He laughed, too. "Bring her in, Katarina."

I called in Anya.

Presently she too had her card, and then we were led to an enclosure containing a few barracks. How many such barracks I was to see! The longish, gray painted buildings and, inside, the rows of cots. But aside from their appearance, few were to be like this one.

As the door opened, bedlam struck us. Singing, laughter, harmonica music, drunken shouts. The place was swarming with men and women, peasant lads and girls, mostly Polish, a few Ukrainian. They were clustered on the cots. For an instant, as they looked us over, there was a lull, and then the noise broke out again.

The barracks master told us to find beds. If we were hungry, we could still get something to eat. Tomorrow, the train for Kraków left at seven; breakfast at six. Be ready. He left.

We were in that other world, the world without Jews.

At once, the boys began to mill around us, sniffing us out. We knew well enough the heartiness of the peasant lads and girls. A pinch on the breast, on the behind, was nothing to take offense at. The thing to do was to laugh good-naturedly and make some earthy remark. Bull, go back to your cow! But in spite of myself

[ 25 ]

a pinch of that kind set my blood boiling. They offered us vodka; they tried to pull us down on their beds. "Wait! wait!" we cried, trying to laugh. "We've got to wash, we've got to get settled."

We managed to install ourselves on cots in a corner. Clearly, they could already feel that we were not their kind. But this place was only for a single night. Perhaps in the big center in Kraków we would not be thrown so closely together with everyone.

That was a ghastly night. The roistering continued. Several of the boys dragged us over to their group. We sang with them, we drank, we laughed uproariously at their crude remarks, and we made crude jokes in our turn. It wasn't so hard to fall into it. At home, we had always had a farm girl in the house—even the poorest Jewish family had a *shikseh* to help out—and so I did as any one of our *shiksehs* would have done. But all through the evening my dread kept growing. Already, some of the roisterers were coupled off, on the beds, on the floor. And so many of the farm girls were free and easy with themselves. When Anya and I drew back, when we pushed hands away from our persons, we could sense in the men a questioning, a puzzling—these girls were different from the others. What was wrong with these girls? What were they?

We tried to stay with a whole group, and if one fellow became too persistent and attached himself too close we tried to play him off against another. And I could always whisper to a persistent one that I had to be careful, I had to behave myself because my family was very strict and they had sent Anya along to watch over me, and she would let them know at home everything that I did.

At last the barracks master came through and ordered everyone to their beds. The lights went out.

We huddled in our corner. But they left us alone. Most of them were too drunk to bother any more, and the others had found their partners. We tried not to understand the sounds, the scufflings, the occasional outcries and gasping bursts of joy amidst the giggles. But once, in the woods near Hrebenko, I and a few of the most daring of our girls, Rosa Gelb and Alla Blumenfeld, had followed a *shikseh* and her beau. We had even slipped close enough to see their coupled form among the bushes. And we had heard the girl's cry. And we had run away, ashamed of ourselves, dreadfully ashamed.

All night I lay awake, feeling, knowing such forms in the dark all around me, in that crowded barrack, with the warmth and the smell of their bodies, and with their grunting and their snoring. I lay awake fearing them with a doubled fear. That they might find out who I was was only the fear underneath. Now there was the fear of something so ugly, so repulsive, overwhelming me, the fear of living like this.

I lay tense, imagining that some movement was coming near, that one of them was creeping in the dark toward me. I waited, waited, holding my breath. Then, hours later, when the room was quieter, I must have dozed, for I awoke with a fragment of a dream. I saw the yard behind our police station. The station was in one of the newer buildings in the center of town, on the same street where Papa had had his store. And in the yard behind the station there were still some old sheds, and there was even a poultry pen. I saw one of the policemen going into the pen, as they used to do, to pick out a number of chickens. It was Meister Klein. The birds ran squawking into the corners, into their coop, but he strode among them and took as many as he wanted for the time being, and then, after he left the pen, the remaining birds, one by one, came out from their hiding places, and soon they were stirring around and pecking at the earth, busily scratching for food. And Meister Klein went away laughing, his fists around the throats of a dozen birds, and they were not birds but Jews. Jews from our town.

And so I lay awake with my eyes open in the dark and I knew

[ 27 ]

that Anya also lay awake. I was still thinking about Meister Klein. Though he had yelled and cursed at us—always yelling in that raucous voice—he had never actually struck one of the girls sent to work in the station. And there was a strange thing about him: he spoke Yiddish. From the first moment when he had taken charge of the Jewish population of Hrebenko and issued his commands, he had shown that he could speak Yiddish. It was as though the Germans had prepared certain people for this task. Had they been taught Yiddish, or had the Nazis chosen persons who had lived among the Jews and dealt with them? We had puzzled over it, but we had never dared ask.

And that was one of the strange new things, one of the changes in the world. Ordinarily, if someone spoke your language, this at once made a bond between you, and you would ask how they happened to learn it, and perhaps a friendship would begin. But now nothing could be asked.

There was another peculiar matter connected with Meister Klein. He had brought a woman with him. When we were sent to clean his rooms, we found her there—a large, brash, redheaded woman. And she too spoke Yiddish. Perhaps she had even worked in a Jewish house and learned it there, or . . . She even talked about Jewish dishes and asked if I could make a good *tzolent*. And then, as she was not Frau Klein and I didn't know what to call her, she said, "You may call me Eva."

"Eva! But that's my name too!" I cried. After that she didn't want me there. And we never learned who she was, or anything about any of them.

Then perhaps it was so in the world. You could move among people and they needn't know who you really were.

Then finally it was dawn. We washed, we stood in line for breakfast. All this was easier. There was hurry, there was confusion. The Poles were in bad spirits. They were all compulsory

[ 28 ]

workers, taken from the farms and villages; only the few Ukrainians were volunteers, lured by promises of good pay.

Now we were herded to a train; we filled two special cars. We were on the way to Kraków. Already, Anya and I found, we didn't have to rely on our false papers. We had the Arbeitsamt transit cards in our hands.

The Kraków camp was huge, with row on row of barracks. Here the atmosphere was more businesslike. Men and women were separated. We were taken to the showers, then told to form a line, naked, for medical inspection.

As the line crept forward, I saw the doctor. I knew him! He was from Hrebenko! Often enough, in the old days, he had stopped into Papa's store for a soda. A Ukrainian nationalist, he had been arrested by the Russians, but now the Germans had freed him. Surely he would recognize me.

I couldn't leave the line. Perhaps he would say nothing. And then I even began to hope that he would not recognize me. It was several years since he had seen me, and I had grown. Besides, my hair hung wet, bedraggled, and girls looked so different with their hair undone. I had noticed it myself when swimming in the river near our town. Sometimes, for a moment, I hadn't been able to recognize my own friends.

The doctor was giving the girls the most careless of examinations—a tap on the chest, a question or two, cough. He had seen hundreds, day after day. Surely he no longer really saw anyone.

My turn came. I tried not to think that I knew him, that he might know me. I was Katarina. He didn't look up at my face, even when he asked his questions about childhood diseases. The examination was automatic. I was passed. I was moving on. I had only to circle behind the showers for my clothes.

Then I saw Anya, still in line, waiting. And from her eyes I saw that she too had recognized the doctor. It was as though I had to go through it all again myself. And I didn't dare linger to watch what might happen to her.

At last Anya came hurrying behind the showers. With the other girls milling around us, we couldn't even exchange a word about what we had been through. But if on the very first day this happened to us, how long could we hope to go unrecognized? If only we could get out of Poland.

As each worker had yet to be interviewed, there would be days of waiting in Kraków. Meanwhile there was nothing with which to occupy ourselves. Groups stood around on the walks, getting acquainted, gossiping, flirting. In all this idleness, people had ample time to satisfy their curiosity.

We could not risk making ourselves noticed by staying always together away from the rest. So we decided to be apart during the day. We wandered separately around the walks. And a couple of boys began to follow me. They began to tease me. Every time I turned a corner, they would appear suddenly in front of me, laughing. I didn't respond. Presently I found them in the middle of the walk, barring my way. One of them, the more handsome and the leader of the two, now began to speculate about me in a loud voice.

"What do you think she is?" he asked his companion. "Polish?"

The other looked me over from head to foot, screwed up his face, and said, "Maybe. Maybe not."

"She speaks Polish," the smarty said. "But she speaks Russian, too. Does she look Russian to you?"

His companion stuck out his underlip, pondered.

By-passers were beginning to notice the game.

"I'll tell you. I think she's too clever to be Polish. Maybe she's Jewish. What do you think? Is she Jewish?"

The companion opened his mouth, knit his brows, stared at me even harder, and announced, "You know, that could be possible. A Yid."

[ 30 ]

I spat out the most vulgar of peasant insults and pushed past them.

For a long while I sat in the toilet. Then I went into the barracks and arranged and rearranged the things in my satchel. I wandered to a far section of the camp. The two tormentors didn't find me again.

Though the men and women were at least in separate barracks in this camp, there was a great deal of visiting, and only when lights-out came did I feel safe from those two. Now the *shiksehs* got ready for bed, as did we; one after another they dropped to their knees and prayed. We did the same; we had learned the Hail Mary and other prayers by heart, and now we mumbled them with the same murmur as the other girls. Though all my life I had watched Christians cross themselves, I still did not feel quite sure but what there was some secret detail of the gesture that had escaped me. I crossed myself, saw Anya do it, and we lay on our cots. Again, I was sleepless, and I could feel her next to me, sleepless.

Another day passed. On the second night I kept telling myself, Sleep, sleep, it's all right, nothing will happen now.

But the door opened, and I saw an officer with a flashlight coming into the barracks. He walked down the aisle toward me. It couldn't have been the doctor who had given us away. It was that inquisitive young Pole with his nasty jokes—it was from him that my end was coming. Then perhaps they didn't know Anya was with me. Perhaps she could still slip through.

The officer stopped, stood near my cot for a moment, then turned and went out.

Nothing, nothing, I told myself. Sleep.

A few moments later the door opened again. He was back. And behind him were four girls; he brought them along to the empty cots. But as the group came nearer to me, my first feeling of relief was drowned in terror. Two of the girls were from Hrebenko. I knew them by sight, from school—two classes behind mine. They were Jewish.

I turned to the wall and pulled up the blanket so as nearly to cover my face. Anya did the same. Yet as I lay there, a strange small pride grew underneath my terror. Already our example was being followed. Two more Jewish daughters were trying to save themselves.

Anya and I arose early, so we would avoid meeting the girls from Hrebenko in the barracks. After breakfast we lingered near the mess hall, and as they came along we let them see us and then started walking toward the lavatory. They followed. Inside, the four of us were alone, but we did not dare stay more than a moment. "You don't know us," I said to them. "We never saw one another before. The two of us are not from Hrebenko."

They were even more frightened than we, for Anya and I were the veterans, by an entire day. The two newcomers agreed to keep clear of us. If only we two could already be on our way out of Poland!

There were several more days in Kraków, but fortunately they were busier. Our interviews came. We were asked if we had any preference as to where we would be sent. Anya and I had agreed to ask for Austria. I had thought of Austria only because of the friendly telegraph operator from Linz. Perhaps other Austrians felt as he did. And when I was a child my father had gone, a few times, to Vienna on business, and he had spoken of the Austrians as a decent, cultured people, among the best of the *goyim*.

Then the interviewer asked me, "Any particular place in Austria?"

I said, "Linz."

"Have you any reason?"

"Among the soldiers—" I giggled—"I had a friend who came from Linz." If only he wouldn't ask further. I saw him write Linz on my card.

[ 32 ]

Anya, when asked, said she had no special place in mind. She was marked for the Arbeitsamt in Vienna.

Now we had new identity cards, stamped with our destination. And yet we waited. Each day groups left the camp. But they were all going to Germany. Comparatively few workers asked for Austria, and so we had to wait for a group to be collected.

But nothing more happened. A few days later we were assembled with a dozen other young men and women and taken to the train. It was almost a carefree journey. Weren't we under the enemy's own protection, with the enemy's own papers in our hands? We reached the Polish border. The control was quickly completed—nothing! To pass over this border had seemed the most awesome of obstacles; we had been sure that each item of our identity would then be scrutinized. But now the border hardly seemed to exist. Everything was all one vast area that was the Greater Reich.

And as the train moved out of the land of my birth I felt suddenly, surely, released from dying there. It was as though the locomotive were pulling me free from my grave. At that moment I was so absorbed in myself that I didn't even feel it was our family grave. There was a life surge within me, in my very belly —something I hardly understood then, for it was like an organic discharge of love, happening of itself, without any connection with my personal being.

The Poles were singing, and I sang, and Anya, too.

And the deeper the train moved into the enemy land, the more secure I felt. I would be hidden among them, in the very midst of them. Only there would I be safe.

Late at night we arrived in Vienna. Searchlight beams crisscrossed the sky; I had never seen this sight, nor such a great city, and in spite of everything, I was stirred with a sense of adventure, and of the beauty of the restless beams roving the sky, meeting and holding together for an instant like lovers.

[ 33 ]

Again we were taken to a lager, the same rows of barracks, the same rows of beds, and even this familiarity began to be reassuring. In the morning, we again stripped naked for inspection.

But instantly I sensed a difference. Now the staff was German. We foreign workers were mere objects, not people. Our train companions were at once subdued.

And as we entered the shower room, I received a shock. The attendant handing us soap and towels was a man. In that moment, something else that was precious was extinguished. I had never been looked at naked by a man, except for the doctor, and a doctor didn't really count. But this, because it was so needless, was like being flung naked before all the men of the world. It was as though I had had snatched from me my very womanliness.

There had been in me that girlish dream, that vague image of how it would be; it would be on my marriage night when I would first uncover myself, my own self, to my husband. And in this moment in front of the shower attendant there arose a kind of rage in me; why did they have to give people so needless a hurt! Wouldn't it have been just as easy to place a woman there?

And so one more human pride was lost. But in a moment the shock was to be worse.

The medical examination was more extensive than what we had had in Kraków and included a gynecological inspection. I mounted the table. It was the first time I had seen such a device, where the legs are trussed up. Before the doctor, an elderly man, I at first had little feeling of shame. But he was an unpleasant man, and as he bent to his inspection he suddenly let out a roar of laughter.

"Come, come look!" he spluttered, and in a moment there were several young men gathered around him, only two of them in white medical coats, the others—anybody. Still laughing, the doctor waved my papers. "Twenty-two years old!" It was, of course,

Katarina's age. "Ah, this belongs in a museum! A maidenhead, at twenty-two!"

They had their ribald jokes around me. Some vowed they had never seen the phenomenon itself. Perhaps the specimen should be pickled, for exhibition?

Then at last they went off to their work, and the specimen could get down.

I was now marked ready to proceed to Linz. In the barracks, I saw Anya for a last moment. When she was settled in a job, she would write to me in care of the Arbeitsamt in Linz and give me her new address.

A hug, a kiss, like ordinary comrades; what we had been through together only we two could know. And now each was on her own.

They had provided me with a railway ticket, and I could simply go, unattended, and get on a train. This small freedom was almost too much for me. I could linger on the way if I wanted and look at the shop windows, at the kiosks. All was still bright in Vienna. The people were well dressed, with only a touch of the grayness of war. Victories continued—only victories.

And on the train I was suddenly overwhelmed by the beauty, the serenity, of the landscape. From Vienna to Linz, the countryside glowed with the full warmth of autumn; everywhere the wooded hills, the habitations, looked so peaceful and settled. It was all so good, so clean, so healthy, the world was so filled with beauty; it was worth anything to live!

At the information counter in the Linz station, someone phoned the Arbeitsamt for me, and presently a translator came to meet me, a Yugoslav. He was pleasant enough and even, to my astonishment, took my satchel. I was again a person, a young woman.

And we walked through the town. What clean, wide, shaded streets!

It wasn't far to Camp Bindermichel, he said. He was garrulous, full of curiosity. I had come alone? That was a bit unusual; others came in groups, in transports. And I was a bit of an unusual type, too. He smiled. And with his smile there came over me a new realization. In the midst of my difficult situation, there would also be the complexity of my situation as a woman. A girl.

In those other camps, it hadn't mattered, for I had only had to stave off the annoyance of a number of boors. But suppose a man were attractive to me? For, like any other girl, with each man I met I would be asking myself, Do I like him? And suppose even this engaging, smiling Yugoslav had his reports to make to the Gestapo? Oh, how could one live in such a world, where no smile could be trusted?

Then I told myself that I must somehow avoid all natural impulses; my only work was to survive. I must find a shelter, some little corner where I could burrow in and be alone.

And presently I found myself again before an endless vista of barracks, gray rows, fenced in with high barbed wire. On one side of the road, where the gate was open, was a resident camp, the Yugoslav informed me—a *Wohnlager*. Although there was a sentry, the gate stood open, and I saw young men going in and out. They were quite well dressed. These were Czech workers, he told me.

And across the road was the transit camp, the *Durchgangslager*, for newcomers such as I, who had not yet been placed in jobs. There I saw a poorer-looking crowd, both men and women, moving about behind the closed gate. Some of them were in peasant clothes, and some looked like shabby town folks; there were elderly people as well as young men and women in the compound. And most of them wore large emblems on their chests.

[ 36 ]

The ones marked *P*, my guide explained, were Poles, and *OST* was for Russians.

"And the Ukrainians?" I asked.

"Ah, you are Ukrainian! You're lucky!"

The Ukrainians didn't have to wear identity patches, since the Germans considered them allies.

The green-uniformed guard checked my papers and opened the gate. I entered Bindermichel, which I was to come to know so well.

The young man delivered me to the first barrack, the reception office, making some cheerful remarks to a pair of young women who sat at neighboring desks. They were chattering together in Russian, a natural Russian, and their voices seemed quite refined, cultured. They wore no identity patches. Both young women looked at me and smiled.

From the first moment, I felt a connection to them. I was still tense, concentrating, as I did before every interview, on the details of Katarina's background. Again I had my finger over the tiny writing on my wrist.

The Yugoslav first placed my papers on the desk of a middle-aged German officer, obviously the chief. He merely glanced at them and waved me over to the nearest of the girls. She looked a bit older than I and was blond, with a fine skin. She asked me pleasantly whether I was thirsty after my journey? Tired? Why didn't I set my satchel down there, beside her desk, where it wouldn't get kicked over?

She was studying my papers. "Ah, Ukrainian. I am Russian," she offered. "Clava, here, is Russian, too." She nodded toward the girl at the next desk—a soft-faced girl, with a sensual mouth, and rather short in build. "Not so many Ukrainians come to us," she said, "and very few like you." She read off my qualifications. "*Gymnasia* graduate. Languages. Typing." Again there was her warm smile. "Well, Katarina *rodnaya*, what would you like to do?"

[ 37 ]

Katarina *rodnaya*—Katy my dear! And what would I *like* to do! I was ready to burst into tears. It had become so easy!

There were all sorts of jobs, she said. First, of course, came the munitions plant.

I quickly reflected. Working in a factory would mean being right in the midst of the multitude of foreign laborers, whose numbers would constantly be changing. Someone from home might turn up. I said, "I thought perhaps . . . housework."

"Housework?" She stared at me, surprised. "Oh, that's not for you!" And then she suggested, since I could type, she might find a place for me right here in the lager, on the staff.

Here! Every single worker arriving in Linz would see me! I couldn't really type very well, I said. That wasn't true. When the Russians had taken away Father's store and made him a night watchman, I had had to go to work. Our town notary had been sent off to Siberia by the Russians, and his secretary had taken over his office. She needed a helper. I took the job and finished *gymnasia* in night school, and while in the notary's office, I learned to type quite well.

"But if you can type a little," the friendly girl persisted, "you'll pick it up very quickly."

"Do I have to decide now?" I asked.

"No, no. There are two or three weeks of medical quarantine to begin with anyway. So take your time. But first we've got to get you settled."

She called Clava, who dealt with such matters, and they talked of this barrack and that. One was too crowded, and another was full of sluts, and then the first girl, Nina, said, "Why not put her in with us?"

There was a special barrack for the office personnel and the nurses, she explained. I'd be a little more comfortable there.

Were they suspicious? Did they want to keep a close watch on me? No, I told myself. They could have me watched anywhere.

Why couldn't I accept the fact that this girl was simply being friendly?

She went over to the director, and after a few words he shrugged, indicating that their decision was all right. And so Clava took me along. The barrack was divided into small rooms, each with two beds, clean, neat, bright. My roommate would be one of the nurses, she said.

With my things set down, in a room with a door I could close, I found myself all at once exhausted. For the first time I felt the weight of the whole journey from Hrebenko to this place. In so many ways, I could have been caught. It was as though the terror that accompanied each step of the journey had accumulated, had been rolled together into one huge force that bore down on me. I dropped on the bed. It's all right; you're safe, you're safe, I told myself. But I wept.

For the next few days, I huddled in the little room. My roommate, the nurse, was scarcely ever to be seen. She was a Belgian woman, in her thirties, and I was glad that she left me alone and asked nothing about me even in the moments she spent in the room changing her clothes. I asked nothing about her. The two girls from the office, Clava and Nina, met me at mealtimes in the huge restaurant; they would inquire if I needed anything. They lent me a few books and magazines and told me to get a good rest while my papers were being processed. Could it be that in some unspoken way they understood? Or perhaps it was only that there was some other bond, a bond of foreign workers against the Germans, an unspoken agreement to take every little advantage. Or perhaps it was simply that they saw in me another girl like themselves, alone away from home.

Then one morning there was a knock on the door. It was the

Yugoslav, Peter. "Come, you must come out and get some air," he said. He was driving a truck to the town market. "I'll take you along." I went.

It was an open market, with rows of stalls filled with fresh green things—green beans, cabbage, cauliflower. People joked, jabbered, bargained, and my Yugoslav filled his hands with beautiful ripe tomatoes and laughed. "Look, Katarina, as red as your cheeks!"

I noticed several women turning to look at me, and I even caught their remarks: "Ah, there's a type of Russian girl! Now, that was an acquisition!"

Suddenly Peter beheld a stall piled high with melons. One of them lay cut open, full, ripe. But melons were severely rationed. Seizing my hand, he whispered, "Katya, you're pregnant." And he pulled me to the stall. Behind the melons stood a fat woman, with lively eyes.

"Ah," said Peter with a sigh, "you see our little Russian friend here; she had a sudden craving—you know how it comes in her condition—a sudden craving—"

"Zo?" She looked at me, with the engulfing look of woman for woman, in the womanly condition. There was certainly nothing to show that I was pregnant, but my Ukrainian skirt was full, and my blouse was ample. "Zo," she said pleasantly, "*fargeloost!*" And, laughing, she chose a large, ripe melon and placed it, sun-warmed, in my hands.

Peter paid for it and we hurried to the truck. And I heard myself gaily laughing. Laughing out loud.

And as we drove back, I became more and more gay. When we reached the lager, I slipped the melon under my skirt band, and together we marched into the barracks, confronting Clava and Nina.

"Did you know our Katya was already pregnant?" Peter solemnly inquired. They stared, and as I produced the melon they burst out laughing. Clava called in the nurses, and the woman doctor. We had a feast.

That night I tried to reach back to them at home in my thoughts. I could hear Mama saying, "Yes, yes, live!"

The weeks of quarantine passed. Several times, transports of workers arrived, from Czechoslovakia, from Belgium, from Italy. For in Linz, though I had not known it, was one of the largest arms factories of the entire Reich, the Hermann Goering works. But Nina had decided that I should not go to work in the factory, as I would then have to live in the barracks on the factory grounds. It would be confining, unpleasant. A job in town, perhaps in a restaurant, meant hard work, too. Again, why shouldn't I remain at Bindermichel? I pleaded that I was really too inexperienced to do office work. What I really wanted, I said, was to find a place with a family.

All right then, said Nina, if I had made up my mind, she would help me. The requests for domestics were combed. Peter made a list of them and took me around the city. There was a family with three children. The mother would hardly let me out of the house. But Peter said the Arbeitsamt would let her know, and he pulled me through the door. "I'll find you something really good." And presently he had it. A nice, middle-aged couple, all alone. Their villa was in the finest residential district of Linz—Froshberg.

We entered a garden, went along a flagstone walk and up a short stone stairway. Frau Eberhardt herself opened the door. She was tall, flat, with straight hair, in her middle forties. She looked me over quickly and I saw that I was wanted. Maids were scarce.

The house was impressive. Downstairs, the living room, with a beautiful long carpet going through the archway into the dining room. In the archway stood a huge Japanese vase. In the dining room was an elaborately carved buffet, with porcelain and silver on show. On the living-room walls were oil paintings in gilt frames —landscapes, and portraits of important-looking people. Even Lawyer Segal's house, the showplace of Hrebenko, had not touched this for splendor.

The kitchen was large, immaculate, and equipped with devices such as I had never seen. There was an electric egg-cooker with a bell! There were clever little potato-peelers, and intricate coffeepots. Upstairs, I was shown two bedrooms, the bath, and Herr Eberhardt's study. He was, Peter had told me, the director of railways for the entire region. Then, up an attic stairway, we came to a pleasant little maid's room, with a dormer window overlooking the rear garden, where fruit trees bordered a neat vegetable plot.

I would receive my keep and twenty-eight marks a month.

I had found my haven.

I FETCHED MY THINGS and unpacked in my own little room, with its armoire, its washstand, its little writing table, and its chair for a visitor. That, I told myself, would never be used. Alone, alone. I would be a perfect housemaid, irreproachable, if they would only let me stay here, alone, safe in my little nest.

As I laid out my things, Frau Eberhardt climbed upstairs to tell me I was to take a bath. Despite everything, I was still a specimen from uncivilized lands.

She had set out a snack on the kitchen table, so as to start me off in good spirits. And then she took me around to show me my tasks. Was I familiar with housework? Unhappily I knew very little, I told her, since at home we had always had help, as my father had been a well-to-do farmer. But I would learn. She sighed. But for her, I could see, even an inexperienced girl was better than none. She would show me, teach me. Opening a closet, she brought out a strange object with a long tube; it was a vacuum cleaner. There had been no such article in Hrebenko. I was intrigued. Quickly, I mastered it. My lady was pleased. "At least, you seem more intelligent than the rest," she complimented me.

Frau Eberhardt explained her schedule. She worked on several war-aid committees and was busy most of the day. Just now she was doing special work at a hospital and could not even take the time to supervise the midday meal. So for the coming few weeks

I would eat my dinner with her and her husband at a near-by restaurant. She would arrive home in time to supervise supper preparations. And during the daytime hours, alone in the house, I would clean, I would do the laundry, I would press Herr Eberhardt's things— Did I know how to iron? No? *Ach!* In what sort of primitive land had I been raised? I could not tell her that Mama had always done everything for us, sewing our clothes, making sure that her daughters were among the best-dressed girls in town, washing, ironing, with only the help of a *shikseh*. And after the Russians had come the *shiksehs* had run off from their jobs, but we girls had still been too busy with other things to help Mama out around the house. Oh, we had been so busy with ourselves! And as for pressing a man's suit—when in Hrebenko had Papa ever worn a pressed suit!

The iron, too, Frau Eberhardt was explaining, was electric. Yes, I said quietly. Such, I had seen.

When Herr Eberhardt arrived, Frau Eberhardt presented me. "Our Katarina!" she said, with the flourish of a wife who has ferreted out the unobtainable. Herr Eberhardt was very tall, graying, with a sharp, serious look. He wore a brief, distinguished mustache and was dressed with precise care. I would have plenty of pressing to do. Shoeshining I had already learned from Meister Klein.

Without too much awkwardness, I served the supper, which on this first day had been prepared by Frau Eberhardt. Then I was told to set my alarm for six, when I was to shine shoes, prepare breakfast, and set out a sandwich for Mein Herr to take along to the office.

I washed the dishes, cleaned up the kitchen, went to my room. How perfect it seemed. How snug. What better hiding place could I have found? I would wait out the war here, and afterward . . .

Afterward? Who would be left to know Eva? I would still

[ 44 ]

be Katarina. I would be Katarina Leszczyszyn—that was who I now was.

I prepared for bed and found myself about to kneel automatically for the Christian prayer.

It wasn't the Christianity that mattered. That was a religion, a faith, and when it helped people and they were true to it, I could respect it. But it was the sudden, overwhelming conviction that I would never again be myself, Eva, a Jewish daughter, that overcame me. And why should it matter so deeply? Why should this make me tremble?

I lay awake, waiting for the alarm. At dawn, I slipped downstairs and took their shoes and cleaned them, for fear that after six I wouldn't have time. Then, in the kitchen, I faced my task. The coffee. There stood the shining coffee-making machine. Frau Eberhardt had shown it to me, with a quick explanation of the mechanism; in my eagerness, I had nodded, and now I had no idea how it worked. Indeed, I had never in my life made coffee. At home, Mama had always done everything; she had been such a *beryah* that even when she asked us to help out, she would end by doing everything herself so it would be done right. I knew in general that the coffee was mixed with boiling water and that the Eberhardts put chicory into it. Desperately, I filled the pot. I dropped in a teaspoonful of coffee. Coffee was precious. Wasn't it a spoonful that she had said? I put in a spoonful of chicory, too, but the mixture didn't look dark enough, so I put in another. And then I let the pot boil and boil.

Presently, Herr Eberhardt walked in and sat down. He tasted my brew and exploded. "Tell me, Katarina, is this coffee? Do you even know what coffee is?"

"In our village at home," I stammered, "we drank tea."

He arose and called out to his wife. "What sort of jewel have you got here?"

Frau Eberhardt hastened down. I stood abject. Suddenly I recalled how Mama had been with some *shikseh* straight from the farm—for from Frau Eberhardt I heard the same resigned sigh, the sigh of the desperate housewife who realizes that she must somehow manage to train an ignorant and uncivilized girl.

Patiently, Frau Eberhardt supervised my every move as I made fresh coffee. Their way was to pour the boiling water over the grains. She turned to her husband, triumphant. "You see, she can learn!"

And he was gone, to his office.

My mistress set out my tasks for the morning. I would not have a moment to spare. At noon I was to come to their restaurant.

Couldn't I just fix a little something for myself in the house? I asked.

*Nein, nein,* there was nothing, and besides she had received restaurant coupons for me. I would be needing my strength. I must eat the main meal. She gave me the address, on a near-by street.

There I was, alone in their house. I worked busily. Yet a thousand little curiosities about the personal things in a home assailed me, not only because this was an enemy home, but because a life was lived here. In their bedroom stood a framed photograph of their son, who lived in Berlin, with his wife and baby. A serious, chubby baby, elegantly dressed for the picture. Was this the future ruler of the world?

I could not resist looking into Frau Eberhardt's closets; she had a passion for knitted things, but among her dresses there was nothing that really excited longing in me. And even the slips and underthings, neatly folded in the drawers, were plain.

My mistress had left the radio turned on for me; it was a large Telefunken set in the parlor, tuned to the national station. There

was music, interrupted occasionally by news announcements—
our forces are advancing, always advancing. Rommel was plunging
ahead with his Afrika Corps. Would he plunge on even into
Palestine? Would they track us even to that last refuge? And my
older brother, Nahum, would he be caught even there, and would
they do with him as with Tauba? It was so hard for me now to
bring him before me. I saw him only as he had been that last day
before he departed, that day when he had come home from Warsaw after giving up his efforts to get into law school. He had spent
his last money on gifts for us children—books for Tauba and a
violin for me—oh, why had I never learned to play it?—and a
tricycle for Yaacov. And then all of Nahum's friends from his
Zionist youth group, the Gordonia, had come to say farewell to
him, and all the grown girls had looked at him with longing, ador-
ing eyes, and he had taken a walk in the woods with his best girl,
the lawyer's daughter, Ida Segal, and then everyone had seen him
off at the railway station. They had stood there singing *Hatikvah*.
And where was Nahum now? Was he perhaps a soldier in
Palestine? Was he watching the approach of the enemy, listening
just as I was listening here in Linz to the same dreadful news? Or
could it be that this news was false? That it wasn't all true?

I was tempted to try to find some foreign broadcast, but I didn't
dare touch the radio knobs. Suppose a secret mark of some kind
had been made by the Eberhardts? A hair that would be displaced
if a knob were turned?

But at least I could turn it off.

I worked on, dusting, wiping the furniture. There was a piano
in the living room. I dusted the lid, lifted it, and idly touched the
keys. I could not play. But suddenly I thought of Tauba.

In Lwów, while she had been going to normal school, she had
learned to play the piano. And when I had brought her back from
Lwów I had heard her play once.

Our family was still living, then, in the rear of our own building, for we had not yet been ordered to move back to the Jewish section. In front, the three stories of Papa's building were occupied by German officers. We had to clean their rooms.

One morning when all the officers had left the building, I slipped upstairs with Tauba, to what had once been our own room. It was on the third floor. When Papa had built the house he had built a kitchen and a living room for the family, behind his store, and there he and Mama and Yaacov had slept. But he had managed a special room for his two girls, on the third floor, in front, next to a rented flat. And in that room we had passed the best years of our girlhood.

Now the room was changed to a man's room, the furniture was changed, and the Germans had even brought a piano there, taken from a Jewish house. It stood against the wall.

"Tauba," I said, "now you can show me how you play. Play something."

First she looked in the hallway, to make sure every one of them was out. Then she sat down and played a popular love song, a favorite just then. As she played, she sang.

> *For even though you do not care for me,*
> *It's you alone whose name spells love to me . . .*

And I sat looking at her, my sister, a sweet girl playing the piano, and something in me said, Look at the wonderful thing a human being is! How complicated the fingers, how swiftly they move, how the head remembers every note, every word. And even then an anguish had gone through me. What did they want of us? What did they want of us!

I heard the last reverberations of the note I had struck on Frau Eberhardt's piano. It was noon. I had to go to their restaurant and eat.

[ 48 ]

It seemed to be a neighborhood place, where clients always kept the same table. The Eberhardts were already there; they motioned to me. As I entered, a silence fell, and then, while everyone watched me as I walked to the Eberhardts' table, it seemed to me there was a kind of murmuring. Had I already done something wrong?

Frau Eberhardt hissed, "Katarina, you didn't Heil."

Her husband said, "Doubtless you do not know it. But in entering a public place, you must Heil Hitler."

"I'm sorry," I said. "Should I do it now?"

Frau Eberhardt shook her head. "But see that you don't forget."

The next day I did it. There was no sensation in me. I could even tell myself that I was using the salute against its meaning, using it to protect a Jew.

They ate busily, even dutifully, wiping their plates with the last bit of bread. In such refined people, this surprised me. I had left on my plate some remnants of a vegetable. "Katarina," Frau Eberhardt admonished me, "in these times we must not waste a single morsel of food." And so I took up the habit of cleaning my plate.

A few days later, in the restaurant, I had a shock. The loudspeaker was always on, with popular tunes. All at once I heard a song that pierced through my whole being, pierced through Katarina to Eva.

> For even though you do not care for me,
> It's you alone whose name spells love to me . . .

It was Tauba's sweet voice I heard singing those words. I suddenly felt that if I remained one more instant among them I would shout out her name, I would shout out who I was, I would scream out all my accusations. I rushed from the restaurant.

I ran to the house, to my room, threw myself on the bed,

shaking. The song still sang itself. In the room we had watched Papa build for us, with Tauba sitting at the piano, with her fingers still moving, each finger, each joint of each finger. I saw her, saw her smile as she turned her head to look up into my face. And it was no longer for them that my heart burned with bitterness and horror. It was for myself. What was I doing here, living, living among them? And over the horror came a wretchedness, a grief, a limitless grief, and I wept and wept.

I heard Frau Eberhardt on the stairs. "What happened, Katarina? What is wrong?"

I got myself under control. I opened the door. I saw her standing there, a middle-aged woman with real concern, with kindness on her face. She was not angry; she was worried over what had happened to the girl, to Katarina. And it was all I could do not to burst out weeping again, or not to laugh hysterically over the world, the insane world.

I said I had been seized with a sudden, dreadful cramp; I had been afraid I would be sick in the restaurant. She sent me to a doctor. He gave me black pills. I told Frau Eberhardt I felt better. But a new dread was growing in me. Something so innocent as this song, coming back from my real life, could betray me when every false paper passed inspection. My feelings could betray me. I must have no feelings.

I tried to concentrate on my work, to tire myself. I scrubbed, I did the heavy washing, I learned to be a perfect maid. For the first time I learned to cook. In their house, they were not badly off for provisions, except for certain items. Bread was strictly rationed. Butter was scarce. But in the cellar they had stored up hams, sausages, potatoes. Though it was forbidden for city folk to go out to the country for provisions, it seemed possible for the

[ 50 ]

country to come to the Eberhardts. They had ducks, geese, and wild fowl brought to the back door by a "friend," a keeper on a large estate. He would arrive a few times a week with eggs, cheese, and meat. They would invite him to spend an evening and would treat him with the most solemn respect, as though he were at least a cabinet minister.

Once, after such a reception, there came a barrel of apples. I had to lay out the fruit on specially built tiers in the cellar, each apple separated with exactitude, so as to avoid spoilage.

I was hesitant about touching any of their food supply, except for what I was told to prepare, and even though they had good things to eat, I found myself often hungry. There was an abundance of tomatoes—at every meal they had tomato soup, tomato salad, tomato juice, tomato sauce. And I had always had a peculiar aversion toward tomatoes.

"What is it, Katarina?" Frau Eberhardt asked me one day. "You don't like our menu?"

I confessed.

"Ah, you have been pampered," she said.

And yet I saw that I had gained another point in her esteem; I was not merely a brutish peasant girl but a person with likes and dislikes, a person of taste.

Nevertheless, I was hungry. At home we had eaten a great deal of bread. Here, the bread ration was carefully shared out each morning by Frau Eberhardt. She would divide each portion into three, for the day's meals.

Sometimes I would devour two of my bread portions at breakfast.

"You'll be hungry, Katarina," she would warn me.

During the day the gnawing hunger came. On a shelf in the pantry I discovered a jar of cookies. I stole one. It was delicious, a kind of butterfly-shaped delicacy, but solid and crunchy. I could not resist and reached for another.

The jar was high enough so that I could reach it but could not look into it. I could not see the level go down.

Each day I helped myself. And a few days later Frau Eberhardt took down the jar, remarking that she was going to send these cookies she had baked to her son in Berlin. Then a gasp broke out of her. "But they are half gone! The jar was full!"

She stared at me. I admitted my theft. I had been there only a short time; perhaps she would now send me back to the Arbeitsamt with a bad record. I would never get such a place again! How could I have been so greedily foolish!

"Katarina, I didn't think you were that kind of a girl—to take things."

"I was hungry," I pleaded. "I was hungry for bread." And then, "I never realized I had taken so many. I just reached my hands into the jar, and they tasted so good, I . . ."

Something had come over the face of the German woman. "Like a child," she said. "A child with a hand in the cooky jar." She shook her head. "But you are a grown-up woman, Katarina. Twenty-two years old."

We were looking directly into each other's eyes. I almost wanted to plead that I was only eighteen. Then she said sternly that she would talk to Herr Eberhardt about the incident.

The next morning, to my astonishment, I found an extra bread ration on my plate. Frau Eberhardt explained that she had got it from her mother, who hardly ever consumed her bread.

Herr Eberhardt gave me a long, quiet look. I wanted to say something, to pledge that such a thing would never happen again, but I could only thank them for the extra food.

And even so, something like it did happen again, though I wasn't caught. I had a terrible longing, now, for fruit. I kept seeing the apples in their tiers. Once, when no one was in the house, I stole down to the cellar and took an apple, eating it on the spot. I hoped they had not methodically counted each piece of fruit.

[ 52 ]

And suddenly, as I bit into it, there came to me the memory of Papa and his apple tree. All through my childhood in the old house, the *shtube*, as the dwelling with its one large room was called, I could remember Papa longing for his apple tree. "On Sabbath," he would say, "a Jew should be able to take his ease in his garden, to walk around, to pluck an apple from his own tree, and eat it." We had no garden, no apple tree. We lived on the street that led to the market place; it was the street of traders and grain dealers. As the peasants drove into Hrebenko with their wagonloads of grain, the dealers would run after them in the street, shouting their offers. And when the peasants had sold their produce, they would come into Papa's store for provisions. Sometimes he would take bucketfuls of eggs in trade, and he would in turn sell the eggs to Yankel Chazanovitch, the egg dealer across the courtyard, a long-bearded Jew who had a strange rule of his own —he would never step outside the boundaries of his yard. He would not run in the street after a peasant. Let the peasants come to him.

On Sabbath the street was quiet, and then Papa would put on his long coat and go off to the synagogue. Once, on a weekday, I took his Sabbath coat and his fur-rimmed hat, his *shtrimmel*, and I donned them and went swaggering along the street with my flock of little girl chums laughing and cavorting around me. I got a good slap for it. Poor Papa, I gave him no peace! On Sabbath I couldn't keep still around the house. Papa would lie down for his afternoon nap, and then he would jump up roaring. "How is it in every other Jewish house children tremble, they go on tiptoe when their father lies down for his nap, not a whisper is heard! But in this house there are only hooligans!" And then he would speak wistfully of his dream of Sabbath ease, of walking in his garden and plucking an apple from his own tree.

Soon afterward, times changed for us. First there was a bad time. The peasants organized a co-operative, with a store. Their leaders forbade them to buy from the Jews, and slowly they stopped buying from Papa, and his business died out. He roved around town, he went to Lwów, desperately seeking a solution. "A Jew must find a way for himself," he always said. "A Jew must give himself a bit of advice." He found a way. He opened a soda stand, sharing a sausage-seller's kiosk, opposite the courthouse. Lawyers and even judges stopped at his stand. Then Mama thought of enlarging the business with a stamp-selling permit, for every legal transaction had to be sealed with a tax stamp. It was always Mama who went, when there were officials to be seen. She would put on her fine brown dress and wear her beautiful knitted blue shawl, and she would stand before them in her stately way, speaking her flawless Polish, and they would respect her even though she was a Jew. And so Mother obtained the stamp permit. And then, condiments were added. And bottles of vodka and cherry brandy. And soon the half store was too small for Papa, and he cast his eye on a vacant plot across the street, and there he conceived his plan to build a fine modern building, with three stores downstairs, one for himself and two to rent out, and three flats upstairs. And behind it all would be a garden. And even before he began to build, he would plant his plum trees and his apple trees.

And he had done it. At least, before the war came, Papa had lived to realize his dream, to walk in his own garden of a Sabbath, and pluck an apple from his own tree, and eat it at his ease.

And as I thought of all this, standing there in the basement in Linz, a shiver went through my arms, a twinge. For since that day of the shock over Tauba's song, I had not once thought of my family. I had shut them all out of me, in my fear. Was I, too, killing them, only that I might live?


Day by day as I grew accustomed to my work and became a "jewel" of a maid, I sensed a personal interest in me growing in the

Eberhardts. They discussed me a good deal, speaking always of *"unser* Katarina.*"* Herr Eberhardt was to me, of course, an elderly man, and there was nothing in the least bit out of the way in his regard for me, and yet I could not help feeling it was a pleasure for him to have a young woman in the house.

I did not want them to become personally interested in me; I dreaded it, and yet I could not help feeling pleased and even a little proud of myself when I heard Frau Eberhardt boasting to her friends of the wonder that she had acquired, of the talents of *"unser* Katarina,*"* who was not at all like the other Russian farm girls but was cultivated and even sensitive. A girl who asked for books to read.

It was not that the Eberhardts were in any way lenient about my duties. If a shirt was not perfectly ironed, Herr Eberhardt would sternly admonish me, "Katarina, do it again, and do it well, or I will send you off to the lager. You know, we have concentration camps where you will learn such things as discipline and order. You should see the lines of beds in these camps—not a hair out of place!"

Yet they kept showing their personal concern for me. Herr Eberhardt installed a radio in my room. Frau Eberhardt gave me some nice clothes. Why didn't I go out on my days off? I was young; I should amuse myself. I should visit the centers for foreign workers, they advised. There, gay times were to be had; dances were held.

I said I didn't know anyone and didn't care to pick up with just anybody at all.

At moments I would feel toward Frau Eberhardt a sudden sweep of warmth. Perhaps it was because she was teaching me every household task, the things a girl usually learns from her mother. "Ah, now, you see, Katarina," she would say, "when you marry, you'll be able to take care of your home." And so the talk would turn to boys. "Surely a pretty young girl . . ." I ought to find friends. I ought to go out. Frau Eberhardt even sat me down at her own dressing table one day and helped me to arrange my hair in a different way. It was becoming.

They seemed so worried about me that I decided I had to make a show of going out on my free afternoon, and so one Wednesday I dressed quite nicely and under Frau Eberhardt's approving smiles left the house.

I couldn't think what to do. I took a tram, rode to the end of the line, got off, walked about a bit, and then took another tram back to Froshberg. Hardly an hour had passed. I took a long walk. Still, I was home early.

"What! So soon!" my mistress exclaimed. And what had I done with my afternoon?

I said I had met some acquaintances from the Arbeitsamt, in the square, and we had gossiped a bit.

Ah, but I must go out more and amuse myself.

The next time I went to the cinema, alone. Several times I did that, until even the ticket taker knew me and said, "But what's this? Such a pretty girl, always alone!"

I began to see that I was perhaps in greater danger by attracting attention to myself in this way than I would be by exposing myself to ordinary company. Frau Eberhardt had been suggesting that I meet the girl across the street, at the Webers'—they too had a Russian maid. And so one evening she took me there.

The Webers welcomed me warmly and led me upstairs to introduce me to their Marinka. She was a nice enough girl, but utterly dull-witted; we spent an hour looking through her album of photographs from home and chattering about our mistresses, and then I asked her to come and visit me. And so we exchanged a few visits.

Once when I said good evening to the Webers as I was going upstairs, I noticed a young soldier in the parlor, an airman. It was their son home on leave. A few moments later he was upstairs on some pretext, asking Marinka where she had put certain of his things. He made a little conversation with me. But I paid no attention.

The Webers' son was a typical German youth, blond, with a pointed nose and thin lips. Instantly I felt he was truly one of *them*, the real Nazis. I rarely felt hatred for people. My impulse is to like people, and even in the worst days at the police *commandatura* in Hrebenko, I had felt a personal hatred for only a few. With the Eberhardts, I experienced no inner dislike; indeed, we were becoming more and more human toward each other. In general, for the older Germans, I felt no hatred. It was the young people who aroused bitterness in me, for their entire way of being was antipathetic to me. Among the older ones you felt that this whole Nazi machine had overcome them, that they had simply been too weak to resist what they were forced to do. But with the young ones you felt that they wanted it. They wanted to do everything that they were doing. Their arrogance, their way of talking, their very walk—it was all there.

And because of this instantly upwelling bitterness, I tried to avoid the young flier. But another time, he stopped me in the hallway and talked a bit. "Aha!" Marinka nudged me as soon as I got to her room. "What did he say? What did he want?"

I shrugged.

"From us servant girls, they want only one thing," she said, and she giggled.

Then came the incident with the skates.

The snows had come. Herr Eberhardt and his wife discussed my footwear, and one morning Herr Eberhardt himself took me to a shop and bought me a pair of elegant overshoes, with a zipper. I chattered of the snowfall at home, in my village of Werchrata, and of the sleighrides, and of the ice-skating on the river near by. But I must go skating here, Herr Eberhardt insisted. There was an excellent rink in Linz.

I reminded him that I had no skates. The next day, he told me that he had remembered that the young man across the street had an extra pair and would surely lend them to me. After supper, I went to the Webers and found the young lieutenant quite ready —indeed pleased—to lend me the skates. "They're in the cellar," he said, and down we went.

A garden bench had been stored there for the winter, and there was also a huge umbrella, standing open behind the bench. He made some inane remark about summer in wintertime and asked me to sit down and try on the skates. Then suddenly his arm was around me, locking me against him. Silently, we grappled.

All at once we heard an angry voice. "With a servant girl!" His father stood on the stairs. Young Weber leaped up, red-faced. I left without a word. I took the skates, too, and kept them.

At the Eberhardts, I said nothing of the incident. I went to the rink. It was a new breath of life to me to feel the clean movement all around me. In the grace, in the ease of it, humanity seemed so utterly innocent once more. There were girls in bright, lovely skating costumes, there were couples whirling and dancing expertly together on the ice. For the first time since leaving Hrebenko I completely forgot myself.

Someone glided alongside me and asked if he might skate with me. I had been watching him—the best skater on the rink. "But I'm not really good enough," I said.

"I'll teach you." And off we went. For the rest of the afternoon, we skated together. I became freer and freer on the ice. People were watching us, even applauding.

As soon as I reached home, Herr Eberhardt asked, "Katarina, with whom were you at the rink?"

"Why, I went alone."

"Oh, no, you were with a man. Do you know who he is? He is the star skater of Linz!"

"I didn't know," I said. "He just asked me."

[ 58 ]

He looked at me. "Katarina," he said, "you look too boldly into the eyes of men. I have noticed it myself, sometimes, on the street. "

I was startled. "Why, no—" I began.

"Be careful. We don't want things said about our Katarina."

But what did he want of me? How, then, should Katarina behave?

Upstairs, I stared at myself in the mirror. I stared at Katarina, the Eberhardts' Katarina, and it came over me—this was now myself. And in that moment I once more felt a strange dread. Who was I? I tried to summon my parents, my little brother, Tauba, but their images would not come. Suddenly the past was blank. And then my panic grew. I could not remember the details of our street. I could not remember names. I began to tell over the names of my girl friends. My twin, Alla Blumenfeld. But for a long moment her sister's name didn't come! Why, we had grown up together, been together every day in school! I had left Hrebenko from their house! Alla and . . . Freda! Freda. But how could her name even momentarily have disappeared from my mind? It was only a few months since I had left Hrebenko. What could be happening to me?

One by one I sought to recover my close ones, my friends. I tried to see my farewell party. Who had been there? Alla, Freda, of course, then Rita Mayer, and Rachel Schwartz, who had helped me with my papers, and Milla, Milla with her ripe figure, and . . . and . . . But what was happening to me? Was this the amnesia that I had heard about, when people forgot their past? Could it come over one gradually?

And who was I, really? Why, suppose I had been born a few

versts from Hrebenko, born as a daughter to that Ukrainian family, Leszczyszyn—suppose I had truly been their Katya?

At home I had been a certain person, Eva, because all my friends knew what Eva was like, and they knew Eva's family. But if here I was Katarina, only Katarina?

And then there came to my mind the tales of people, sometimes escaped criminals, who went to a new place and completely changed their lives, married under new names, had families, yet perhaps twenty years later revealed their true identity. When tales like that were told, I had always wondered whether it was really remorse that made them reveal themselves. And now I knew that it need not be a remorseful conscience. It was instead something like what I felt, a terrible fear, a terrible need to be known as oneself.

And that night a memory kept haunting me. It was of a time when I had gone ice-skating in Hrebenko. I had got hungry, and in my usual impetuous way, I had rushed clattering back from the frozen river, along the icy streets of our town, without stopping to take off my skates. I had burst into the store, heading straight for the candy shelf to help myself to some chocolates.

My parents had both been away on business somewhere, and Tauba had been minding the store. I could see her, pulling the chocolates out of my hands. For again and again Papa had complained about our helping ourselves to whatever we wanted from the shelves. And today, Tauba had cried, she was responsible!

In a sudden rage, I had kicked at her. Instantly I felt as though the pointed skate were ripping into my own flesh, and even now, at the memory, I writhed and gasped with the pain of it. Terrified, I had tried to stop the flow of blood. I had screamed for help, and when people had come and Tauba had been carried upstairs, I had knelt weeping at her bedside begging her to forgive me. It had taken weeks for the flesh, cut to the bone, to heal. And no one had ever said anything to me for what I had done—not Tauba, not my parents—and that had been the worst punishment of all. I would break into a gust of weeping each time I came into our room, though Tauba had told me not to cry any more, that she forgave me. Yet the scar remained on her leg, and it seemed to me now that I saw Tauba, I saw her going from the train in Belzec to her death, still bearing the scar I had given her.

In those days, as I kept trying to summon those who were dear to me and feared I was losing them, there kept growing in me a dreadful need for some word, some news of what was happening there. Were they all dead, the Jews of Hrebenko, of Poland, of the whole Ukraine? I scanned the German papers, I listened to all the broadcasts. It was strange that the German people were given no news whatever of what was being done to the Jews. This campaign against the Jews had seemed such an important part of the Germans' war; everything had been so fully prepared, organized, carried out by plan, with persons especially trained to deal with us. One would have thought that there would be constant reports at home of the vast extermination effort, so that the German people would learn how one of their great war aims was being achieved.

But there was not a word on the subject. There was plenty said about the Jews in general; the same anti-Semitic speeches were still being repeated constantly, and the awful caricatures were in the papers all the time. But news of what was being done—nothing. Was it perhaps already finished? Were there no Jews left in that world?

Nor did the Eberhardts or their friends talk of the Jews. I sometimes even yearned to hear them curse us, revile us. Nothing. Had the Jews ever existed? Had Eva ever existed?

One morning as she was laying out my tasks for the day, Frau Eberhardt brought from the closet a military uniform and boots. An important celebration was taking place in Berlin, and her husband was to take part. She placed the uniform in my hands. I stared. Why, it was an SS uniform! And he was an officer!

Yes, said Frau Eberhardt, her husband was a major in the SS reserve. He had been assigned to remain in civilian work because of his age, and because his task with the railroad was as important as front-line duty.

For two days I pressed and shined. For this meeting, everything had to be super-perfect. The Fuehrer himself was to be present.

But if they were Nazis—even SS—how was it they never talked of the Jews? Didn't they believe in all that, after all?

And so Ober-Storm-Fuehrer Eberhardt went off to Berlin and returned, and the great meeting was the subject of conversation at several dinner parties. It had been a celebration of victories in the East. Perhaps the victory over the Jews was too small to be worth mentioning.

Only, that was the winter before Moscow. I knew that the German troops seemed to have stopped their advance. Perhaps they were merely waiting for the cold months to pass.

But one evening Herr Eberhardt called to me from the living room, where he was seated with his wife by the radio. To my astonishment, I heard Russian in the broadcast. But because of the interference, it was impossible to make out more than a few words at a time.

"Tell me, Katarina," he said, "is this language Russian?"

"Yes," I said.

"What are they saying?"

I tried, but couldn't make out the meaning. "I can't tell," I said. "There is too much noise."

Then he said, "You know, Katarina, it is forbidden to listen to foreign stations. I hope that you don't do it."

"No. I listen only to the regular broadcasts," I said.

"Good." He turned back the dials.

But why had they been trying to get news from a foreign station? Perhaps, after all, something was a little bit wrong for the German army. I could contain myself no longer. Once, when I was sure they would both be out for the entire day, I turned the radio dials. Backward and forward, I sought a foreign broadcast. But I could get nothing clearly. It seemed as though in the very air itself I was barred from coming upon an echo of my people.

At last I decided to write. Mother had said to wait a few months before taking such a risk. The months had passed. And so one day I hurried through my work, took pen and paper, and went upstairs. I wrote and wrote, page after page, my tears smearing the ink. Never mind, let them see my longing. Everything had to be said in roundabout language—my dear aunt, how I missed her; though all was well with me, I wondered how things were with her, I wondered about her health, and had she perhaps gone away? Then I described as much as I could of my life in Linz.

I sent the letter to the Polish friends with whom we had arranged things. They would pass it on to Mama. And I knew it would be weeks before there could be a reply—if they were still among the living.

The weeks passed. Then one day as Frau Eberhardt sorted out the mail she cried, "Katarina! You've got a letter!" Seeing how excited I became, she said, "Well, then, the breakfast dishes can wait. Run upstairs and read your letter."

It was in Mother's own handwriting. They were still alive!

"We are happy you are well and have a good job, and we only hope you can keep it." And then came something incredible. "We have also heard about our little dove." The word for dove was *tauba!* "A bird flew in and took our dove with him to his nest in the woods, where they are free and happy!"

A nest in the woods? Free and happy? Was Tauba alive? A bird flew in and took our dove? Someone had got into Belzec and helped her escape? But that was utterly impossible!

Further in Mama's letter I found another hint. "A stranger came to the house one day and left a letter in your sister's handwriting. We don't know where he came from or where he went."

Then that was how they had heard about "our little dove." From Tauba herself! By a letter in her own handwriting! Tauba was alive! Alive!

And still further—Mama had separated the hints—I read, "You remember your father's friend Bistray? We've heard that his brother is free and happy."

My father's friend Bistray? But Bistray had been chief of the NKVD during the Russian occupation of Hrebenko. He had been a friend of our family's, in a way. But I didn't recall his having a brother. What could this strange remark mean?

I tried to remember all that I knew about Bistray. I saw the day of the arrival of the Russians. Despite everyone's worries, I had been excited by the beginning of the war. There had been no fighting, on that summer's day in 1939. The Polish police had suddenly disappeared. Papa had sent me rushing all around town on my bicycle, to his brother Nachman for flour, to the Blumenfelds for kerosene, to the candlemaker. And then the Russians had entered our town, and several cars and trucks had drawn up to the regional police station near our house. Papa had said it was the Russian NKVD that was taking over the station.

Soon enough, some of the officers had come into Papa's shop for vodka. Until then, he had sold liquor only in bottles. But now they told him he could open the bottles and serve drinks in the shop, and presently it was vodka and not soda water that we dispensed. They drank and drank, and some days, when it got late, they moved to the back room and continued drinking. The NKVD chief himself, Bistray, was one of the steady drinkers. He was middle-aged, with gold teeth. Papa said Bistray was a Jew. Mama wasn't sure. A Jew didn't drink like that. But Papa insisted. And then, I demanded of Papa, if they weren't sure, why didn't they ask Bistray himself?

"If a Jew doesn't give a Jew a *Sholem Aleichem*, you don't ask him if he is a Jew," my father said.

Later, Bistray's family arrived in Hrebenko. Mama said the wife was not Jewish, and surely the little boy was not circumcised. "With them it doesn't matter," my father said. "With the Russians, a Jew is like everybody else, and he's no longer a Jew."

Yet once I did ask Bistray the question. It was when the Russians had finished off all of Papa's vodka, and he couldn't get to Lwów to buy a new supply. One day I saw Bistray in his car about to drive to Lwów. Could I go along? I asked. He took me along, and I went to Papa's dealer and got a whole sackful of bottles of vodka, and on the way back, as Bistray seemed cheerful and we even sang some Russian songs together, I tried out a Jewish song. He picked up only the tune but didn't sing the words. "Don't you know the words?" I asked. "I thought you were Jewish, too." He laughed and said that he had been born a Jew, but what of it? A smart girl like myself—I wasn't religious, was I? I didn't believe in all that superstition, did I? A God with a long beard, talking to Moses? And I said no, not that. And we didn't talk any more about the subject of being Jewish.

Now I recalled the day when the Russians were leaving, two years afterward. That morning, suddenly, the sky had become filled with German planes, and the real war had come, and as we were only a few miles from the border, all the Russians had started to pack. Bistray's family was standing beside a truck in the yard behind the police station, while boxes filled with papers, records, dossiers, were being loaded onto the vehicle. And Mama had run to Bistray, begging him, "Take us!"

He kept shaking his head.

"Take only the children!" she begged.

He was silent.

"I implore you, instead of the papers, take the children. Jewish children!"

And he said only, "Don't fear. We'll be back! We'll let those swine come in a way, we'll lead them in, we may even let them cross our own borders—and then we'll break their heads!" He smacked his hands together. "We'll break their heads!" And so Bistray had left us.

And now I read his name again in Mama's strange letter. "You remember your father's friend Bistray? We've heard that his brother is free and happy."

"Free and happy"—the same words she had used earlier in the letter, where she said "a bird flew in and took our dove with him to his nest in the woods, where they are free and happy."

Then it was clear! Bistray's brother—that meant the Russians. In the woods—Partisans! The partisans had broken into Belzec and taken Tauba out with them! There must have been a partisan attack on that place of death! Even with bombings by air—"flown in." Could it be possible? Here, not a word had been heard of it.

I was so borne up, swept up by Mama's letter, I felt I could do anything, go through anything now. I would certainly live! After the war, I would find Tauba and we would be together!

And all through those days, filled with my happy secret, I sang as I worked in the house. I bubbled over. Sometimes, as I looked at the Eberhardts, the news almost burst out of me: "You know, my sister is alive!" Oh, if I could only tell it to someone!

Then one day when the Eberhardts were out the phone rang. I answered, and the call was for me! Nina, from the Arbeitsamt, from Bindermichel. She had a letter for me.

Only Anya could have written to me there. I begged Nina to send the letter at once. And meanwhile, Nina said, why did I keep myself a stranger? Why didn't I come to see them?

I felt the same warmth as in my first contact with her. Yes, there in Bindermichel I had friends. Why was I afraid to go there, to Nina and Clava? And suddenly I felt rich. I had Anya, I had Nina and Clava, and my Tauba was alive! I danced with the broom.


When Frau Eberhardt came home she said, "You had a telephone call?"

"Yes," I said. "It was from the Arbeitsamt. But, Frau Eberhardt, how did you know?"

"Ah," she said.

It was not with malice; only, I supposed, to let me understand that everything was always known.

The next morning, Anya's letter arrived.

"Ah, you have another letter!" Frau Eberhardt exclaimed.

I told her it was from my dearest friend, the girl with whom I had come to the Greater Reich. My friend was working in Steyermark, in the village of Steinkeller am Grumming, on a large estate, as a governess for the landowner's children, and she wanted me to come for a visit.

[ 67 ]

Excellent! It would be an excellent change for me. I must go!

Even then there came to my mind my mother's advice to keep only a distant contact with Anya. But there was such a longing in me, such a need for some contact with home. It was as though I would otherwise lose myself entirely.

Even as a child, I had always calculated my transgressions. If I had been told by my mother not to stay out after nine o'clock, and if nine o'clock came and there was still life and movement and excitement around the town square, I would calculate this pleasure against a good slap in the face when I came home late, and usually I would decide to take the risk. Yes, I was still the same Eva.

Since the trip would consume four or five hours each way, Frau Eberhardt said she would give me an extra half day on Saturday, for otherwise I would spend my whole Sunday on the train, with no time for my visit.

She herself supervised my preparations. I wore my good dress, the one that Mama had insisted on putting into my satchel. Ah, Frau Eberhardt was pleased with her Katarina. I looked quite refined, elegant!

And so I went off.

Here sits the maid on the train—who can tell what she is? A young lady, at ease, relaxed, leaning back watching the scenery.

And indeed the scenery was beautiful. The winter woods, and then a chain of lakes, one more beautiful than the other. Peaceful towns, where it was really accepted that people had a right to live and to enjoy their lives. I closed my eyes, lulled by the rhythm of the wheels.

Now the train climbed up into the mountains. And so I came to the station of Leoben, and Anya was waiting there on the dimly lighted platform; who would say she was anything but a girl of the local countryside?

We fell into each other's arms. "Katinka!"

And then we were in the dark lane, walking together, our

stories tumbling out, the words tumbling over one another. It was a long walk to Steinkeller, and we were quite alone together on the tree-lined road, and I told her the wonderful news about Tauba. "Tauba lives!" And there in the silent nowhere, two creatures alone in the whole world, we hugged each other, because of the feeling that we were not alone. Others lived! And a longing engulfed me. I suddenly whispered, "Call me Eva. When we are all alone like this, Esther, call me Eva."

"I know," she said. "Sometimes I feel as though I'm not sure who I really am, Eva."

And even though I was ready to hear it, the name sounded as though it came from afar; it was already not my name. And then I confessed to her the dread that had been growing and growing in me, the dread that I was losing my family, my friends, my real life in Hrebenko, even within myself. I told her how, even though we had been away only three months, there were moments when I already found it difficult to recall what people in Hrebenko looked like. Even people in my own family!

"And you, Esther. Is it that way with you?"

She pressed my hand. Esther was a little older than I, had studied more. She said that it had happened to her, too. Perhaps it was something within our own minds that was working to protect us, to cover our memory, so that there would be less danger of our being caught. Sometimes, she said, when she was among the other workers, perhaps even in their church, at mass, the memory of her sisters, of her father and mother, would suddenly come to her, like their presence. And it would seem to her that if any of the people around her looked into her face, into her eyes, they would surely see what she saw, and know who she was. And so perhaps for this reason—her hand pressed mine tightly—the mind itself shut off those memories, by a will of its own.

"But if we lose them, Esther, how will we bring them back?"

I must not keep on calling her Esther, she whispered. We might pass someone in the dark. Or perhaps later, among the other workers, I would forget myself. It was still quite dangerous for her in this place. There were scores of foreign workers on the estate; farmhands were endlessly coming and going. She could not tuck herself away, as I was luckily able to do, for she had to sleep in the workers' quarters and to eat in their dining hall. Of those who came from Russia she had no fear, but there were Poles and Ukrainians, too, and these could more quickly sense that she was not exactly the type of Ukrainian girl she claimed to be. But as yet, thank God, nothing had happened.

As to the place itself, it was a paradise. All was peaceful. To be in the country this way among the growing things, close to the innocent beasts, the cattle, the beautiful horses—this alone made her situation bearable. And the children. They were quite young, not yet spoiled or haughty, two little girls of four and six, and she had only to mind them, to read to them, to take them walking in the gardens and the fields. The six-year-old had lessons from a tutor, and then Anya was left alone with the younger child, whom she adored.

But away from the main house, things were more difficult. From day to night, there was the constant pestering of the men around the place. The plucking at her, the curiosity. Why wasn't she like the other girls? Sometimes one or another would take to following her around, for days, even weeks at a time. She didn't know how long it could go on. She was thinking of applying to the Arbeitsamt for a transfer, but what if she fell into something even worse? Here, at least, there was so much natural beauty around her.

And so we came to Steinkeller. There were large central buildings, and then cottages perched on the mountainside, their scattered lights winking through the trees. As we crossed the grounds, away from the main residence, there came the warm, sweetish smell of the barns. We entered the long, two-story structure where the farmhands slept.

At least Anya had a room to herself. And there she had prepared a feast for me: such wonderful sausages, and real butter, and farm bread, and fresh milk. The milk, together with the meat, struck me as a little odd, for at home her family had been so strictly orthodox, and even though Anya was modern she had by habit kept from breaking the kosher rules. Now she laughed ruefully. "Don't you know what kind of sausage it is? Pork sausage." And both of us were quiet, thinking of our parents.

In half whispers, we talked of what was haunting us. "What is happening there?" she asked. "Have you heard anything at all?" I told her how I had even risked dialing a foreign broadcast. Nothing. Nothing.

"It's as if they were gone off the earth," she said. "Sometimes I have a terrible impulse to go back, to run to the train and go back, only to see—"

"I know," I said. "I too."

Then an odd and awful thought came to us. The silence, the void, the emptiness, made it seem as if we would be the only two Jews left in the entire world. And how, if it was ever all over, would we even make people believe that we were Jews?

"We'll have to speak Yiddish, to prove it," she said.

I recalled how Papa would complain to me, "What, a Jewish daughter, and she can't even speak her mother tongue! That I, in my house, should have such a daughter!" But then in the last months, when I had been the errand girl for the *commandatura* and had run ten times a day to the Judenrat with messages and orders and requests—Meister Klein wanted a new gold watch, Herr Meyert demanded new boots, the *commandatura* demanded six fur coats—in those days the poorer folk had always stopped me on the street, begging me for news, speaking in Yiddish, and my Yiddish had grown fluent.

[ 71 ]

And so now with Anya, whispering in Yiddish, I talked of home. All night we tried to remind each other of things at home, of how life had been lived in Hrebenko. Nonsensical memories. The time the new cinema had been built for the Polish police school established in our town, and the cinema had been opened to the public three times a week, so we had two movies in Hrebenko. The time a whole band of us had gone to see the first picture in color—oh, it had been so beautiful, a picture based on an English classic, *Becky Sharp*. That night Lawyer Segal's younger daughter Feigheh had invited us for ice cream, after the movie. Oh, what a horrible girl, a Becky Sharp herself. Lawyer Segal gave her more pocket money than any other girl in town, so she could invite everybody to the ice-cream parlor; otherwise no one would be seen with her. Remember the time she was caught with a boy, in the lockers? And that night in the ice-cream parlor, there had been twenty-two of us! I had been there with my whole band of girls, and there had been that bold band of boys, Henig Weiss and the other boys who made eyes at us, and Esther— Anya—had been there with the slightly older group, with my sister Tauba's group . . .

And so we talked, and then we went to bed, and all night long I lay trying to remember our town, to recall the life we had had "before."

Our Hrebenko was a pleasant town at the bottom of Poland, alongside a river where the horses went down to drink, and where we had our bathing places—the men upstream and the women below. I would go and watch the boys, and once I scooped up a boy's clothes—another boy dared me—and we jumped on a horse, and the naked boy chased us all through town, howling and yelling, "Bandits! Bandits!"

[ 72 ]

There was still another bathing place, farther up the river, hidden among trees and bushes. That was where the Hasidim went; they were, of course, the most pious Jews of our town, and there even a "bandit" like myself didn't dare approach. I always wanted to see if their earlocks floated on the water when they swam.

All around Hrebenko were the fields tilled by Ukrainian peasants. They hated the Poles, and they hated Jews even worse, of course, but that had always been so, and the ghastlier part of it, with the pogroms, was a tale told by Papa about when he was a boy.

We children went out on hikes among the farms, stopping in the peasant cottages to fill ourselves with sour milk and black bread.

Sometimes the family went by bus, past several villages, to the hamlet where Grandfather Yeruham Korngold had his store. Four sons had grown up in my grandmother's *shtube*, and the store was far too small to give a living to all of them and their families. The eldest had wandered away to Paris, and the second brother, Uncle Reuven, lived there in the hamlet, and the third brother, Nachman, had become a flour merchant in Hrebenko, and my father had followed Nachman, to start his own first store.

Hrebenko was not very big, but it had the regional court, and lately there had been built a brand-new institution, the training center for the Polish police and their watchdogs. We used to peek through cracks in the fence into the yard where the dogs could be seen learning tricks.

Hrebenko was large enough to have a "better" section, where Jews weren't wanted, and a thieves' quarter too—what town hasn't? Ours was known as "the sands," and of course our high school had to be right there. My big brother Nahum went there, but for anything more in education, like becoming a lawyer or a doctor, he would have to go to Lwów or Warsaw. And I, too, as a little girl, was determined to become one of the "intelligentsia" and somehow to get into the higher schools and become a lawyer and practice in the district court and be a part of the finer element, even to have a grand house like Lawyer Segal's. Somewhere in it there would be a husband, too.

But meanwhile I had to worry about studying hard enough to get into the high school, for only a very few places were open to the Jews. And ours was largely a Jewish town. Many of the young people, unable to get into the professions, had learned the fur-working trade, and all over the streets you could see the scraped skins, set out on stretching boards.

But our family was still among the "better off" because father, after all—even when he had only the soda stand—was a merchant. Menahem was his name. He was a tall man, very tall for a Jew, straight, solid, with lively blue eyes and magnificent teeth. It was a legend that his own grandfather had lived to the age of ninety, with every tooth in his head. Papa wore a pointed little beard, and there were reddish tints in it, though the rest of his hair was darker. Each year Papa would clip his beard stylishly smaller, until we used to joke that he would soon be no Jew at all. But it was only when the Germans came, and their soldiers on the very first day caught Jews in the street and tore their beards off their bleeding faces, that Papa went into the bathroom and shaved it away.

But I saw him, that night when I lay in Anya's room remembering, as he was in my childhood, a cheerful man who loved to tell comical stories about the slow-witted peasants, and about their cunning, and his own cunning; he had a quick temper too, even with his customers, and he would sometimes shout and exchange curses with them, but it would always end with backslapping over a bargain, and he was proud that his peasants always came back to him with their trade.

He liked to sing a snatch of song after meals and to flirt a bit with the ladies. Papa would tease Mama, describing the attractions of this one or that one who had given him the eye on the way to

[ 74 ]

the synagogue on a Sabbath. Oh, what a fine piece of womanliness was there!

"I'll put her eyes out for her!" Mother would reply as required, but she had no fears. She was herself tall, imposing, quite a lady, although she had grown stout. Papa still loved to tell of the sensation she had made at the time of their marriage, just after the first World War; he had still been in the barracks, a soldier, and when she had appeared there to meet him, with her regal beauty, the whole camp had been stunned.

He was her second husband; her first husband had been killed in the war, and she had been left with a baby son, my big brother Nahum. Perhaps it was because of this that mother had a strain of melancholy. But she would not yield to it. She was always busy, active, the center of all the women of her circle, the advice-giver about everything from a change of business to a marriage. She was always busy in the house and she was always busy with Father in the store, seeming to be in both places at once. And nothing was left undone. Mama was a plain old-fashioned *berya*, a perfect housewife. Her *tzolent* was the richest in Hrebenko, her *lokshen* (noodles) were the thinnest and finest. Even though "aristocrats" like Feigheh Segal bought their dresses in the Bon Ton shop— styles said to come straight from Vienna—Mama would already have dressed her daughters in the same mode, copied from the samples in the windows.

It is on her knees that I see her, pinning a hem on a new frock for me, circling me on her knees, in the kitchen. And it was at these times that I found it easiest to talk to her about "womanly things." Alla Blumenfeld and all the other girls said I was lucky because they didn't even dare open such a subject with their mothers, and they marveled because my mother was so advanced that a girl need not be ashamed to speak to her. And so, during these fittings, pinning a seam, her hands acknowledging how I was filling out and becoming "already womanly," Mother would speak to me of how it would be for me. With a Jewish girl, it couldn't be like with our little *shiksehs* from the farms. With us, a girl, a woman, had to hold herself to her real value. She would cheat not only her future husband but herself of the greatest treasure of her life if she became too free before marriage. Unquestioningly I knew that so it would be: as a good Jewish daughter I would bring myself to my husband, who would be the man I loved, chosen out of love. And of course there was no thought that he would be other than Jewish. Deep down, in the dark recesses of the soul, there was the fear and yet the fearsome curiosity over what could happen, otherwise. There were always the whispered legends of Jewish girls who had been "led off their paths" by gentiles. But how could it happen? In our town, in our school, Jews and non-Jews hardly even spoke to each other.

And so, having touched upon womanly things, mother would rise from her knees, she would brush her hand over my dress, smoothing the cloth over my new curves, and she would say, "Take it off and run outside. Put on your old dress and go run in the fields. Sing, yell, you are still only a child!"

For all through childhood I had had such wild energy in me that sometimes I would run in the fields and shriek out loud, out of sheer exuberance. Each summer Mama moved to the town of Ulanov, where she took the baths for her rheumatism. At first we had stayed at the Mayers' pension—their little girl Rita was my own age—but I made such a commotion, climbing trees, peering into people's windows, shrieking and yelling and laughing, that Mama had to rent a cottage just outside of town, and there she could let me run in the fields, shrieking my head off, and tumbling and fighting with my little brother Yaacov.

But as soon as I got into high school, being accepted only because my big brother Nahum had become a legend as the school's most brilliant student, I tried to subdue myself. I even wondered whether there was something wrong with me, for being so filled with energy. I made solemn attempts to become ladylike; I would practice walking with short steps like our mincing Milla Stein, and I would try to hold down my voice and speak softly like my sister Tauba.

When Poland was invaded in 1939, I was thrown into such a frenzy of excitement, of activity, that I remember my mother trying to quiet me. "Eva, Eva, you don't know what war is." And she told me about the first war when her husband had been killed, and how alone she had been, with Nahum a baby, and how there had been scarcely a family untouched by death and disaster.

Yet, as the Russians came into Hrebenko, the first words were "It will be good." By this was meant, of course, good for the Jews. There were new edicts by the dozen. All were free and equal, even Jews. No longer would we have to compete mortally with one another for the few places assigned us in the schools. I was almost sorry that my big brother Nahum had gone off to Palestine, for now he could have entered law school.

All the Communists of the town were jubilant. There was dancing in the streets, and the noise of the loud-speakers never stopped. The Russians rigged off parts of the square every night, for dancing. The young people came out; everything came alive.

And indeed things seemed good. The swarms of little brown-clad soldiers were on good behavior. They were from far-off Tashkent, and even our refinements of Hrebenko were a marvel to them. From Papa, they bought every trinket, every flashlight, every toy. And everywhere, they were continually pulling the chains of the water closets! When we made jokes of this, the answer was always the same: "Ah, you may have toilets, but we have tanks."

The NKVD moved into the fine new regional police head-quarters that the Poles had built, only a few doors from Papa's store. They had scarcely settled when we saw one of their cars drive up with Dr. Miller, one of the leading Zionists of our town.

He went into the station with two Russians, and we didn't see him coming out.

Soon we saw others going in: our town notary with his pince-nez, some of the leading lawyers. I watched anxiously for Feigheh Segal's father. No. At least, not yet. But others—teachers, and even judges. Rita Mayer arrived alone from Ulanov and told how her parents had disappeared. And one day I saw Mother sewing some bags out of stout cloth. They were a certain size, like small sacks, and I knew what they were. Each bag could hold twenty pounds of clothing and necessities. That was what the NKVD allowed people to take along. If they came to your house for you, they gave you fifteen minutes to get ready, and so it was best to have the sacks on hand.

Yet in spite of the disappearances, the town remained cheerful. Things happened only to the old ones. The world was for the young. In the schools there was a rush of activity, new teachers came, new subjects were taught, capitalism belonged to the dark ages, religion was a superstition, and we had a special new choir-master, Starshusky, who came straight from the Soviet Union, and we sang, we sang our heads off.

Jews and gentiles sang together. We even talked to each other! I had a new chum, a Ukrainian girl named Lucia Rosenska, and she came to the house every day to do her homework with me and to practice singing, for our choral society was going to become the biggest and the best in the region. There was going to be a competition—the Russians were always holding competitions, socialist competitions for everything one could imagine—and the best choral society in our region would be sent to Odessa for the grand finals!

One day I came home from school and walked first into the shop, as always. A strange man was behind the counter. Mama was serving vodka at one of the tables. As I passed, I said to her, "Where's Papa?" She whispered, "He's in back in the house;

they're making him a night watchman at the grain bins. Go speak to him, Eva."

I hurried back there and saw him sitting in the gloomy kitchen in the half basement. And his bitterness poured out. Oh, he understood; he knew what was happening to him. He was a capitalist; he was the owner of three flats and three stores that he had managed to build with his life's blood, scraping, borrowing, paying fantastic interest rates. He was a blood-sucking capitalist, and though he and his wife labored from morning till night to give an education to their children, to give them a decent life, he was to be flung aside on the refuse heap. And all that he had labored for—what good was it? A daughter running around with a gentile, everyone laughing at him.

I couldn't speak. For it was true. It had started at school, but not with a fellow pupil. Not for Eva! For Eva it had to be different from anyone else, And so it was with a teacher. My teacher of literature, Andrey Putko.

Why had I had to give that last pain to Papa, and Mama too? I didn't want to think of it. It was one thing I didn't want to talk of with Anya. I shut it from my mind, reflecting bitterly how, if any one good thing could be said to have come with the arrival of the Nazis in Hrebenko, it was that their coming put an end to my being seen with Andrey Putko. For most painful of all was to remember what he had done, later on.

In the morning, Anya brought our breakfast up to the room. Everyone around the estate knew, of course, that she had a visitor, but she didn't want to expose me needlessly. She brought a tray heaped with good things—real cream, hot bread, fresh eggs. Then, she said, we had to go to church. "All the Polish farmhands go," Anya said, "especially the girls. Don't you have to go, in Linz?"

I explained that the Eberhardts were not churchgoers, and so I had told them that I too was not really observant, and they saw nothing wrong in my not going.

It was mass that we would attend, in the village church, Anya explained. I was afraid I wouldn't do things exactly as they should be done, but Anya assured me that she was by now an expert, and that I had only to murmur when she murmured, and all would be well.

Though I had watched the maids pray at home, I had never been to a service. The little church was bright, as though everything, even the walls, were embroidered, and the atmosphere was different from what I had expected. It was not sanctimonious, but earnest and fresh. The girls from the farm were all freshly scrubbed; their checks glowed. Some came with their young men, who walked stiffly in their Sunday clothes.

Everything was orderly and quiet instead of tumultuous as in a synagogue, where people kept moving about, gossiping, each one praying in his own way. Here, it was like a small theater, with a beautiful show, with singing, and fine costumes, and bells.

There was no danger that I would ever be tempted to a conversion, I said to myself, but I liked the way they did everything, and I liked the way the people were solemn here, in their religion— if they could only be serious and pure like that all the time. But for them, too, it seemed to me, the time inside the church was like play-acting. They were more serious with one another than was natural, and more solemn with themselves, and when they came outside, except for a few girls who looked truly spiritual, their faces instantly changed, as though they were actors coming off the stage.

Just outside, Anya introduced me to one or two of the girls, and we chattered for a moment, but I could see how distant she was from them. Was there really no one for her here? Not one person? I thought of the few weeks I had spent at Bindermichel, and how

friendly Nina had been, and Clava, how instantly I had felt a
rapport with them. But it was true that here all the girls seemed
like Marinka, at the Webers'. Poor Anya.

We walked in the fields. "You don't know, you don't know
what it's done for me, to have you here, to feel myself close to a
human being again," she said.

"I know. It's the same for me. I know." And I confided, "Sometimes there's such a longing in me, I'm afraid that I'll do anything
just to have a friend. Sometimes I have such a longing, just to be a
young girl going out with a young man. I'm afraid, if I should
encounter one who is nice . . . "

I had said it. I had brought out my most intimate fear. Anya
looked directly into my eyes. Her own eyes were quiet. "At least
here, for me, there's no danger of that," she said dryly. And I
thought, She is older than I; what nature is doing in me has already
happened in her; the longing, the need that is growing in me has
been known to Anya, too. And I felt somehow reassured. We
walked on, over the winter fields. Ours would have to be a long
winter.

Soon it was time for my train. Anya hurried to the kitchen and
brought me a huge package to take home—cheese, eggs, and, most
important, a solid lump of real farm butter.

I gave it all to Frau Eberhardt, who was overjoyed. What a
wonderful friend I had! I must go there often. I must have my
friend come and visit me. The trip had done me so much good.
It had made a changed girl of me.


And it had. For days, it was as though I were still with Anya,
telling her things, asking her advice, babbling of home. I talked to
her in my mind. But then the hunger for companionship became
even worse than before. The excursion, the outpouring to Anya,

had opened something in me that could not easily be closed again. My sense of isolation became unbearable.

I thought more and more about Nina and Clava at Bindermichel. While I could not be as close with them as I was with Anya, could not really be myself, I could nevertheless feel that I was among friends. Though they were not Jews in hiding, they were foreign workers, like myself, in a strange land among an enemy people. I could even hear forbidden jokes about the Nazis. I could even laugh with them. And there would be the warmth of chattering with young women who were not clods like the maid across the street.

And so I began to visit Bindermichel, even though I knew it was somewhat risky for me to expose myself in the transit camp. I would slip into Nina's and Clava's room, and sometimes Nina would be sewing on a new dress, and Clava would be primping while she gossiped about her adventures with her friend Hans, an Austrian who always risked arrest when he was seen with her, as it was forbidden for Aryans to consort with foreign workers.

Nina had a man friend, too, named Karlus; both Nina and Clava had already been married and had lost their husbands in the war. Always, between the two of them, there was man-talk, and in my innocence I would often ask some naïve question that would provoke gales of laughter. Partly because of this, I felt, they loved to have their little Katya about, and they insisted that I come out with them to the movies, when they had dates to meet Karlus and Hans. I didn't want to be a fifth wheel, yet I went.

And so in this atmosphere I began to feel myself more and more stimulated. There were always little remarks from the girls—did I like this man or that man? Was I attracted to this or that movie star? Among the Czech workers there were some fine young men, and Karlus would be glad to bring one along. What was my type?

I bantered, I hinted that I was being loyal to someone at home. I even thought it might be best if I stopped seeing them altogether, and yet when I saw them brighten as their men were coming, when I saw the little attentions that Karlus gave to Nina, and heard their little private jokes, I too longed to live that part of my life.

Then, on one of my visits to Bindermichel, I saw a young man loitering at the entrance to the barracks; he was handsome, neatly dressed, dark, with that look in his eyes of someone who has his own opinion of the world and can say sharp things. I was attracted. I could not help asking Nina who he was.

"Ah, at last!" She laughed. "She's really a woman—our Katinka!" The young man was a newcomer, she said, a Hungarian. She knew nothing more about him.

All week I kept telling myself it would be foolish, foolish. To risk everything for a little flirtation. But on my next free afternoon I went again to visit the girls at Bindermichel, and again I saw him in the yard. This time he struck up an acquaintance. Could he meet me in town on Sunday, perhaps take me to a movie?

I agreed. I was nineteen, warmhearted, and my young woman's body could not be halted in its ripening. In my solitary room, where the solitude had been so welcome, so prized, I had begun to feel hungers, and to weave my girlish fantasies of someone who would be there with me, fantasies of being enveloped, held so close that everything passed from my body—all the tension, all the longing, all the fear.

And yet in the few intervening days the apprehension grew. What could it lead to? He was a *goy*. If anything happened, it would be again a betrayal of my mother, my father. Was it for this that they had sent me out to be preserved? After the pain I had given them through my romance with Andrey Putko?

The whole affair came over me as though it were happening again. I saw him from my seat in the classroom—a small, tense man with an over-large head, not even handsome. His face was rather thick, and the features seemed always to twist themselves together before he could get out what he wanted to say. We girls had always made fun of him.

And then the girls started saying, "Putko keeps looking at you, Eva. He looks at you." That was how it was among us. Boys were very shy about approaching girls. But there would be a long period of "looking." And even a grown man could look.

"Looks at me? He looks at everybody!" I retorted. "He's just trying to catch me out!" For Andrey Putko loved to catch his pupils passing notes to one another, and I was a frequent offender.

But several times my eye caught his. He *was* looking.

How could such an unbelievable thing happen? A teacher, a Ukrainian, and a Jewish girl!

Besides, we girls knew all about Andrey Putko, as we knew the intimate lives of all our teachers. He had a girl in his home village, only a few versts away. A pretty girl, too. He had been going with her for years.

But now I found myself looking at him. He was not so ugly. The way he twisted his face around showed a certain earnestness. And he was a sensitive man; he loved poetry. And his voice, I now noticed, was quite warm and agreeable when he was not speaking officially as a teacher.

One day toward the end of the winter term he called on me to recite a poem we were to have learned by heart. Although I had become a good student since the Russians had livened up the school, it just happened that I had neglected to do my homework for that day. So I admitted it.

"Very well," he said in his schoolteacher voice. "Then I'll fail you."

"Fail me!" I stood up, indignant. "You know I am a good student! Just because for one time and only once you catch me without my homework done—"

He stared me straight in the eye, and I felt a strange inner thrill.

I knew he had had to dare himself to do it. "You're failed," he said. And I saw him mark it in his book. I sat down.

Walking home, the girls couldn't stop questioning me. What was I going to do about Putko? It was surely a sign that he was in love with me, that he persecuted me, Milla Stein said. "That's how men are. If they feel soft toward a girl, they act hard toward her."

We had seen that in many movies.

That night I deliberately didn't study my literature lesson. The next day he called on me again. "I haven't learned my lesson," I said, "as you've already failed me."

We stared at each other. And then he said, in his official voice, "I have decided to let you take the final examination after all. But you must make up these lessons."

Out of the corner of my eye, I saw Alla's yellow braids vibrating as she shook with suppressed laughter.

After school, as I was going out, the teacher fell in step beside me. "Are you going home?" he asked.

I had a little bundle of cloth under my arm. Mother was working so hard in the store that she was letting a seamstress make a dress for me. I told him I was going to the seamstress.

"Do you mind if I walk with you?" he asked.

I was astounded. But perhaps he wanted to tell me something about my schoolwork. We began to walk. Right through the main square, to the other side of Hrebenko, we walked together. I was sure that every head turned.

And he didn't talk about my lessons. He talked about movies, about the girls in the class, making me laugh again and again with the sharp way he had noticed things about each one. He talked about the changes in the school, the new activities, just as though I were someone on his own level.

When I went in to see the seamstress, he waited, and then he started walking me home. But when we passed his house—I knew where he roomed, in the block next to ours—I said he mustn't trouble; I would go the rest of the way alone. And he understood; I was unsure of the effect this would make on my parents.

He said, "What are you doing tomorrow?"

Then he meant it.

And I wondered, Why me?

I was lively, I knew. But I was not the class beauty. I had fine teeth, a wonderful skin. My mouth was too large.

I knew more. I knew I had a full, warm bosom, and when by accident or half by accident a man brushed against it, waves of feeling, between excitement, shame, desire, embarrassment—a whole muddle together—attacked me, and the best way out was to be boisterous and laugh.

And so now it was starting, with a real grown man, not one of the gawky schoolboys. A teacher! And a *goy!*

Several times more we took walks after class. Then came the examinations. In the finals, the teacher would remain in the room, ready to help, if there was something a student didn't understand in the way a question was put. He would come and sit down on the edge of the seat and explain.

I saw Alla call him, and he sat with her.

Then there was a question I honestly couldn't understand. I raised my hand. He didn't come. He walked out of the room.

After class, Andrey met me. Indignantly I demanded, "Why didn't you come to me? You helped everyone else."

"Don't you see?" he said. "I couldn't sit down with you. Anyone else, I could. But with you, they would make something of it."

"But why?"

"It's just so."

And I knew perfectly well that certain things had to be answered by "It's just so." Something deep and womanly in me answered in the same way when I asked myself, "Why me? Why does he choose me? And why am I attracted to him?" Something, a warmth, flowed through me, as though to put such questions to sleep.

We took our bicycles and rode to the end of town, to everyone's favorite trysting place, a little grassy hillock overlooking the river. It was an artificial hillock, made of earth heaped over a storage pit where Alla's father kept his stores of gasoline, for he owned Hrebenko's gasoline station.

I suppose every couple who went to sit there had to listen to the same joke: "Watch out! If things get hot between you, you'll set fire to the gasoline!"

As we sat there looking at the river, I said suddenly, "Why me? Why did you choose me?"

He laughed softly, and repeated, "It's just so." Then he sang a popular song.

*It always begins this way*
*You don't know why or how*
*But suddenly you're taken with a girl*
*And after that it's too bad.*
*At first you see her just a little,*
*And then you keep wanting to be with her more and more,*
*And in the end though you wish it wasn't so*
*You feel you can no longer bear to be without her.*

I kept looking straight ahead, afraid to look at him. Straight ahead, so as to keep track of what was happening to me. A Jewish daughter out with a *goy*. I still tried to talk, of little things. I told him a comical story about the wives of the Russians. A number of them had come to stay in Hrebenko, and they had seen the window display in our best shop, where a few nice things were still to be had: sheer nightgowns embroidered with lace. The Russian women must never have seen anything like these things at home, for they had bought them and worn them to a ball—as evening gowns!

[ 87 ]

We laughed. And then, as he put his arm around my waist, I flushed, confused, for I realized I had talked to him of nightgowns. And just then he kissed me on the mouth. It was my first real kiss. A kiss meant real love. I was upset, and at the same time impatient to run and tell the girls. We had promised one another, as soon as one of us really "felt something" with a man, she would tell the others. Had I "felt something"? And as we kissed again, and I tried to know what I was feeling, everything came into a tumult within me. I could never marry Andrey; he was a *goy*. Even in the new times I could still never do anything like that to my parents. So here I was, playing with love, and I was ashamed of that, too—one must not play with love.

And what of his village sweetheart? We never spoke of her.

The next day I told Milla Stein, and Alla, and Rita. After the giggles and the laughter and the gasping were over—about his kissing me—the earnest, secret, feminine questions began. Had I really felt "it"?

Yes, I said, I had felt it. It was indescribable.

And so Andrey and I kept on meeting. We would stay out until the hour when people came home from the movies, and I would say we had been to the movies. And one night, lost in kisses, we found we had outstayed the hour. I became frightened, and Andrey said that this time he would take me to the door and face my parents.

Papa flung open the door as we approached. "Please, it's my fault," said Andrey. "I know I should not have kept your daughter out so late."

Papa quietly accepted the apology. And even when Andrey went off, Papa did not turn on me in anger. There was more of deep sorrow in his face as he went to bed, silent. But Mama had come out, and she spoke to me in a tone more intimate than ever before, touching to the very center of our lives. "Eva, I know. I remember very well the feelings of being a young girl. But what will happen? Suppose you really fall in love with him? Does he want to marry you? Are you still a Jewish daughter? Would you marry him?"

"No, Mama, that will never happen," I promised. And we looked at each other as woman to woman.

And I tried in those nights in the spring of 1941 to think, to find out in myself what I really believed, what I really felt. For now I was grown; we girls were grown and coming into the age when the presence of a man, a certain man, unexpectedly could tug at the very insides of a girl. Yes, now I knew what it meant to "feel something." And now everything was changed around us, too. Things were more free; we knew that all people were the same, even Jews and Ukrainians and Poles; we knew in our schools that there was no God, Christian or Jewish, so what did it all matter? And yet I knew in my heart that I could never do it, I could never do it to my family. It was one of those things that had to be answered by "just so."

I could not give up going with Andrey. I did not know how to stop. And then the answer came of itself when the Germans invaded Russia that summer.

Andrey Putko went back to his village, and a few months later certain stories were heard about him.


I did not want to think of those stories. I did not want to believe them. But I began to have a dream, in the days before I fled from Hrebenko, and even in my little room in Linz the same dream would sometimes come to me. I would be sitting with Andrey on the hillock overlooking the river, with his arm around me and my head against his shoulder. And then I would be fleeing, fleeing from a troop of SS. And I would look behind me for an instant, and every one of them would have the face of Andrey Putko.

For the story was that a number of Jews had paid peasants of his village to hide them, and my Andrey Putko had given the Jews away to the Gestapo.


That was all I had known of love. And now I was again attracted to a man, "just so." And again, a *goy*. But how could it be otherwise, in my present circumstances? Wasn't I too a gentile, so far as he was concerned? And wasn't he, if he was here in the labor camp, in some way also a victim of the Nazis?

On Sunday, I dressed quite smartly, wearing a fine woolen jacket that Frau Eberhardt had given me and that I had tailored to my own size. And I wore my high-heeled shoes. She sensed my excitement, for she complimented me on my appearance and said, "You are going to meet a young man, Katarina?"

Yes, I said, one of the foreign workers, and we would be going out together with my friends at Bindermichel.

She smiled approvingly.

His name was Lazlo, and we went to the Centralkino together with Nina and Karlus. He was well-bred, gallant, and his opinions about the film were in good taste. After the movie, strolling back to Bindermichel, each couple walked separately, and then he began to make little roundabout remarks, as though he were searching me out, while careful not to show too much of himself. When I asked what sort of job he wanted to get, he said he couldn't tell yet; this was not really the place for him—and it was not a place for a girl like me, either. Why had I really come?

For adventure, I said, laughing. And I too talked in roundabout ways, and all the while I felt that there was something—that there could be something—if only we could reach each other truly. And this was the most awful of all the feelings, in our condition: that you could not show yourself, even when your heart went out to a person.

It was the hour when the gates closed at Bindermichel, so he could not take me home. I went alone on the tram. And after that it was Lazlo whom I imagined, in my girlish fantasy, coming to me, being with me. Night after night I imagined him, I imagined that the door of my room would open, and he would come into my room. His face would lean over mine. And in our secrecy we would tell each other everything about ourselves. And in our secrecy I would whisper my true name and he would whisper it back to me. That would be his name of love for me. Eva.

And then I imagined something even more strange. Perhaps he too was Jewish! Perhaps that was why he was so roundabout, and troubled? Could it be possible that a man could hide his identity through all the medical examinations? But, after all, there were gentiles who were circumcised, for medical reasons, I had heard. And there were also Jews whose parents had detached themselves from their religion, or had even converted to Christianity and had not had their sons circumcised.

Could it be some bond of that sort, unknown to us, that had nevertheless drawn us together? And I imagined how we would one day reveal our secrets to each other. And after that we would feel so close, so intimate. His fingers would caress me. Perhaps his fingers would even touch my breast. And I touched myself. I was afraid and ashamed, I could not know that all girls did the same, in their fantasies.

But I was never to know his secret, if there was one. For the Hungarian disappeared. Nina knew only that his card was no longer in the files, not even in the job-assignment files, and he was no longer at Bindermichel. Things happened that way sometimes. Nothing.

And yet the longing that he had awakened in me grew and grew, and with it my sleeplessness. My unrest, my yearning, my secret fear and shame at my nighttime desires—all this had to be hidden. It increased the part of my life that had to be submerged, and I became more nervous. At about this time I began to feel the pains in my arms.

And as a result of these pains there developed an episode that took my thoughts away from love and brought me back to my danger.

At first, I felt only twinges at night. Sometimes during the day when I was lifting something heavy, a shooting pain would go through my arms, and I would have to stop work for a while. Then the nighttime pains grew more prolonged. I would rise and sit for hours by my window, waiting for the twinges to subside.

I was certain the trouble was rheumatic. All day my hands were in water, laundering, scrubbing. I had not wanted to complain of anything, in my job, for the Eberhardts' house was so perfect a place of refuge, and I feared that if I could not do the work or became troublesome they would send me away. But Frau Eberhardt herself noticed that I was becoming pale, my face drawn. And one afternoon, right in front of her, as the needlelike sensation shot through my arms, I dropped a panful of water.

"What is it, Katarina?"

I told her. It was particularly when I had to do the heavier work, the washing and scrubbing, that the pains came. That night the matter was laid before her husband. He questioned me about all my symptoms. Herr Eberhardt was most considerate. It was perhaps too much for me, a girl who had never been used to such work at home, to do the heavy washing. Let the linens be given out to the laundry.

The next morning I gathered up all the soiled sheets and table-cloths, until there was a huge bundle. How would I get it to the laundry?

"Put it on our little wagon," Frau Eberhardt said. Like every family, they had a small pullcart. But as she pointed to the cart on the back porch, something happened within me.

In Hrebenko such carts had had a special use. On such little

[ 92 ]

carts, the hog butchers had pulled their wares from house to house. No respectable person would be seen pulling a hog wagon!

"No, no, I can't do it!" I cried out.

Frau Eberhardt was astonished. Why, it was an ordinary little shopping cart! On the streets of Linz, the best people could be seen pulling their little shopping wagons behind them.

This was, of course, true. I had seen them myself. But an irrational obstinacy had taken hold of me. I burst into tears. I couldn't. I couldn't!

She called her husband. "Our Katarina is too refined to pull a shopping wagon in the street!" she snapped.

Herr Eberhardt drew himself erect. "Katarina! You will take the laundry in the wagon!"

"I can't! I can't!"

They stared at me. And even through my convulsive feeling, it came to me that I might somehow give everything away. I tried to control my sobbing but could not.

Somehow this affected them. Their Katarina was indeed in some peculiar way a refined person. Frau Eberhardt, without anger, said, "I will go with you and you will pull it, Katarina."

We loaded on the laundry. I regained control of myself. With my mistress stalking at my side, I drew the wagon along the pavement. I became quieter. I tried to explain to her, even to joke about how one could not possibly be seen pulling such a cart at home where I came from.

Not long afterward there was another incident.

It happened at Christmas time. For a week I was busy with preparations. The house was polished and festooned. The Eberhardts' son, with his wife and baby, was coming from Berlin. But in addition to the family festivity there was to be a huge dinner party, a traditional Weinacht feast.

I spent long hours in the kitchen preparing puddings, cooking, baking, piling up delicacies for the great day. The young couple arrived from Berlin, and in addition to all my other work, I had to wash the baby's diapers. It happened that I had never before done such a thing, and the first time, I vomited.

"Ah, Katarina! Our Katarina is so delicate—you would not believe it—a girl from a farm! Never mind, Katarina, it's good training for you when you have one of your own."

The dinner hour arrived; there were a dozen guests. The Eberhardts had invited their most exalted connections for the occasion; everyone was at least an Excellency, and there was a retired general who came often to their house, a little apple-cheeked grandpapa. Indeed, the general had taken quite a fancy to me and would never sit down at the table unless "*die* Katarina" brought along a chair and sat beside him.

The cider flowed, and there were innumerable *heils* and toasts to all the Nazi chieftains. And as the guests filed in for dinner, there was my general protesting that he would not sit down without his Katarina. So the chair had to be brought, and in between serving the courses I would sit beside him, and my presence provided a great subject for conversation. How serious a girl I was, a constant book reader, and what an excellent cook I had become— I was a wonderful example of what could be done with a girl from those primitive lands. And one of the ladies kept teasing Frau Eberhardt: "Ah, where did you find such a jewel? I'll steal her away from you! Katarina, would you desert the Eberhardts and come to me?"

I was almost at the end of my nervous strength, from all the chatter about myself, all the questions. But at last the time came for departure. As the guests stood at the door, Herr Eberhardt reminded me, "Their coats. Help them with their coats." And one of the men, when I helped him on with his overcoat and handed him his hat, pressed some money into my hand. A tip.

Suddenly unnerved, I flung the money down, ran to the kitchen, and collapsed at the table, sobbing uncontrollably. The general

[ 94 ]

was the first to rush in. "But, Katarina, nothing was meant. A little Christmas money! *Trinkgeld!*"

He stroked my hair. Frau Eberhardt stood over me, worried. "Katarina, what has happened to you?" And now Herr Eberhardt was in the doorway. I rose and said I was sorry. I had been taken by a fit of nerves; I was exhausted.

As I helped the rest of them on with their coats, I heard Frau Eberhardt explaining that it was all because Katarina had become more like a daughter than a house helper. Over and over she declared that they loved me and treated me like a daughter.

And everyone wished me a Merry Christmas, and I wished them the same.

And strangely, this idea that I was like a daughter seemed to have taken hold of them. Not that I had to work any the less hard; I was like a good daughter who keeps very busy around the house. But the atmosphere became still more personal. And with Herr Eberhardt I increasingly sensed that curious, unspoken feeling of a woman who is aware that a man feels her presence. I had no understanding of it; I had not ever considered that an elderly man could be disturbed, as a young man might, by a girl's presence in the house. But I felt his awareness when I came near, to serve him at the table, and sometimes when I passed him on the stairs, and there were times, too, when I found him "looking," exactly the way the boys at school had done.

Yet there was nothing ever in the slightest way irregular in his manner with me. One evening when his wife was out at a meeting he brought a bottle of liquor from the cabinet, and two glasses, and asked me to sit with him. The conversation was commonplace, and yet the sense of something between us could not be broken.

Then suddenly the bell rang. "Don't open," he said. "Take the glasses to the kitchen." He put the bottle away and went to the door. It was his wife. After a moment, she came into the kitchen. I had washed the glasses but had not put them away.

"Ah," she said, "you had a visitor?"

"No," I said.

"But there are two glasses."

"Herr Eberhardt used them."

She said nothing more.

They must have had a long talk about me. For it was then that their unusual idea was put forward. It was so strange a proposal that at first I could not quite realize that they meant it seriously.

Late one afternoon, as we were in the kitchen together, Frau Eberhardt, while supervising the dinner preparations, broached the subject. "You know, Katarina, Herr Eberhardt and I have been discussing your future. We have become very fond of you. We would like to keep you with us always. What would you think if you were to become our daughter?"

I said I was really touched that they could even think of me in that way, but of course I understood it was only a manner of speaking.

But no, she said, it was serious. A sensitive young girl like myself—I needed someone to be responsible for me. And perhaps when the troubles were over they could make it possible for me to continue my studies, as I was so eager to improve myself.

I looked into her eyes. She was serious. I felt tears coming, tears from some helpless sense of the world's utter insanity.

I thanked her again and I said I couldn't do anything such as she had suggested because I still hoped my parents would one day return alive, from Siberia.

Well, naturally, she said, if ever my parents returned and I wished to go home to them . . . But a girl like myself—my possibilities shouldn't be wasted. And did I realize the advantages that

[ 96 ]

would come to me as their ward? I would become a citizen. A German citizen! And the main thing, my children would be German. Completely! I must think about it, not only for myself but for my children. I must think about it seriously.

I said I would.

I thought about it, of course, more seriously than they could imagine. For in their good intentions lay the most terrible of dangers for me. In order to go through with an adoption, I would have to be investigated down to my grandparents on both sides. The village that Katarina Leszczyszyn came from—Werchrata—was in German hands. The authorities had only to write to Werchrata for the Leszczyszyn family records. And then they would be informed that the said Katarina Leszczyszyn had died in 1939!

I lay there, picturing the arrival of the information exposing my false identity. Would it come first to the Eberhardts? Or would the Gestapo appear?

The bell would ring; I would go to answer it. Or would it be in the middle of the night? After I had answered the door, the Eberhardts would come down—and I could see the shuddering horror on their faces! All these months that I had been in their house, they had been contaminated by me! And their friends, and the general with the dried-apple cheeks—contaminated! "Our Katarina? Is it really possible?"

And then I had images of that mysterious place, Belzec. The train went through the gate. Would I sense, there, around me, the last hovering presence of Papa and Mama, of my little brother Yaacov, of my sister Tauba? No, Tauba had escaped! And I could escape!

And in my sleeplessness I writhed, as though struggling against some crushing wall that moved slowly, inexorably, closer to annihilate me, as in some horror film seen in childhood. I clawed, as though to seize hold of the smooth metal surface, to seize the wall, to clutch the floor that now tilted to slide my body, all our

[ 97 ]

bodies, into the deep black pit where my body would be dissolved in a bed of quicklime. My fingers clawed, tore at the metal, at the stone, and sharp electric pains pierced through the very nightmare. My nightly pains. And half awake I vowed I would escape. Then I saw a band of partisans, fierce, with their fierce eyes and dark mustaches. They leaped over the walls, and there was pandemonium in the deathly prison. With our bare hands we fought, we seized the weapons of the guards, and I ran back and seized my little brother Yaacov by the hands. But no, why did I see him so small, a child of six, when Yaacov was already a big boy—thirteen—when I left home. Fourteen now, if he was alive. He would fight! He would himself become a partisan. And later, we would arrive together in a boat, to the shore of Palestine, and we would see Nahum standing on the shore waving to us!

And then I drew myself out of that fantasy, foolish, doomed girl, and I pulled at my hurting arms as if to pull them off and end the pain. I got up from the bed, bathed my arms in cold water, and sat and stared at the wintry night sky.

And a heavy, dreadful knowledge assailed me, something I had known and not wanted to know—by now they were all dead.

Since receiving Mama's letter about Tauba, I had written back, and written again, to the address of our Polish friends. And no answer had come. Yet to my first letter from Linz, Mama's answer had been immediate. Even if my second letter had gone astray, what of the third? And why had neither been returned?

I had argued to myself that the silence was perhaps only a sign that contact was dangerous. Once more I gave myself this answer. I must wait. I must hope.

And so I went to lie down again.

And then in the midst of this dread, the yearning came. Oh, for someone to hold me. All this was too much for me, alone. I was only a girl, a girl who should be held close, protected, and so now he would come, my unknown one, like some medieval knight climbing to my bower, and he would carry me away.

And the pain stabbed and burned in my arms.


For a week nothing had been said about the adoption idea, and I began to hope it was only a passing notion. But then the subject was revived. They were at dinner. "Well, Katarina, have you been thinking of our plan?"

Thinking? If they could know what thoughts it had given me!

And Frau Eberhardt said, "Katarina, we don't want to hurt your feelings. But who returns from Siberia? The Russians are primitive, they are murderers, without the slightest human conscience. Do you know how many millions of their own people have perished in Siberia? Even before the war? People like your own parents, the well-to-do peasants who would not give up their farms to be collectivized. The Communists have sent three millions of them to Siberia, and not one has returned. I do not want to make you feel sad, Katarina, but we must face life as it is."

Then Herr Eberhardt said, "And if by some miracle they should return, Katarina, think what life would be for them. They would be elderly, broken people, and in a subjugated land. We must not delude ourselves that once the war is ended things will be easy. As our ward, our daughter, you could then be of help to your parents. For you would have become a member of the German race."

"How is that?" I asked. "I was born Ukrainian."

And would I not give that up, they asked, to become German?

But how could it be possible for a person to change what he was? I asked.

And now Herr Eberhardt explained to me that in special cases it was possible for someone to become a German. Before the adoption, I would have to undergo an examination as to whether I was fit for acceptance into the German folk. Since I was from the Ukraine, and not from the distant reaches of Russia, filled with Tartars and Mongols, I was undoubtedly Aryan. Therefore the basic qualification existed. And so, if I would agree, he was ready to make arrangements for me to go through the formalities of this examination. There was no need to wait until my family documents arrived; it would be that much time gained. Meanwhile, I must write to my native village for these records.

I stood there, silent.

Agreed, then? Both were smiling at me. Would I write for the records that very day? And Herr Eberhardt would meanwhile write to Vienna to make an appointment for the examination.

Could I refuse? Were they testing me? In spite of the warm relationship that had grown between us, were they suspicious? Was this simply a way to examine me further, without losing their precious maid?

That night was again sleepless, but I was able to think clearly. And I came to a series of decisions. First, there was no way to refuse what they asked. I had to agree to face the examination. But secondly, I must do everything possible to escape from this idea of adoption before the question of my records from Werchrata became an entanglement. That meant that within a month at most —when the papers would be expected back from Werchrata—I must detach myself from the Eberhardts. I must leave their employment. But how? I did not have the right simply to quit. Perhaps Nina could help me. Yet I knew that she could not send me to another employment unless the Eberhardts were dissatisfied with me. How could I make them dissatisfied?

The twinge in my arms gave me, for once, some comfort. Suppose, because of these pains, I could no longer satisfactorily do my work? Suppose the pains became worse?

So my course was clear. For the first part, compliance. They expected me to write the letter home, for information about my family. I would give them a letter to mail, in the morning.

And I wrote a letter. I wrote it directly to our Polish friends. I have had no news of my aunt for some time, I said. In her last letter, I learned that she was ailing, and I began to fear for the worst, since I knew her condition. Please do not try to spare my feelings, as I would rather know the truth. If she is gone, please write to me and tell me so.

The tips of my fingers could not feel the pen, and yet they burned, they stabbed and burned unendurably.

In the morning, Herr Eberhardt himself noticed that something was wrong with me. The coffeepot shook in my hand. "Katarina, you are not well?"

I showed him my hands. Even from the first hour of house-work, my fingers were already wrinkled and pale from immersion in water. Herr Eberhardt touched my fingers, pressed the skin, and even then I could feel nothing. "It is poor blood circulation," he said. I must go to see the doctor.

I said no, no, I was too much trouble for them.

Herr Eberhardt went to the stairway and called his wife. She came down and studied my hands. She questioned me about my sleepless nights. And she too insisted that I must go to their doctor. Surely, her husband added, I must now see that I needed someone to take care of me? Had I come to a decision about their proposal? Had I written the letter to my village?

Yes, I said. To someone in the town near by, who could get the records for me. And I gave him the letter to mail.

The doctor told me that my pains were undoubtedly rheumatic; he recommended massages and gave me a salve. Also, I was to refrain from lifting anything heavy until my condition improved.

That night the Eberhardts again held counsel over me. What could Katarina be allowed to do, and what must she not do?

The problem was attacked item by item by Herr Eberhardt, in much the same way, he said, as he would attack a problem in railroad administration. As each item was disposed of separately, the problem would be solved.

Now, therefore . . .

Bed-making. This was light work so long as the beds did not have to be moved. Katarina could make the beds every day.

Laundry. The heavy laundry was already being sent out. Katarina could continue with the light washing, being careful not to keep her hands too long in the water.

Cooking. This was light work.

House-cleaning. The floors. Scrubbing was done by means of brushes attached to the feet, and as there was no pain in the legs, but only in the arms, floor scrubbing could be continued. Also waxing.

However, moving the furniture during floor-scrubbing and house-cleaning was heavy work. A thorough scrubbing and cleaning twice each week—or perhaps only once weekly for the duration of this emergency—would suffice. And for this weekly cleaning, someone else would have to be present to move the furniture. Herr Eberhardt looked at his wife. "You are quite strong, my dear."

"No, no!" I protested. I could not have Frau Eberhardt do the hard work for me. I would have to call her each time there was something too heavy for my arms. I would be ashamed! And it was not only the furniture-moving. When curtains had to be put up and taken down, my arms were always in pain. No. And I heard myself suggesting, in a sad voice, that perhaps it would be better for them to ask the Arbeitsamt to supply them with another girl.

"Katarina, what are you saying?" cried Frau Eberhardt.

"Unheard of! Out of the question!" said Herr Eberhardt. Did I take them for unfeeling people? These pains had come upon me in their service, and it was their responsibility to see me through until I got well. Certainly in a few weeks, with massages and treatment, the pains would disappear. Meanwhile Frau Eberhardt would do the heavy work around the house.

And she did, once.

A few days later, opening the mail, Frau Eberhardt informed me, "Ah, Katarina! The appointment has been made for you in Vienna!"

In Vienna?

For the examination, for the adoption. In Vienna, there was a special commission for the consideration of candidates who applied to become part of the German folk. I could take an entire day off for the trip.

From this trip I felt certain I would never return.

Yet, what could be seen on me? Had I not passed a dozen physical examinations, the most complete, the most intimate, from Przemyśl to Linz? What new thing could they ask that might lead me to betray myself?

I took the train to Vienna.

The office was in an imposing building on the Ring. I found the right door, lettered *Commission for the Determination of Qualifications for Integration with the German People*. Inside, a receptionist verified my appointment. I saw no one else waiting. It was apparently not a busy office; this was an uncommon opportunity and privilege that the Eberhardts had obtained for me.

The receptionist led me to a dressing room and told me to disrobe completely. Naked. Again, naked. I undressed and waited. What did they want of me now?

In a moment she returned and led me to the examination chamber. It was a large room in which the commission sat in full session. There was a long council table, and twelve men turned their eyes on me as I entered. Near the head of the table sat a stenographer.

I was merely a specimen, I told myself, and I would not even blush for them. I would look in my turn at each of them; they would be my specimens. Yet I could not look into their eyes. I saw each of them, but with my eyes opaque, as though I were not looking.

The head of the committee was a fat individual with the traditional thick, creased neck of the Germans. He was half bald, with light eyebrows, and looked like the comical German bandmaster in some childhood schoolbook rather than the tall, blond godlike youth of the Aryan posters. And his colleagues were an assortment such as one might see at a professional lecture; a few of them looked quite professorial, with glasses and bookish complexions. And one was quite small and dark; he might even have been taken for a Jew. And another was white-haired and pompous, and another was rather young, with bad teeth, and then there was one who frightened me. He had dark pouches under his eyes, and heavy brows. He was quite thin, hollow-looking. And he kept looking at me steadily, unblinkingly, with pale eyes, looking not at my nakedness but at me, with a slight, cynical expression around his mouth, as though he knew everything, everything.

The examination began with family particulars. I recited them as usual. The fat one at the head of the table, the chairman, or the director—whatever he was—asked the questions in a bland, patronizing voice. He had a folder before him, but it seemed necessary to have the same answers come from me again, in their presence. The stenographer wrote down the data. I felt almost angry at her, a woman, seeing me standing naked there and not even giving me a glance of sympathy.

Werchrata. One of the professors repeated the name of my village. And he arose and went to a map that I had not noticed, hanging on the wall behind them. It was a huge map. But would such a village as Werchrata even be shown on a map?

"Near Lwów," I said. "And the nearest town is Hrebenko." Even in uttering that name, I felt I might give myself away.

"Ah, Lwów. Lemberg." He repeated the German name for the city as he placed his finger on the map. And then he found Hrebenko. And then, to my astonishment, peering closer, he said he had found Werchrata. He seemed satisfied that it existed, and came and sat down.

From an anthropological point of view, he remarked, it should be noted that there had been Germanic population in the Ukrainian region for several centuries. Admixtures were common.

The white-haired one said to me, with a laugh, "You are sure you did not have a grandmother, perhaps, who indulged in a little admixture, Katarina?"

Several of the others laughed, and I felt my nakedness. Only the cynical one had not changed his expression, nor had he taken his pale eyes from me. Their pallor, set in the dark circles of his eye pouches, was terribly disquieting.

I said that as far as I knew my family had always been completely Ukrainian on both sides.

Another of them made some remarks about the name Leszczyszyn, using the word *etymology*.

I said it was a fairly common name in our area.

Had our family originated in Leszczyn, then?

That I didn't know.

Another asked whether the members of my family were dark-haired, as I was, or were some of them blond?

My mother was flaxen-haired, I said, and on her side of the family almost all were blond. My father was dark, and on his side of the family, it was about half and half. I gave the name of my mother's family. They, too, were from Werchrata.

One of the examiners now rose and approached me. As he stood by my side, he began dictating particulars to the stenographer.

"The specimen is a young female of good bearing, unblemished, twenty-two years of age . . ."

He asked me to open my mouth, and he looked at my teeth and described them. My two front teeth have a gap between them; this was a mark, in my real family. He noticed the gap and recorded it.

Then he produced a tape measure, and he began to measure me as a modiste would. Shoulders, bust, hips—he called out each measurement to the stenographer. Thighs, ankles, the length of my legs, the length of my arms.

He asked me to hold my arms extended. And he proceeded to measure the length of each finger!

Then he studied my fingernails and described them. "Pigmentation," he said, and he noted their coloring, and even the size of the moons.

At the far end of the room was a scale. I stepped on the scale; my weight and height were noted.

And then the examining professor said, "A specimen of the hair, please."

For an instant I failed to understand. But he pointed, and I took a few hairs from my head and pulled them out.

"Thank you, *Fraulein*." And he went to a table near the window on which there stood a microscope. He placed the hair under the microscope and sat there, studying my hair!

Meanwhile one of the others approached me, to take his turn. It was the little dark one who looked Jewish. He was, I suppose, an anthropologist, for he carried a large, shining pair of calipers. I had never even seen such a tool, except in the windows of instrument shops. Now I was asked to sit down, and he proceeded to measure my skull. He measured it lengthwise, and frontwise, and sidewise, and he called out the measurements to the stenographer. He measured the height of my cheekbones, the width and length of my jaw, the depth of my eyes. And then he took a smaller instrument and measured my nose.

When he had finished with me, it was the turn of the white-haired one, who seemed to be a medical doctor. He asked me about the regularity of my period. Had I ever been pregnant? He asked about childhood diseases. And then he too dictated particulars to the stenographer, describing my abdomen, my hips, my breasts, even my nipples, and adding that the specimen was well adapted to childbearing.

And yet, it was not over. There was another medical doctor, a ponderous man with thick hands, thick lips. He was perhaps in his forties. As he approached, I had an instant feeling of revulsion; it was something about his skin, perhaps even his odor.

"Step into the cabinet," he said, indicating a little booth with a curtain.

The feeling of revulsion became even more intense as he followed me into the small booth. It was so narrow that I could hardly turn without pressing against his bulk.

First he produced a syringe and jabbed it into my arm, looking steadily at me, as though this were something personal between us. He drew a blood sample and handed it out to one of the other men. Then, with a small flashlight, he peered into my eyes, and I could feel his warm breath. He examined my ears, even my nostrils. He used a stethoscope against my chest. Finally he grunted that he was finished.

The entire examination had lasted an hour. Now I was told I could go and dress. The cynical one's pale eyes still followed me. He had asked no questions. He had never joined in the discussion.

I went and put on my clothes. Whatever would happen would happen.

To my surprise, they called me in again. The fat one at the head of the table addressed me. *"Fraulein,"* he said, "I have the honor to inform you that the examination has proven you to be extraordinarily qualified to become a member of the German people. You are a perfect specimen of the Aryan race."

I thanked them all. Now that I was dressed, the cynical one was not even looking at me.

Then, as I shut the door behind me, I was filled with a sudden great wish. That one day I might open it again. It would be a day when the war was ended, and when by some miracle it would be possible for a person to be what he was.

I would open this door and I would walk into the room where the twelve scientists sat, the anthropologists and the etymologists and the historians and the physicians and the biologists, and that one with the circles under his eyes. And I would say, "Gentlemen, you pronounced me a perfect Aryan specimen, extraordinarily qualified to become a German. I must decline. I am Jewish, my parents on both sides were Jewish, my grandparents on both sides were Jewish, and so were their parents and their parents' parents, down to the days of Moshe rabenu."

I would turn and walk out.

Ah, if that day would come.


But on the train back to Linz my amusement evaporated, my spirits dropped. For surely the Germans would win; they would conquer the world, and even if I remained alive there would not be a Jewish man alive to give me a Jewish child. And what was I dreaming of? Here I had passed their examination; I was marked qualified. So the adoption process would continue! I would have to produce the Leszczyszyn family records or they themselves would send for them. How long could I delay? A few weeks? A month? Unless I got free of the Eberhardts, I was doomed.

That night I told the Eberhardts the joyful news of my acceptance as worthy of becoming a German.

"A toast!" cried Herr Eberhardt, and he brought the bottle out of the cabinet, with three glasses.

"Ah, now you will truly be our Katarina!" said Frau Eberhardt, and she embraced me.

The glasses were filled. "May we be together always!" proposed Herr Eberhardt. And we drank.

And the next morning, I could feel nothing with my fingers. I could not even manage the buttons on my dress, and when Frau Eberhardt arose, I had to ask her to help me. It was a strange sensation—almost as when my mother fitted my clothes on me, sewing my dresses.

Frau Eberhardt was now really worried about my rheumatism. I must go to the doctor again, at once, this morning.

This time he prescribed a program of electric massage. But I had plans for a program of my own.

That evening a plate of soup fell from my hands, smashing on the dining-room floor. I wept. "I can't! I can't!"

Herr Eberhardt soothed me. The electric massages would surely help. Meanwhile I must do only the lightest work, and rest every day. The following morning they were both solicitous. Frau Eberhardt stayed home and not only moved the heavy furniture but did all the housework herself. Each day they were more concerned for me, more kind, as if I were truly becoming their daughter. I was in despair.

I saw that I would have to make a drastic attack. On the sideboard was a Venetian vase, one of their most cherished and admired possessions. It was a memento of a trip they had taken in the early years of their marriage. Of cut crystal, shining like a great diamond, it was a beautiful piece of glassware, and yet I had to make up my mind to break it.

I chose an afternoon when Frau Eberhardt was in the house. I was dusting. I picked up the vase, to wipe it, and it slipped from my fingers and was smashed.

She came running. "Katarina!"

I burst out in anguish. "Send me away! It fell from my fingers; I can't feel anything. Oh, to have broken something so beautiful! It had such memories for you! I know it can never be replaced! Send me away!"

Even that wasn't enough; they merely sent me on another visit to the doctor. This time I asked him to give me a letter stating that I could no longer do housework. He stated only that I was to avoid lifting heavy things, or doing tasks that would strain my arms. I presented the letter to the Eberhardts and again suggested that they had best get another maid.

No, no, they said. We would manage. Was I not like a daughter to them?

Meanwhile the formal notice from Vienna arrived, of my acceptance for Germanification, and Herr Eberhardt asked, "But, Katarina! Haven't you received a reply to the letter you sent to your village?"

"No," I said.

And to me, that *no* meant much more. For if our Polish friends had not answered my last plea for information about my family, their silence was itself an answer—of death. Mother, Father, Yaacov were no longer there, no longer alive.

"You must write again, Katarina. Your people are so slipshod! I'll have to write to the German authorities there to forward your family records. That way we will be sure to get a reply, and promptly."

I said that the mails were slow because of the war. He needn't trouble. The records would surely arrive in a few days.

Now all sorts of wild schemes went through my mind. I would have to get away from the Eberhardts, even if it meant burning down the house! I would tell them I had contracted a dreadful social disease. But no, that was so easily checked on. I would ruin the meals, let the house get dirty.

In my despair, I consulted Nina. All I could tell her was that they wanted to adopt me; I said I feared that I would be tied to them, become their slave forever if the adoption went through. Oh, if I could only tell Nina my real reason, and how desperate things were for me!

Yet, Nina said she understood my feelings. But it would be a delicate matter to have me transferred, since they had not expressed dissatisfaction with me and were, on the contrary, so much attached to me. She could think of only one way. She would have to say that I was needed on the staff of the camp. She could say that there were no other girls with my language qualifications—Ukrainian, Polish, Russian, and now German—who could type.

Even though I was still afraid of being exposed to all the workers coming through the camp, I agreed. But on my next visit, Nina told me she had sounded out her chief and that he had refused. "Are the Eberhardts dissatisfied with her?" he had asked. She had had to say no. "Then why make a change? You can manage without her."

So now I had to find my own way.

In the archway between the living room and dining room stood the Japanese vase. It was waist-high, with silver and blue and green inlays, picturing graceful kimono-clad ladies with their enamel-white faces and their delicate hands, fanning themselves. This was the Eberhardts' showpiece, far more valuable than the Venetian crystal. Once every month, in the big house-cleaning, the rug on which the vase stood had to be taken up and dragged out the back door to be beaten. The vase was meanwhile pulled aside, so that the rug could be lifted.

For a few days I reported that the pain in my arms seemed to be diminishing under the electric treatment. That Friday, Frau Eberhardt forgot to offer to help me with the heavy task of rolling up the carpet and carrying it outside. I did not remind her, and she left the house.

Afraid that I would lose courage, I went immediately to my job of destruction. I pulled the vase out on the stair landing, let it balance on the edge of the stairs, and then let go. It toppled down the back stairs, shattering. The foliage and dry cattails which it had contained spilled into the yard.

Then I went up to my room and packed my satchel. I brought it down and set it in the entrance hall. After that I completed my housework.

Frau Eberhardt arrived home, saw my satchel in the entry, and called, "Katarina, what is this?"

I came to her, white-faced. "Frau Eberhardt, what happened today is too much. You and your husband have been so good to me, and I . . . I can't help breaking things—"

"But what has happened?" She took a step into the living room and then rushed out to the back stairway. "*Mein Gott!* What have you done?" she wailed. "The Japanese vase!"

"The Japanese vase!" I moaned. "First your Venetian crystal, your precious memento! And now the Japanese vase! I can't bear it!"

Frau Eberhardt had burst into tears. I had never seen her so truly undone, and now I too burst into tears. We stood there facing each other, sobbing and wailing.

"Katarina, Katarina!"

"I broke it! I've broken your most precious things!"

"You can't help it. You have worked your fingers to the bone for us."

"You have been so good to me, and I cause you only grief."

"What will become of you?"

We fell into each other's arms. I couldn't stop crying. Everything, everything, was behind my tears, even the realization of the most insane situation of all—that instead of suffering cruelty and hatred from the Germans, I should find my greatest danger coming from this couple who were kind to me.

At last we were quiet. Nothing more was said until Herr Eberhardt came home. We were downstairs waiting for him. I had carried in the shards of the vase, in a vain effort to see if they could be glued together, and they now lay like a corpus delicti on the dining-room floor.

He walked in, saw the remains, looked at me, looked again at the shards. There was one piece on which a hand holding a fan had been broken off at the wrist. I felt not only like a murderer but like an utter barbarian. Herr Eberhardt said not a word. He walked upstairs to his study. This time I knew I had cut him to his very soul.

He came down to dinner. He had prepared a letter to the Arbeitsamt, which he handed me. I took it to the kitchen and read it. The letter was warm, regretful. I was a fine girl and had proven a tireless worker, intelligent, cheerful, and of the best character. Unfortunately I had fallen ill and was no longer able to carry out my duties; hence they were forced with the utmost regret to relinquish my services. They hoped that the Arbeitsamt could find me useful, light employment, suitable to the state of my health. health.

I thanked them. I had been there for eight months, snug as in a bomb shelter. Now I must go out again into the open.

WHEN I ARRIVED at Bindermichel, Clava and Nina cried, "You've done it!" Nina hugged me. "Now you'll stay with us! What an idea, to be a housemaid!" And when I told them about the Japanese vase, they shrieked with laughter. For a while I was dumfounded, and then I found myself laughing, too. We rollicked like schoolgirls.

"But what's wrong with your hands, really?" Nina seized them, examining my fingers. "No wonder. It's from keeping them in the water all day long, washing dishes, scrubbing floors. You'll see, now you're here, it'll go away."

And strangely enough the pains did disappear, almost immediately.

My life was completely changed. I no longer had privacy, it was true, but I had friends around me. Nina arranged for me to work in the office with herself and Clava; after all, she had declared to the boss that she needed me. And soon we were not only working together but all three living in the same room, a room that, according to the regulations, could be occupied by only two.

On the first night they had found me a bed in the same barracks; my roommate was a young Frenchwoman, a translator. I would have the room practically to myself, Clava said, winking, since Jacqueline always came home late. Oh, there were ways to stay out after hours.

[ 115 ]

I met Jacqueline in the morning, a very pretty girl with gorgeous reddish hair, extremely fussy about her clothes, vain of her elegance, untidy, and not a pleasant roommate. I kept out of her way. This was easy enough, with her busy nocturnal life.

But a few nights later the situation happened to be reversed—I was the one who came home late, having been sitting up to all hours with Nina and Clava in their room. And as I entered I was startled. In the dim light that came from the hallway, I saw Jacqueline's head, as I thought, reposing on the chair. I let out a shriek. At this, Jacqueline sat up in bed, head and all. On the chair was a wig. Her own hair was clipped very close.

Wearing a wig was the latest mode in Paris, she assured me. But I couldn't get over the sight. When she had again fallen asleep, I went back to Nina and Clava and pulled them out of their beds. They sneaked into my room, and gawked. "The latest fashion?" Clava tittered. In France, she had heard, the girls who went out with German soldiers were sometimes caught, and they got their hair clipped off. No wonder Jacqueline had volunteered to work in Germany.

Perhaps Jacqueline sensed that I knew, for it became more and more unpleasant to room with her. Then Nina and Clava had a thought. Why shouldn't we have an extra cot moved into their room? I was there all the time anyway. It would be crowded, but we would all be together.

The chief had to be asked. He even made a joke about it—so long as the third bed was not for a man, he would approve. And so I moved in, feeling safe and snug with my two friends.

In the evenings, they would insist that I come out with them. Mostly they would go to the movies or stroll with their men. As Clava had to be careful not to be seen with Hans the Austrian, she had acquired a second friend, also named Hans. We called him Hans the Czech. And the girls twitted me about my handsome Hungarian. Soon, they said, they would find me another beau.

"Ay, Katinka," Nina would say, "you'll see, you can even be happy here. We'll find you a handsome young man. I'll ask Karlus to look around."

I protested that I didn't want to get involved, yet I knew it was bound to happen sooner or later, and secretly I was eager. If it could only be someone like Karlus. He was a quiet man, with a nice sense of humor; he could take down someone with just a single word, a word that would send us into gales of laughter. He was what I thought of as a real man, dependable and devoted. Nina was always showing off little gifts that he managed to buy for her. He couldn't buy anything expensive, but even if it was only a handkerchief or a scarf, Karlus would select it with a thought to her coloring, her gray-blue eyes, her personal taste. And he always managed to find little ways of surprising her with his gifts. Those two were truly in love.

Although Nina kept up a mild pretense that they were just devoted friends and managed everything else quite discreetly, I knew quite well that Karlus was her lover. He lived in one of the camps for Czech workers, not the one across the street, but a lager at the Hermann Goering works, where he had been conscripted as a draftsman.

With Clava, things were different. She was a trifle sluttish, but in the most appealing way. Her face was round, soft, and her mouth had an expression about it, a looseness, that I imagined could be seen on prostitutes. She even talked like one; her language was shockingly foul, a soldier's language. Every word was preceded by a sex word, and yet in her this didn't really seem offensive. It was just Clava's way. She had no temper whatsoever, was calm and agreeable, while Nina could fly into a temper over the slightest annoyance.

Clava's first Hans, the Austrian, was ugly, thin, with a sluggish speech that was almost defective, and with nothing interesting to say. He kept the canteen in the Czech camp across the road.

"What on earth do you want with him?" we would tease.

"Oh, he gives me things. A girl has to have a man who will give her things."

They were not the small gifts of Nina's Karlus. These were really substantial presents—a radio, a wristwatch, a new dress, shoes. But still, it was not a pay relationship. Hans was a good soul, and she was truly fond of him. He was what my Papa would have called a *nebish*, a nobody, but warmhearted, and wonderfully helpful to the foreign workers. So, though we felt he somewhat lowered the tone of our company, Hans the Austrian was tolerated.

Clava made no bones about her relationship; she would manage to slip out after ten-o'clock curfew, through a gap in the fence on one side of the camp, where the barbed wire had been arranged in such a way that a piece could be detached—a convenience to which I had quickly been introduced. Clava would scuttle across the road and spend entire nights with Hans the Austrian, in the rear of his canteen, though it was, of course, a crime punishable by imprisonment for Hans to sully himself with a female of a lower race.

Clava's second Hans, the Czech, made up by his handsome physique for anything that was lacking in Hans the Austrian. Sometimes she alternated, breaking up with one while she went with the other, but for long periods she would be friendly to both.

Even before coming to live in Bindermichel I had wondered how it was that I felt so close to these two young women who were after all so much more grown up than I. They had passed the border; both had been married. Before leaving home I had never had close friends of this sort. There had always been a segregation between "those who knew" and the still-virgins, no matter how sophisticated the maidens pretended to be. Sometimes, with Nina and Clava, I felt that they cherished me, that we got on so well together, really, because every woman wants in her heart to

[ 118 ]

pretend that she is still only a girl—just as Nina kept up the pretense that nothing actually happened between herself and Karlus. And even Clava pretended that all that, on the sexual side, with men, was of no great importance. Perhaps, too, this remnant of girlishness was kept alive for Nina and Clava by our way of life together. We were like schoolgirls in a regulated dormitory, always scheming to break the rules, to stay out after hours.

We were free to go in and out, provided we were in bed at ten. But even though one of the supervisors occasionally made the rounds to check the beds, this rule was regarded very lightly in the personnel barracks, for the veteran inhabitants, like Clava and Nina, had their understandings with the guards. And there was always the hole in the fence.

The supervision was light enough, and the atmosphere was good, except for the presence of one elderly couple, a pair of White Russians who had lived in France. Both were poisonous tale-bearers and intriguers. They loved to make surprise visits at night. And they were dreadful anti-Semites, as well. One hardly ever heard Jews spoken about in the camp, but with them the word Jew was the most vile of epithets, and it was always coming into their talk. They had a dangerous way of throwing the word at people they disliked.

There was a dark-complexioned girl named Liza who worked in the kitchen, a generous-hearted girl who could always be counted on for a pot of tea. "Ach, Liza, that Jewess," the Russian woman, Tamara, would say. "What? You don't think she looks Jewish? She even acts Jewish." So, although I would have liked to become friends with her, I was careful to steer clear of Liza.

Of those two tale-bearers, I was most careful. Fortunately they were almost alone in their passion for intrigues. The head of the camp, an elderly Austrian named Seifert, was interested in nothing but efficient operation. All he wanted was for the transient workers to be quickly sorted out and sent to the right jobs, so that he would have no complaints from the various managements whom he supplied with labor.

My work was on the reception team with Nina and Clava. A Russian woman doctor completed our crew. Transports of workers would arrive at any hour of the day or night; we would meet them and work straight through until everyone was registered.

Just as I myself had gone through the inspection naked, so they came, lines of women, lines of men. And I found it equally embarrassing to be on the other side of the table. I could not raise my eyes to look a man in the face. Clava would tease me. After all, she would say, it would be less embarrassing for me to look up than down. But I told myself that if I kept my head down there would be less chance for anyone who happened to come from the region of Hrebenko to recognize me.

On Sundays the three of us, perhaps with Karlus along, would take our rucksacks and board a small local train. We'd get off at a siding less than an hour from Linz. Some of the farmhands imported from Italy had started their own little truck gardens there, and we would load our sacks with fresh green cucumbers, lettuce, carrots, and the tomatoes I had once despised. Our diet in Bindermichel was altogether lacking in vegetables and greens.

And then we would stroll the fields, dipping into our sacks to crunch the fresh vegetables, warm with their tang of the earth. Even fruit was to be had. On a lane off the main road, we came to know a little Austrian lady, a retired schoolteacher, who had plum trees on her tiny estate, as well as pears and apples. She sold her fruit only to the foreign workers, telling us how she sympathized, knowing that life was hard for us.

So we would regale ourselves of a Sunday.

During the week, the men would come along the fence to

whistle for their dates, as we were not allowed to have them visit us in the barracks. Sometimes when Nina and Clava were going out, I would insist on staying home, as I did not want to be a fifth wheel on every date. But on one particular evening Nina declared that she would not allow me to sit at home alone; besides, Nina said, Karlus already had a ticket for me to go with them to the movies.

So I dressed and joined them. At the theater, Karlus met a friend who happened to have the seat next to ours. Slavek was his name, and he also happened to be a draftsman like Karlus, and also happened to be a Czech, and even happened to work in the very same shop as Karlus.

I glanced up at Slavek. Though I am fairly tall for a girl, he was even taller for a man. And there was a handsome fellow! No need to look at the screen! He was just like one of those devil-may-care movie stars, with soft brown eyes, a piquant mouth, and a sort of glow, a glow of life. Only, he didn't seem particularly interested in me. He wasn't even looking.

Our seats were close to the screen, in the third or fourth row, and the light from the projection was reflected off the screen toward us, so that I could see him quite plainly. I found that I wasn't watching the movie. I was looking at him. And I wasn't the only one. There were other girls around me whose heads were turned. As for my cavalier, he calmly watched the picture.

Afterward we went for the usual stroll. He paid no particular attention to me, and I felt suddenly lumpish. I was no coquette. I didn't know how to attract a man. Indeed, this Slavek had a terribly annoying way of looking around at other women, remarking, "There's a pretty girl!"

And so we separated at our fence, and there was nothing. No talk of meeting again.

Yet I couldn't help chattering to Nina. What a handsome fellow!

"You see!" she said. "If I get you someone, he's someone!"

I had no way to measure my feelings. I had to reach back through so much that had happened to me, to the days when a high-school girl had let herself be embraced by her teacher. Then, I had felt myself being led on, led on by a man, and I had responded more out of curiosity to discover if I would feel anything than out of a true longing for him. Now I was surprised how in the midst of my work, in the midst of my chatter with the girls, in the midst of every thought, the longing stayed in me; it was a new condition in my life. It was like everything everyone had ever said, and yet it was more, more. And this was happening to me even here, in the midst of my hiding and my anxiety! This part of life was not being denied to me, nor could it be escaped.

Two days later, Nina was getting ready for her date with Karlus. We heard his whistle. She looked out the window. "Katya, you'd better get dressed. Slavek is with him."

And so it began. The movies, the walks, the four of us. But Slavek was in no way like the good Karlus. Slavek was impulsive, crazy. He might turn up at ten in the morning, unexpectedly, having somehow got away from his job. He would whistle or even shout my name, or demand of some girl inside the gate, "Go to the office and tell Katya to come out." I'd make some excuse and get away for a minute. He'd want me to come to town. Sometimes I even managed it.

And in town he was likely to do anything. I was still quite shy; I didn't like even to hold a man's arm in the street. "Take my arm!" Slavek would demand. "If you don't, I'll walk on my hands, right here in the middle of town!"

And if I refused—as I discovered the one time I did refuse—hup! there he was, walking on his hands! I tugged at his coat. Slavek righted himself and I took his arm. He pulled me close to his side. And I knew that strange, heady feeling, in early love, perhaps more exquisite than kissing, than close embrace—that tender, excited feeling of the limbs, walking together.

There on the street in Linz I suddenly remembered my girlish questionings with Alla, about "feeling anything" with a man. Now I could really have told her.

Where were they now, Alla and Milla, so I could run and say, "Everything before was childishness. Only now I know; I know how it feels."

And like some balance of pain for love, the thought of them was with me again, constantly. What was happening to them, there in Hrebenko? What had happened? It was like staring out into some absolutely dark night, listening for some sign of life.

Once, a transport of workers came from Galicia, with Ukrainians from the region of Lwów. Unable to restrain myself, I risked a few general questions.

"How is it back home?"

"Hard, hard."

My head pounding, I dared. "But at least, I hear, they've finally finished with the Jews."

"Oh, there's not a Jew left. They've all been burned to death. Their houses, everything burned."

I was seeing Slavek every day. He was irrepressible, a real bandit, a bohemian. I would have wanted him different. I wanted him to be respectable, like Karlus. Karlus was always carefully dressed; he even wore cuff links. Slavek wore unpressed pants, a weird jacket with a slit in the back. His hat was twisted into some crazy shape and tilted so that a curl peeped out. Karlus always arrived on the dot; Slavek might show up an hour late, or even an hour early. That, I liked.

I fussed, objected, told him he'd get me into trouble, but it was always a thrill when he appeared unexpectedly. More than once he whistled for me when the lights were already out, and I was in bed. And I would go out to him, risking the terrible vengeance of the White Russian, who might come around with his flashlight to check the beds. Already he had caught Clava, and he had reported that she was said to be going out with an Austrian named Hans. She had been called to the Gestapo, but had talked her way out, declaring that everyone knew her friend Hans was a Czech. Yet none of these dangers deterred me. When Slavek whistled, out I went!

Nor did Slavek bring me little gifts, such as Karlus brought to Nina. Slavek was not considerate but bossy, a dictator. He began to tell me what to wear, what not to wear, how to comb my hair. Ugh, that Polish peasant hair-do! I must comb my hair off my forehead, in the Czech fashion. There! It made me look more womanly. And then he began to demand, Why didn't I use make-up? Why didn't I use lipstick like a real woman?

This had been a matter of absolute principle with me. As a young girl, I had made a code of "being myself." Tauba too, and several of the girls in our circle, had believed in this code and had scorned the use of cosmetics as deceitful. A man should love a woman for what she was. That was our credo. We were derisive of Milla when she appeared at school with her cheeks rouged, and all the girls who copied her we branded as brainless. Ours was the real sophistication!

Besides, I had always thought, since I had such high natural coloring, what did I need with cosmetics?

But now Slavek began to pester me. No wonder I was such a prude. I was even afraid to use lipstick. And he got Nina to join in the campaign. "What does it hurt? Put on a little make-up!"

[ 124 ]

"A man must love a woman for what she is," I announced. "I don't want to wear a mask of smears and daubs."

"Don't be so stubborn, Katinka!" She laughed. "Be what you are, but add a bit."

One Sunday when the four of us were out on an excursion, Slavek produced a lipstick from his pocket. He caught hold of me, and while the others hooted, he smeared it on thick. "There! Now maybe you'll become a woman!"

He had of course from the first frankly embarked on the campaign of "making me a woman." And just as frankly I had told him that this was excluded. If he wanted to go out with me, it had to be with such an understanding.

Why? I would argue with myself. What was I waiting for? Never again would I live in that ordered life of my childhood where a girl could expect to fall in love and get married. Like everyone else, I had now to forgo the rule I had absorbed from the first moment of my upbringing, that my life as a woman would begin with my husband.

Surely it had been only natural, in Hrebenko, to believe that I would never marry except for love, and that when I was in love I would marry, and so the rule about making love hadn't seemed prudish at all. But now I was no longer sure what was honest. If I was in love, it was only honest to yield. And yet I couldn't. Perhaps it was a desperate clinging to all that was left to me of home. It was as though by giving way I would at last admit that my mother was dead.

We went out more than once on overnight excursions to the mountains. I would remind Slavek in advance: "Slavek, I don't want you to be disappointed. I don't want us to go if you think it will be any different."

Of course he would agree to behave, and I would know he meant to change me if he could.

Once we went to climb the Feuerkugel. It was an almost painfully beautiful day; the sun was so warm we had to take off our coats, and yet there was snow on the mountainside, and the peak was covered with snow.

There were cable cars, but a long line had formed, and it looked like a three-hour wait. "Come on!" Slavek called, and he started up like a goat, afoot. Though we weren't dressed for it, we followed. He leaped and cavorted ahead of us, came catapulting back down the mountainside to seize me by the hand and drag me along with him. Soon we had reached the snow line. On, on! he commanded. He dragged me into the snow, till it filled my shoes; he went back and dragged the others. We romped in the snow like children, washing each other's faces, throwing snowballs; we plunged into drifts ankle-deep.

Suddenly Slavek appeared on a huge boulder, near the mountain top. He stepped to the edge, there above us, flung out his arms to the world, and shouted, "I am I, Slavek, and the universe is mine!"

Who but Slavek could do it, a conscripted worker in a foreign land, living behind barbed wire.

Laughing, we plodded through the snow, we girls in our thin shoes and dresses, until we came to the peak. We took off our soaked shoes, our stockings, the men rubbed our feet, and then we sat in the sun. Afterward we had coffee in the *Gasthaus*, and danced there. And on the way down, this time by cable car, we all sang, but in the whole medley of voices I heard only Slavek's, so vibrant, so charged with life! And everybody looked at us. We had become tanned up there in that one afternoon of sunshine; we glowed, and who could say but we were four happy people!

That night we stayed over, at an inn. We took two rooms, but as Nina still kept up her pretenses, it was with the understanding that the girls would be in one room, the men in the other. Before

[ 126 ]

going to bed, we walked in the dark fields, and Nina and Karlus drifted away.

Then Slavek and I fought.

Only once before, I had known something of this, and then it had not been the same. Not long after the Russians had come to Hrebenko, and I had made trips to Lwów for Papa, to replenish the vodka supply, there had come one time when I had been given a ride back from Lwów, with my sack of bottles, in a small truck driven by a sort of sergeant. There had been a second one, who had got into the back of the truck with me. And along the way he had suddenly seized me, and I had fought him. Silently, almost impassively, intently, he had exerted his strength, and it had been almost as though there was a rule to our battle, that a man was allowed to force a girl, simply if he were able to. I had twisted, and clawed, and somehow when the truck lurched I had broken out of his hold and tried to leap. And only then, in that moment, I had screamed. The driver had stopped the truck and come back to see what had happened; then he had laughed and called to his comrade to let me alone, and to come and sit with him, in front. And that had been the end of it. I had never told it at home. The scratches on my face and arms, I had told Mama, had come from the low-hanging branches of a tree, under which the truck had passed. And I had run up to my room, for it was still the time when Tauba and I lived in our third-floor room. I had crept into my bed, and shivered, and wept, for I had felt then that I knew what it meant to be a woman. Tauba had come, and stroked me, but I hadn't been able to tell her what had happened. Until much later, at night. Then she had held me in her arms, and we had clung to each other, as sisters.

But now with Slavek, it was a different fight. This time I was fighting the man and myself, too. I writhed within myself. And my anger at myself made me only more violent toward him. I struck him, hard, and he let go of me.

[ 127 ]

For several days we didn't see each other. Partly, I was angry because I knew that Slavek went out with many girls. Oh, he had a great reputation among the foreign workers. It was said that even a number of respectable German women of Linz had had their meetings with Slavek. And if it was not with respectable married women, or with girls from the workers' camps, then it was with prostitutes.

One night I had to talk it out, with Nina and Karlus. "Katya," Karlus said, "I must tell you one thing. I know him well. Slavek has never gone with a girl in this way before. With Slavek it was always only to go to bed. If a girl goes, fine. If not, next day there's another."

"Then why did you bring him to me, if you knew he was that kind?"

"Even such a man longs for a girl with whom he can stay for good."

I wanted to cry. I wanted to run to Slavek wherever he was. And yet I said, "Karlus, then why is it, there are times when we all go out together, and you two boys bring us home to the barracks and then you go off—Karlus, at those times, he doesn't always go home to the lager with you."

"No, he goes off by himself," Karlus said. He looked me directly in the eyes; I could no longer be naïve.

And all day long, in my tension, I kept wondering. Could it be for Slavek as for me, even though he went to bed with those other women? Could he feel as I felt, as though all life were suspended because of our separation?

So we met again. We walked hand in hand, on that path away from the barracks, away from the city, into the fields. We stood and embraced, and I felt terribly dismayed, helpless, and I couldn't help bringing up all those things to Slavek, about the rest of his life. "What do you think, I'm made of wood?" he snapped. And then, holding me by the shoulders, "If that was all I wanted, why would

[ 128 ]

I come to you, where I know I won't get it!" He struck himself on the forehead. "*Ach*, Slavek! You had to go and fall in love with a Katinka, with such a little Ukrainian oxhead!"

And all that night on my cot I kept hearing those words, better than a whispered "I love you." Those words of admission to himself that he was in love. With a Katinka, a little Ukrainian oxhead. I began to see them as a couple, Slavek and Katinka. He was standing there in the woods embracing her; they were melted together. Slavek and Katinka. Katinka. Not Eva.

And all at once it seemed clear to me—that was why. That was why I had not been able to free myself for complete intimacy with him. For I wanted him to love me, Eva. Eva. To know me truly, the person that I was in truth.

And then a terribly insistent urge took hold of me. With my incessant dreaming and thinking of Slavek, day and night, was mingled an unending urge to tell him I was Eva, a Jewish girl. Not Katinka, his little Ukrainian oxhead, but Eva.

I couldn't shake myself free of this idea, any more than I could shake myself free of my endless longing to be with Slavek, to see him, to have him make me angry with his antics, to have him touch me.

The intention kept growing in me. Yes, he had to know me, to love me for myself. I was sure of him, and yet how could I reveal this terrible, mortal secret that I had kept for a whole, long year?

Nina and Clava were as close to me as sisters. Could I tell them? Surely not. I could not burden them with it. Slavek would never betray me, no matter what happened between us, of that I was sure. But, drunken, sometime, or in the arms of some slut? No, no, I was being unfair to him!

But there came another fear. Suppose I told him. Would it make me someone different to him, someone strange? When he lost his Katinka, would he still want to be with me, with Eva?

And meanwhile, perhaps because I was thinking so constantly of this, there came the only fright that I had had in a long while. A Polish worker, in his interview with me, suddenly remarked, "You speak Polish perfectly, except for your R. That soft R—that's the way the Jews talk."

No, if he meant anything by it, he wouldn't have said it to me but to others. He had told me he was from Katowitz, in the south. I mentioned a city in the north. "I come from Poznań," I said. "That's how we talk in Poznań."

He kept on. What a funny way they talk in Poznań! What an R!

And then I realized what an idiot I had been. Suppose he mentioned the incident around the camp and repeated that I had said I came from Poznań? In the records, I came from the opposite end of Poland! That very day, I placed him in a factory, to get him out of Bindermichel.

But from my reawakened fear, there came a new thought, in my worries about Slavek. If he truly loved me, if we should become bound together, he had a right to know everything that might happen to him because of me. Suppose I were caught. Before having anything more to do with me, he should know this risk. And so I determined to tell him.

I set it in my mind, that it would have to be on a special day. I was making over my good dress, according to a pattern in one of the fashion books that Jacqueline had brought from France. For since I had moved out of her room, we had become friends. I told myself that the special day, when I told Slavek my secret, would be the day on which I wore my new dress. I would look elegant. Eva would have the best of opportunities for herself.

He was outside, calling for his Katya. It was twilight, and as I came out in my new, shining dress, Slavek seized me and whirled me around, there on the street in front of the camp gate, calling to the guards, to everyone, "Look! Look at Katya! There's a lady of fashion!"

We walked off, arm in arm. We had to celebrate, Slavek insisted. We'd go to the Rosenstube and dance!

No, I said, I didn't feel like going into town. I wanted to walk the other way, toward the country.

What! With a new dress? There was his contrary Katya! If Slavek says left, Katya has to say right. If Slavek says the city, Katya has to say the country, even though she's dying to go to town.

I was so tense with my plan that I couldn't even squabble with him. Slavek must have sensed that something unusual was in the air. He wheeled and walked down the road, and I had to walk quickly to keep up with him. I was silent. We passed the edge of town. The sun was setting; the whole sky was red, the haze around us was reddish. We turned off the road, down our favorite path. We were always so gay when we came here, teasing each other and laughing.

"Katya, what's wrong?"

How could I say it? Blurt out the words?

I walked a little farther, then halted and drew him aside, among the trees. I put my hand against his chest.

"Slavek, I know that you love me enough so that I can tell you something about myself without the least worry."

"Well, what is it? What is it? What's wrong?"

"I want to tell you . . . Slavek, I'm Jewish."

[ 131 ]

He looked at me, his eyes burning in that still-reddish light. And he said, "What of it?"

"But, Slavek—"

"But what? What does it matter to me if you are Jewish?" He saw the tears in my eyes, and he put his hands on my shoulders, hard. "Now I love you doubly. Oh, yes. Now I see. Because you really love me, you had to tell me this. Katya, I love you doubly."

"I'm not Katya," I whispered. "I'm Eva. My name is Eva."

He repeated it softly. "Eva." And as he said my name, an overwhelming joy rose in me, a bubbling feeling of release, something such as I imagined I would feel if the whole war ended and the world was at peace.

It was foolish, foolish, I told myself, to feel so much over so simple a thing. But the tears burst now, flowing, and he kissed the tears on my face, holding me, fondling me with a new tenderness, repeating the name in a hundred endearing diminutives, "Eva, Evaleh, Evinka, Eva."

Then we sat down on a fallen tree trunk, and everything burst from me. I told Slavek of my family, my hopeless fears for all of them, except perhaps my sister Tauba, who might be alive with the partisans. But my mother, my father, my little brother, were surely gone. Then I told of my brother in Palestine, and Slavek swore that we would one day find him. As soon as the war was over we would be married; first he would take me back to Prague to his parents; he would work, earn a great deal of money, even get rich—he had all sorts of ideas for inventions—and then we would visit my brother. Why, we would even go to live in Palestine!

He pressed my hands. "Eva, Evinka, if ever a time should come when you are in danger, you must tell me at once."

"If that time comes, nothing can be done. I would want only one thing—that you should not become involved."

"No! You must tell me," he insisted. "We have ways."

I knew that some kind of an underground existed among the

Czechs; they had a hidden little radio on which they listened to foreign broadcasts. But how could they possibly help anyone who was caught as a Jew?

We would escape, Slavek said. We would get to Czechoslovakia somehow, and we would be hidden by his parents. Perhaps we should even go now, right away, without waiting.

No, no, I said. That would only call them down on us. So far, nothing had happened. The more time passed, the less likely it was that anything would happen. And just now, the war was going a bit better.

Then suddenly he laughed.

Without even knowing why, I laughed with him. I felt so happy.

"Evinka, now I understand," he said.

"What?"

"There's always been a saying with us—Jewish girls are the hardest to get."

I pulled away my hand. He put his arm around me. Still, I had to laugh with him again. It was a compliment. I was a good Jewish daughter, after all.


And now, the next days were heavenly. Slavek treated me with such tenderness! A new delicacy appeared in his behavior; everyone noticed it. Nina said to me, once after the four of us had been out together and she and I were getting ready for bed, "You know, Katya, whatever it was with him until now, Slavek is really in love with you now. He's like a man just before marriage." There was such a softness in her voice, I knew she was thinking about her own husband, of whom she spoke so little. She caught my eyes. Then her tone became lighter. "He's even ceased to bother you."

It was true. Slavek had ceased to press me, that way, and for my part, I didn't even think about whether he was going with other girls, for that had suddenly ceased to matter. I was at peace.

Slavek had gone to Vienna to arrange some documents about things at home in Czechoslovakia; he was gone for two days and when he returned he had a gift for me. What could it be? He teased me; there was no package to be seen.

Then he put his hand into his pocket and brought out some folded slips of paper. Ration coupons for dress goods! Only Slavek would have thought of such a gift! It was comical, and yet it was just right.

He had spent all his money on the black market for these coupons. There were four, each valid for a meter of cloth. Since it was forbidden to buy cloth except to be used in mending, only a single meter of any one pattern could be bought.

I went from shop to shop in Linz, and in each of three shops I bought a meter of the same elegant black fabric. In the fourth, I used my last coupon for red silk trim. Night after night we girls pored over Jacqueline's fashion magazines. Finally a pattern was decided on. I sewed as though it were to be my wedding dress. And I was satisfied. The dress was stunning. Black was always in the height of fashion in Paris, Jacqueline assured me, and the dash of contrasting color went well with my red cheeks. I even had enough material for a hat, and so my costume was complete.

I had finished it in time for a great occasion. The four of us were going on a weekend trip to visit Anya.

Slavek was irrepressible. He announced that his Katya was the belle of Bindermichel, and he posed me at the gate while he took snapshots, as though I were a fashion model.

And so we took the train.

I had been to Steinkeller several times, and Anya had come to Linz, so that it was well established that we were old friends; there seemed less and less to fear. Anya was still alone; she had thought it best to keep her distance from the farmhands, and so our visits were almost her whole social life.

Anya met us at the station, beaming. This time, it turned out, she had outdone herself. She had rented a room in a near-by village so as to be away from the estate. Always a good manager, Anya had found a charming place for our weekend. The room was in a farmhouse, one of those ample, peaceful houses that seem untouched by war or by any outside catastrophe. The farmer's wife, good-hearted, fat, welcomed us and laughingly asked where the third young man was. She made sure we had everything we wanted and then kept out of our way.

The room was vast. Side by side stood two grand double beds, topped with the customary mountains of feather quilts and pillows. At the foot of the two beds was a cot. Everything smelled fresh; the house was Sunday-scrubbed.

We looked at the beds and looked at one another. We laughed, and everyone said there was safety in numbers.

On a round table, Anya had prepared our feast. She had brought every imaginable delicacy: roast goose, and wonderful sausages of three kinds, butter, and goose fat, and jellies, and pears, and liver pâté, wonderful Viennese cream cakes, and tarts, fresh cream, real coffee! We gorged ourselves. There were pitchers of cider and bottles of beer and wine. We told jokes. Slavek knew all the latest Hitler jokes. And there were new jokes about the troubles of the Germans in Russia. We sang, we danced.

And as it grew late we made more and more jokes about the beds. Anya laughed maliciously, saying she had no problem. The cot was hers. As for the two large beds—well, we couldn't deny that she had provided plenty of room.

The men were driven out while we undressed. I still did not know for sure how things would be arranged. There are moments, times in our lives, when it seems that just some little clumsiness about the way things are arranged makes a fateful difference.

[ 135 ]

Everything had been so gay until now, I felt so immersed in happiness, in Slavek's love, in the love of my friends, that the whole occasion was like a wedding party. Surely never in my life would the time again be so good.

Perhaps if we had that night taken separate rooms, everything would have happened naturally. And perhaps the presence of Anya, even in another room, still would have held me, like an admonition from home.

Anya lay down on her cot and merrily bid us good night.

The men returned, in their pajamas. Nina looked at me quietly, even with a tiny smile of compassion and, sitting down on one of the large beds, said, "Karlus and I will sleep here. Is that all right, Katarina?"

I knew already, with a dreadful feeling of disappointment in myself, with a sorrow over the circumstances, that it was not all right. Not like this, half in jest, for our beginning. Oh, why hadn't something happened to arrange this differently? And yet in another part of me I was dreadfully grateful; I had a feeling that things had to be this way so that I would be spared, so that I could still be faithful for a while to everything Mother wanted—a good Jewish marriage. No, I told myself angrily, I would not let myself feel spared because Slavek was not Jewish. For if I truly loved . . . No, it was the image of a real marriage in a settled world that I was clinging to; for that, I had been spared. It was the image of a girl who was waiting for her husband, who believed in the solemnity of marriage as well as the joy. Otherwise, everything would be spoiled for her.

And so we lay together that night, a dreadful night.

He whispered, "Eva." I closed his lips with my fingers. He bit them. I drew away.

In the next bed, Nina, heavy with wine, was asleep in the arms of her Karlus, and soon we heard him, too, snoring gently. With Slavek I kept up a whispered struggle. No, no, not like this, not

[ 136 ]

here. And then I pretended to sleep, but I felt his wakefulness, and then he said bitter things to me, in a hushed anger, and then he apologized, grew tender again, and I wanted him, I tried to sleep in his arms but knew his torture and drew away. Then I must have half slept, for a distorted whirl of thoughts and images kept passing through my mind; at moments it was even as if Tauba were there in the cot where Anya lay, and if I bent down to her and touched her it would be my sister. And still in half sleep I told myself, No, no. It's a dream. And then what held me from reaching to touch her was the fear that I would prove my dream and know Tauba was gone, and then I was fully awake and I heard every creak and whisper of the house but kept my eyes closed and pretended still to be asleep because Slavek was lying open-eyed beside me, smoking a cigarette.

In the morning we were moody, silent. We all tried to retrieve our gaiety, marveling over the good things for breakfast, but our lightheartedness was painfully effortful. Then we went walking in the fields, and we could scarcely think of anything to say to each other. We uttered the most banal remarks, about the weather, about the trees. It made my heart heavy for Anya, that all her efforts were spoiled; I even hoped Slavek would flirt with her. But the spirit was gone. We attributed our mood to tiredness. At last it was time for the train. I begged Anya to come to see me soon at Bindermichel.

On the train, too, Slavek and I could find little to say to each other. We had lost contact. I even prepared words. I would declare that I was sorry, that it was my fault, that I knew I had to make up my mind one way or the other, but because of the way I had been raised . . . I remained silent.

When we parted at the Bindermichel gate, instead of asking to see me the next day, Slavek said the day after, and then I said no, the end of the week. And yet every day all day long when I wasn't with him, it was the same as before; my longing was incessant.

And then once he was to meet me after work, and I waited and he didn't appear at all. I told myself it was good that I had failed to give myself to him, because with him, it hadn't really been love. And I went into the barracks and went to bed and wept. Nothing any longer seemed important; to remain uncaught, to live, to see the end of the war—all this dreadful struggle for life seemed a ridiculous pretense, some artificial comedy, and the only reality was that I was a girl in love, and that I had not known how to keep my lover.

The next day when Karlus came for Nina, he called out that he had something to tell me. I went to the gate with her. Slavek had gone to Vienna for a few days, Karlus said, and had asked that I be told.

Several days passed, and Slavek did not return. And then one of the girls in the office laughingly remarked, "Have you been to the hospital to see your Slavek?"

What? Didn't I know? She had been to visit a friend in the hospital—why, yes, right here in Linz—and there was Slavek. Oh, nothing serious; he claimed to have hurt his leg.

I confronted Karlus. Yes, it was true, he admitted. Slavek had wanted to spare me from worrying, but he had hurt his leg in a fall and was in the local hospital.

"Then I'll go to see him," I said.

It was not a visiting day, but through the fence I saw him in the yard. He appeared indeed to be having trouble with his leg. I called to him, and Slavek came, half limping, to the fence.

"But what happened to you? Why did you have to tell me that story about going to Vienna?"

He looked at me in a curious way, a bit embarrassed and yet

[ 138 ]

amused. "Well . . . I fell," he said, and laughed. "A few more days and I'll be cured."

All at once I felt myself blushing. I understood. I recalled how often he had pleaded, "You know I'm not made of wood."

I could feel only fury at Slavek, at myself, at the way people were made, at the conditions in which we had to live. Everything was so repulsive; why was the most beautiful part of life made so ugly? It was as though I had unknowingly put my hand into something slimy.

I told him I understood; I was sorry. And I went home.

One morning while I was at work, Clava came in and said, "Slavek is waiting for you at the bridge."

Unchanged! In spite of everything, to demand me like that, in the midst of working hours. Nevertheless I went to Herr Seifert, our chief. "My friend has been in Vienna; he's been ill for some time and he's just back. He wants to see me for a few minutes. He's waiting on the bridge."

Herr Seifert looked at me, as a man who knows what it is to have to deal with women. "All right, Katya, go and see your friend."

I approached, determined to keep down my excitement. "Well, how was it," I asked sarcastically, "in Vienna?"

"Oh, I had a miserable time." Slavek laughed.

"And how is your leg? Is it better now?"

"Yes, the cure was complete," he said. And for a moment longer we kept up our remarks. Then he burst out angrily, "Katya, you know what it was. You can't leave me over a thing like that."

We tried again. We met. We walked. But the true moment had been lost. One night I told him we had better not see each other any more. He was silent.

[ 139 ]

Then for weeks I remained in my room all the time I wasn't at work. I managed even to take my meals alone. I refused to go out with Nina and Clava, refused the dates they offered to arrange for me. Then, one night I did go out, with the whole band—Karlus, Nina, Clava, and Hans the Czech. We went to the Centralkino, and afterward we sat in a café, and there was Slavek with a band of his own, two girls among them. He came over to us and we chatted a bit, almost formally, like distant friends, and then he went back to his own group. The girls were attractive . . . .

The winter months passed in a kind of deadness. Once, Karlus came with a bright face and a pot of jam, for a celebration. The Allies, he whispered, had landed in North Africa. The might of America would now be felt in the war.

But North Africa? So far. So far from us. How could that save anyone now? As Karlus gave us his bits of news, I found myself listening, instead, with a secret hope that he might drop some word about Slavek, relate some new tale about that crazy Slavek's exploits, even tell about Slavek's affairs with women.

But, perhaps out of consideration for my feelings, the name never passed his lips.

Presently something happened that made me realize I could not be just a girl mooning for her love; I was brought back to the reality of my situation.

One day in the office Herr Seifert called me to his desk and said he had just received a call from the Gestapo. They wanted to see me. He gave the name of the officer, the room number, and said the appointment was for three o'clock.

I had two hours. And during all that time, a certain thought stood before my mind. It was as when you shut your eyes to some nightmare vision, and yet it stands before your closed eyes. You know it is false and yet it persists. It stands there.

Even my fear was blocked out by this dreadful thought. I knew in my heart that Slavek could not have betrayed me to the Gestapo. And yet the worst horror in all our helplessness is in the things that come unwanted to the mind. Even one's deepest feelings are smeared with distrust. If he could not have done it deliberately, my mind kept insisting, he might still have betrayed me by accident. He was the only one who knew. Perhaps he had accidentally spoken my name? Before some girl?

A scene arose, complete, in my imagination. I saw Slavek lying with some girl, and she was a girl truly in love with him—oh, I could believe that well enough. And perhaps it was so, that Slavek longed for me. And perhaps in his love-making with her, he called out my name, my real name, Eva. Evinka. I had read of such scenes. And had I not called and whispered his name, Slavek, Slavek, night after night in my restlessness, with my very skin crying out for him?

But even as this imagined scene struck a doubled pain in me, I tried to examine it sensibly. Suppose such a thing had happened. Suppose he had called out for Eva. How could any girl have known it was I, Katya? No, but a girl who was familiar with all the gossip in the camp—almost any girl among the foreign workers —would know that Slavek had been going out steadily, for months, with Katya, and if the girl loved Slavek she would instantly feel it was Katya that he wanted, Katya whose name he called, under that Jewish name.

But why Jewish? Suddenly the whole ugly scene was blown away in a simple thought. Eva was not necessarily a Jewish name. What of Meister Klein's mistress, brought to Hrebenko? Her name, too, had been Eva.

And I almost laughed out loud. In that instant, when the unwanted suspicion of Slavek was dissolved, it was as though every cause for despair was gone, almost as though I had not even been called to the Gestapo.

And then I tried to fathom the message. What of my chief in the office? Why had he given me the message as though it were utterly routine? Did he perhaps know the reason for the summons, and know that it was of little consequence? Or did he already know that I was being accused of being Jewish? And was his offhand manner a bad sign? For, surely, no one took a call from the Gestapo lightly.

There even passed through my mind that incident with the seemingly stupid Pole who had kept puzzling over my *R*. And I had told him that I came from Poznań. How idiotic of me to have felt so superior, to have become careless with him because he appeared stupid. Suppose it had been a pose, to catch me off guard? Or suppose he had babbled about his interview and someone like the White Russian had been struck by my saying I was from northern Poznań when I was from the south of Poland? But that incident had taken place months ago! No matter. They might, all this time, have been checking.

So I tormented myself. But once on the way, I forbade myself any nervousness. I must be calm, self-possessed. I must show no sign of worry.

The building was in the center of Linz. Just inside the entrance was a reception desk. There was nothing sinister about the place; it looked like any other office building. I gave my name, and the name of the person I had been told to see, Herr Kroll. She telephoned, confirmed the appointment. I walked up to the second floor. As I passed an open door I happened to glance in and saw a long room with several men standing with their faces to the wall.

I came to the Foreign Workers Section. Opening the proper door, I found myself in an ordinary office occupied by two young men in civilian clothes. One sat behind the desk, the other at his side, glancing through an open folder. They greeted me pleasantly

[ 142 ]

enough, even courteously, asked me to sit down, and the one behind the desk, Kroll, began with routine questions. My name was Katarina Leszczyszyn. I worked in the registration office at the *Durchgangslager*. How long had I been there? Nine months, yes. And I roomed in the personnel barracks. I shared a room with two other young women, Clava Kriloff and Nina Ilanova. They were also my intimate friends? Yes. I was quite close to Nina?

For one deathly moment I thought, Even she? If Nina had betrayed me, I would rather die than live in such a world.

But now he was asking, What did I know of Nina's background? Where she had come from, what she had done there? And suddenly the curtain of the play was open for me. It was not about myself!

So they were concerned with Nina! As though coming up from half drowning, I needed a moment to shake out the dazed feeling from my head. I must be just as sharp, just as clever, in protecting Nina as in struggling for my own life. Only now, feeling safe for myself, I could be stronger.

What could they want of Nina? I said only that I knew she came from Kharkov, and that she had studied philology at the university.

"Did you know that she was Jewish?"

I stared at them. Nina? Jewish? My dumfoundedness was genuine, for this really struck me as absurd. If there was anything Jewish in her, I would surely have sensed it! And now I saw the double absurdity in the situation. I had feared they would accuse me, a Jewess, of being Jewish, and instead they were accusing Nina, a gentile! And accusing her to me, as though I were one of them!

"We have good reason to suspect her of being a Jewess," Herr Kroll went on, "and we believe you could help us find out the truth."

I? I held back my feeling of revulsion. Wait. Perhaps they had only a suspicion. Someone had lodged a suspicion. Who? And how could anyone possibly see anything Jewish in Nina? A golden blonde, blue-eyed, with a fair, almost milk-white skin, and a calm, cultured manner that was anything but what one thought of as Jewish.

But the golden hair—it was bleached. I had often seen Nina bleaching her hair and had thought nothing of it; blond hair easily becomes dull, and she was bleaching it to give it tone. Could there be a possibility of truth in the accusation?

Would I help them, Herr Kroll repeated, pointing out that I was ideally situated for the task; I was Nina's closest confidante, we often went out together with our young men—they knew that much, then—and I was in a position to watch her every word and move, without her having the slightest suspicion.

My first impulse was to tell them, But of course she's not Jewish! There's nothing to find out! But if I did that, they might turn to someone else to spy on her.

And if she really was Jewish, I had to do everything in my power to help her. Even had she not been Nina, this would have been true. For anyone. If there was a risk, I would have to take it, but actually it seemed to me that I would be protected by this task. If they thought of Katya as someone who would spy out a Jew, then they would have no suspicion of Katya.

"Of course, I'm just the one who can find out," I declared. "If she's Jewish, she'll give herself away. I knew Jews in school, in Poland; there were several of them in our high school—they have a way of getting in everywhere—and if I watch her closely, and she's Jewish, I'm bound to find out. It's true, I haven't seen any sign of it, but I wasn't really watching for anything of that kind. Am I permitted to know just what is already known about her?"

No, said Herr Kroll, that would be of no help to me. But he was glad that I would undertake the task. And he went on to tell me how important it was. The Jews were the worst enemies of mankind, they were all Communists, and the Communists were all

[ 144 ]

Jews, and the Reich was engaged in a great crusade to rid the world forever of this pestilence.

I said I knew.

Then the matter was settled, Herr Kroll said, closing the folder. I would send him a weekly report with full details of my progress.

I saluted, Heil Hitler, and left.

Instead of taking the tram, I walked slowly back to the lager, through all of Linz. I had to put off that moment when I would face Nina, not knowing whether I should at once warn her of this, or whether I should first talk to Karlus, or whether I should keep it entirely to myself.

The Gestapo had only a suspicion. If they had real proof they would not have set me to spy on her. And where could they get proof? Already, as winter broke, Karlus had brought great news. The war was turning, there in Russia. The Germans had broken their heads at Stalingrad. The Russians were counterattacking to drive the Germans from their soil. Nina's home city was already free, retaken. And if so, the Gestapo could no longer send for her family records! Without records they could prove nothing. Nothing. And at that moment I recalled my own examination by that great board of scientists in Vienna, and I felt a little better. Yes, yes! If the war was turning, we had only to stay close together and wait. If I would protect Nina for the next few months, perhaps by the summer of 1943 the Americans would come and free us!

Nina was home in our room. Even from the corridor, hearing her flow of perfect Russian as she chattered with Clava, I felt reassured. Yet I wondered how it would be to look at her in this new way, with a question in my mind.

Everything was normal. As I entered, I joined their talk. Clava was in trouble again. Her period was several weeks late, but she didn't know whether to start to take her "medicine," a recipe of her own, a horrible peroxide concoction that had "always worked." Nina scolded her. I joined in as though I too were an experienced woman. She would one day poison herself. She would never be able to bear children. And what a slut she was with her two Hanses. Oh, Clava laughed, at least she could safely call the child Hans!

And all the while I was feeling lighter in my heart, for even looking at Nina with the eyes of suspicion, even with the severe test of my own feeling that I could always sense a Jew, there was absolutely no reaction in me to say that she could be Jewish. She was completely, typically Russian.

No one seemed to be aware that I had been summoned to the Gestapo. Herr Seifert had been discreet. And so, for a week, I did nothing. At the end of the week I wrote a long, detailed report. I was proceeding with caution, I said, so as not to arouse the subject's suspicions. But I was observing her more closely than ever and trying whenever possible to introduce into our conservation subjects that would lead her to give herself away. So far, there had not been the slightest evidence. If she was a Jewess, she was an extremely clever one. I would redouble my efforts.

And so another week went by. And I wrote another report. I told how I had engaged Nina in conversation about her childhood, her schooling. I said it was not possible as yet to come to a firm conclusion either way. There was still more I wanted to learn, about the boys she had gone with, about her parents. There was as yet no sign that she was Jewish, but I could not be absolutely sure that she was not. And so on, and on.

They called me once more to the office. We went over my reports line by line. One thing heartened me. The Gestapo seemed to be quite careful about such an accusation. They did not want to make a mistake and take any Christian for a Jew. "What's your impression?" asked Herr Kroll.

I was dreadfully tempted to say, "I'm sure she's not a Jew." Yet I wanted them to feel, when I did say it, that it was a positive and

[ 146 ]

final judgment, that they could rely on it, and that they need investigate no further.

And so I said I wanted more time. They told me to keep on, and to try to bring some real evidence, either way. Surely that need not take me much longer.

What could I find that would satisfy them? I tried to review in my mind all that I knew about Nina's life, but it was scant. Only from her could I get details that would serve as final proof to them. I could not see her childhood, her girlhood, in focus, and it had become dreadfully important for me to know, for myself. Either way.

Then I decided that there was only one thing for me to do. I had to tell her. And it became fixed in my mind that I had to tell her first the truth about myself.

Could I not simply have said, "Nina, the Gestapo suspects you of being Jewish"? I could have given her that warning without exposing myself, and without burdening her with the knowledge of who I was. Yet it didn't come to me that way. Perhaps it was again that terrible need in me, as with Slavek, to have a dear one know me as myself. Perhaps this need was even greater because I was estranged from Slavek. And perhaps there is indeed something in us that works against ourselves. I had for so long been successfully hidden—almost two years; it was as though something deep within me were insisting that things could not be this way, that I could not remain hidden forever, even experiencing some enjoyment in life, while every Jew was dying.

And perhaps also there was the feeling that if I revealed myself to her, and she then revealed herself to me, if it did turn out that she was Jewish, I would have, with Nina, an intimacy even deeper than before. Not only would she know me, but we would know each other, know each other with a doubly secret intimacy in which life itself was kept sealed, and this would forever stop my inner loneliness.

[ 147 ]

But the reason I gave myself for telling her who I was, was simply that I had to gain her complete confidence. I had to bring everything to light in order that we might deal with her situation together. Otherwise the Gestapo might set someone else to spy on Nina.

We would have to talk together alone, with even Clava out of the way. I decided on a Sunday morning. We slept late. Clava, who had a date for an outing with Hans the Czech, arose and went to the mess hall to fetch breakfast for us all.

There had been half a plan for Nina and myself to go along on the outing. But now I said, "Nina, I have something to talk to you about. Let's the two of us stay home."

"All right, Katinka," she said.

I could see that she felt sure it was something to do with my troubled romance.

Clava brought in the breakfast; we chattered, she dressed. "Up, up, get dressed, or the day will be over!"

We protested that we felt too lazy. She shrugged and finally went off.

We were still in our nightgowns, sitting opposite each other on our beds, with the little breakfast table between us. "So, Katinka, what is it?" Nina asked. "You're not in trouble?"

"No, Nina," I said. "I've something important to tell you, but first I have to ask for only one thing—that it stay between us, no matter what happens to us. Even if we should sometimes quarrel." She laughed. We quarreled often enough; we both had tempers. "Don't drop that dress on the chair! You're always the last one to straighten things up" . . . and so on.

"What is it, Katya?"

And as with Slavek, I plunged. "You know, Nina, I'm Jewish."

She laughed, but in a different tone now. Quite loudly, as at a joke that isn't exactly in good taste. "Is this what we stayed home for—for such a stupid joke?"

[ 148 ]

"It's true."

"Katya, do you think you can make a fool of me with such non-sense?"

"Nina, I'm not joking. About such a thing one doesn't joke."

"Ay, Katya! If it isn't a joke, then why would you ever tell me such a thing!"

"I want you to know, because we are so close. I want you to know the truth about me."

She looked into my eyes. There she sat, so near to me, with her golden hair, her light-blue eyes, her soft Christian face, and we knew each other so well, and what did we know of each other? Nina threw back her head and laughed again, more loudly. But this time I caught an artificial note in her laughter.

"Nina, believe me," I pleaded. "Believe me, because it is as important as life itself."

"You're quite an actress, Katya," she said. And she laughed again. But it was difficult for Nina to keep up anything artificial. Her laughter faltered.

I began to tell her my whole story. "You know, I don't really come from the village of Werchrata. I come from a town near by —Hrebenko. And Hrebenko is a Jewish town. My real name is Eva—Eva Korngold. I took the papers of a Ukrainian girl in Werchrata who had died. What's so strange about it? I tried to save myself. My sister was already taken, and my mother drove me to leave the house, to save myself."

She had ceased laughing, but now she took the attitude of someone indulging in a game. "You want me to believe that you are Jewish? Katya, do you know how to talk Yiddish?"

"Of course!" I said. Though in that moment I had a perverse fear—my Yiddish had never been very good. For two years I had been trying to forget every word, every intonation, especially as I spoke in a language so close to it as German.

Nina put her hand on the table. "What's this?"

"*Tish*," I said.

"That's German."

"But it's Yiddish too. Yiddish is a lot like German," I said. "You surely know that. You're a philologist." And I ventured, "Didn't you ever hear Yiddish spoken in Russia?"

Without replying, and keeping up her indulgent, amused manner, she pointed to the window. "What's that?"

"*Fenster*," I said, but with a Yiddish intonation. She looked at me quizzically. The examination went on. Chairs, curtains, the bed, our clothing. But if the word was not German it was Polish, or Russian, except for the Yiddish pronunciation. In despair, I recalled an example my father had given us when he was trying to teach us Yiddish. *Brate* for the German word *Brote*. Pointing to a bit of bread remaining from our breakfast, I said, "*Brate*." Nina raised her brow. "Why, that sounds like early German—low German," she remarked.

I said, "It's Yiddish."

Then she turned to another question. "If you're Jewish, do you know about their religion? I've always wondered what they do in their synagogues."

"Of course I know," I told her, "though I wasn't religious myself." The main things I remembered, I said, were the holidays. Passover, when we ate matzoth and had a big feast called a seder. And I described it. "It's in memory of when we were slaves in Egypt."

Her eyes were changing. "Every family performs this ceremony at home," I said. "The whole family is gathered around the table —grandparents, cousins, everybody. In our family we used to take turns; sometimes we had the seder in our house, and sometimes it was at my uncle's. We would work a whole week to prepare the feast, all the girls with our mothers, and the night before Passover we had to go over the whole house to make sure there wasn't a crumb of bread left anywhere, only matzoth. Then, for the whole week of Passover, we had to use a special set of dishes; they couldn't be touched the rest of the year. And then, in the ceremony, there's a moment when the youngest child asks the Four Questions. My little brother Yaacov would recite them. Why is this night different—"

I couldn't go on. I was weeping. And suddenly a dreadful sob burst from Nina, and she fell on me. Across the little space between the beds, we fell into each other's arms. "I too—" she was sobbing—"Katya, I too, I too, I too."

Then Nina poured out her whole story. She had scarcely thought of herself as Jewish; among the Soviets there was very little observance of religious holidays, and each year in her family there had been less and less memory of Jewish customs. The Jewish language had scarcely ever been heard. She remembered from childhood such Passovers as I had described, but it was many years since she had seen one. And just as I now told her that I had hardly learned Yiddish myself, at home, since it was considered to be the language of the commoner Jews, so she had heard no more of it as she had grown. Her parents had always spoken Russian, resorting to Yiddish only when there was something very private to discuss, that the children must not understand.

She had married a Russian, a non-Jew, and they had had a baby, a little girl named Svetlana. Then her husband had gone off to the war and been killed. And so she had returned to live with her parents, with her baby. But when the Germans had swept through the Russian Ukraine, annihilating Jews wherever they appeared, she had taken Svetlana and fled to another town. With her marriage documents, her Christian name, her golden-haired little girl, she had hoped to live undisturbed. That was when she had first bleached her hair.

But someone who knew her had recognized her there, a virulent anti-Semite—oh, yes, there were plenty of them still to be found among the Soviets, too. And in fear of denunciation she had fled again, to still another town. Svetlana had been a frail child. The disorder, the flights, the lack of proper food, had weakened the child and she had taken sick with an inflammation of the lungs. And so the baby had died. She had been four years old.

Now Nina slipped down on her knees and from under the bed she pulled out her valise; she put it on the bed and opened it. There, carefully wrapped in tissue paper, were the golden curls of her little girl, which she had clipped off before burial. And there were the child's little dolls, her toys, her picture books, her little dresses.

All this time, in the same room, under the bed next to mine, this life had been lying there—this remnant of a life. I had never once wondered what might be contained in Nina's suitcase.

We wept all morning, together.

And so I told Nina, then, about the Gestapo, and about my reports during the past few weeks. She could not think where the suspicion might have come from. But one thing was certain: there was no one here who knew her background, and there was no way in which anything could be confirmed, since her city had been recaptured by the Russians.

We sat down and worked together on another report in which I could give particulars about her schooling, her childhood, details that would help convince the Gestapo that she was not Jewish. We used all the particulars about her husband's family.

And then we talked of every possibility that might confront us. Suppose, sometime, the Germans became suspicious of me? "If they should ever arrest me," I said, "they will certainly bring up these reports I made about you, and charge that I lied. But, Nina, remember what I say to you now—if they should ever arrest me, and then arrest you, and if they tell you that I confessed that I lied in these reports, don't believe it! No matter what they do to me, no matter if they make me confess about myself, I will never tell them about you. Even if they show you something on paper and say I wrote it, don't believe them."

And there did indeed come a time when this warning was useful.

But that Sunday, after we had wept ourselves out and shared our lives, a wonderful feeling of peace came over us. We had joined our lives. And later in the day, again and again, we would catch each other, one looking at the other, and each would shake her head and say, "I never would have believed it!"

I made a few more reports to the Gestapo. Each time I went a step further. "Though it is now my definite impression that she is not Jewish, it is still too soon to say so with absolute certainty." And finally I wrote that I was certain. "We have become more intimate than ever. She has told me her whole life in every detail, just as I have told her my life, and I am certain now that there can be no possibility of any truth in the suspicion lodged against her."

I waited. I was not called again to discuss Nina, nor was she summoned for questioning. They had accepted my final report.

We were indeed closer than ever now. Nina had understood at once that Anya too was Jewish. And Nina told me that Karlus knew about herself; in the end, he knew about all three of us. Clava was not told.

But more feverishly than ever now, we studied the little maps that Karlus would draw for us on cigarette paper which he later burned. There were great battles in Russia. The Germans were perhaps back in Kharkov. Would they find out about Nina? It seemed absurd that they might take so much trouble to track down one little Jewess. Besides, all Kharkov was certainly destroyed.

Both Karlus and Nina spoke English quite well; it had been her major study, and he had passed some time in England as a student. Somewhere the Czechs had their secret radio, but it was only rarely that Karlus could tune in on the English broadcasts. But we heard news of the massive Allied air raids, and this we could well believe, for the alerts even in Linz were becoming more frequent.

And then things seemed to be going well again. The Allies were winning against Rommel in North Africa. The Russians were once more moving forward. Would they even reach Hrebenko? Once my birthplace was out of German hands, I would be much safer. And so would Anya.

BUT THEN, that summer, a change came for me. Every change could hold a danger, but there were still other reasons for this change being unwelcome. It happened that the personnel manager of the Hermann Goering works had taken a notion that he needed me on his staff. Many times I had been to his office with reports, with the records of various foreign employees, dealing with a thousand different questions—family allocations, vacation permits, changes of jobs. Sometimes I would receive an urgent call from Herr Lauterman to find him a skilled welder, or someone with other special qualifications. And so it had been established that Katya was an efficient, resourceful worker, and also cheerful, willing—a model employee. I had succeeded too well. Herr Lauterman decided that I would be more useful in the Hermann Goering works than in the transit camp, and, being more important than Herr Seifert, he arranged for my transfer. Worst of all, the change meant that I would be separated from Nina and Clava. On the new job, I would have to live on the plant premises.

I could not protest. I was promised a room all to myself in the compound as soon as one could be found. In the meantime I was back in an open dormitory with forty other women.

At once, in the dormitory and in the office too, I felt a different atmosphere. It was more animalistic, more excited; there was even something of frenetic sexuality about it. As though the men and women, forbidden any other human outlets, any normal home or family life, were driven to sex. On the cot next to mine was a chubby Polish girl who from the first evening gossiped incessantly about every woman in the room, interrupting herself only to ask me directly, Well, and with whom was I going? Had I ever been with a real German? It was done, it was done, I need have no fear, and there was a great deal more to be got from a German than from the poor foreign laborers. By the second night she had told me her most intimate secrets: that she had a German lover, one of the guards, that he was from this very town, from Linz, and he had even taken her home to meet his parents, who had been horrible to her, and that she was three months' pregnant and didn't know what to do because if their affair became known, then not only would she be arrested but he too, for consorting with an *Auslanderin.*

She babbled on, a little bit sly, but mostly foolish, stupid. There was that little Czech girl—she pointed out the girl's bed to me—you would only see that one up until bed-check time, or early in the mornings, but it was no use looking for her in bed during the night. "That one is called the whorelet. You can tell by the way every man in the plant talks to her that there isn't a one she hasn't been with. Men have a certain way of talking to a girl after they've been with her, a special smile. When you see a man smile that way to a girl, you know he has been with her. I wouldn't be like she is; I am faithful, I can tell you I haven't looked at another man since I started with my Walter, and don't think they haven't tried, the men here." And if I wanted, she would introduce me to a friend of her Walter's.

The first, desperate need was to get away from the dormitory. And so, in the office, I kept reminding my boss of his promise that I would have a place of my own. Had he found anything yet?

There were seven or eight of us in the personnel office, and in the first days it was as though every cell in my body had become alert, sensing them out, for always in a new place there might be someone troublesome, someone who was too curious about people. Besides the chief, there were two men, and the first, a Slovene named Brata, struck me as overly polite. I had an impression of falsity in him. Besides, the Slovenes were even worse anti-Semites than the Ukrainians. With him, care! Avoid lengthy conversations.

The other man in the office was a German, and a problem in quite a different way. He was a skirt-chaser, openly, laughingly, and unremittingly. A handsome fellow, too, he would sit right down with a girl and kiss her, in front of the whole office. He was always saying, "A man like me, it's my nature. It's even my duty." From the moment of my arrival he was after me. "Ah, a real addition," he announced. And he jested, "I'll have to tell my wife about you right away, so she won't be suspicious—she'll know!" There was still something quite shocking to me in the thought of a married man running openly after other girls. Perhaps, I told myself, it was all an office joke.

Whenever he bent down beside a girl's desk to give her some documents, he would put his arm around her. It was difficult to object to this. But after a few days he began pestering me seriously. He would sit down on part of my chair, embrace me and kiss me. I had to break away by sheer force, yet laughingly. Already, Max was making remarks about visiting me as soon as I had my own private quarters. That was why, he said, he was doing his utmost to get me a room to myself.

The chief, Herr Lauterman, was aloof, strict, a ramrod Nazi. He demanded absolute perfection in our work. If there was a single erasure on a typed page, the page had to be done over— sometimes five times—before he would accept it. But this at least could be dealt with. I never showed him a letter that was not absolutely perfect, I would type it over myself four or five times if necessary. Quickly, I was in his good graces: "Katya—there is a worker!"

On my second day in the Hermann Goering works, Slavek phoned me. Would I come and have lunch with him?

It had been so long! More than half a year.

"Why not?" I said. "But if you want to have lunch with me, come over here."

As the plant covered a vast area, there were several restaurants for the workers. Slavek protested that in his shop the hours were strictly kept, and by the time he walked all the way to my side of the plant his bell would be ringing. In such an office as mine, and for a girl, he argued, things were more lenient.

But I said no; I had just got there and didn't want to take liberties. "You come to me."

"Then some other time," he said, and hung up.

I was filled with desire to see him, and yet I couldn't act differently. Perhaps I wanted things to be as they might have been at home. If a girl was courted by a bit of a scamp whom she was determined to tame, she could hold herself proud. Yet I missed him incessantly. My face had become thin, and I was uninterested in the life around me. Ever since I had broken with Slavek, Clava and Nina had been arranging dates for me, and a few times I had gone out, together with them. But none of the men had interested me, and lately I had been refusing to go out altogether.

Once more, Slavek called. Again we argued about which restaurant. Finally he said, rather angrily, "But, Katya, I simply can't come to you!"

I thought of the past when he had found ways to come around, even in the middle of the morning, and I said, "If you want to have lunch with me, you'll find a way to come here." And I hung up. On so foolish a note, it ended.

On my lonely evenings, I would slip back to Bindermichel, and Nina would try to comfort me by singing a Russian love song.

*Don't cry, don't cry, my little Katushinka,*
*Don't cry, my pretty little love,*
*There's so much in our lives that's not the way we want it,*
*But still we know that when the springtime comes*
*There'll be dancing again in our street!*
*So, let's remember, Katushinka, that springtime has to come!*

In the office I was making great progress. So much, in fact, that I even lost some of my dread of the Gestapo. For quite often in my new job I would be called to the downtown headquarters for translations.

I could now walk into that building without a sense of doom. The girl receptionist knew me. I would go upstairs to the Foreign Workers Section, to the office of the chief himself, Herr Mueller. He was a man in his fifties, very neat, with the manner of a middle-ranking executive. There was certainly nothing frightening about him. His private office was good-sized and impressive, with leather chairs, a handsome desk—the office of a man of considerable consequence. And almost always, when I arrived, he would lean back as for a moment of relaxation. "So, Katya, what does this fellow say, here?" And he would hand me some intercepted letter, referred back to him by the censor. These were always family letters, written by our workers, asking how things were at home. Mostly, they were about food. "Don't send me packages if you deprive yourself." There was longing in them; once or twice there were passages from a man to his wife that I did not translate. "Ah, Katya, I see you are blushing. Come, come, what have you left out there?" And sometimes the men included guarded references to air raids. "There are quite a few clouds overhead, and we have had several hail storms. Last week the hail could be heard all around our barracks." Such passages I managed to skip, without blushing.

Soon I realized that I might be becoming overconfident.

I was strolling on the grounds of the plant one afternoon, together with two girls from the office. Behind us a group of boys kept making remarks, flirting. They were a crude lot, Poles from the Ukrainian area, and we walked on, paying no attention to them. Suddenly one fellow began to yell after me, "That Katya, she's a Jew! A Jew!" I ignored him and walked on, chattering and laughing. But a moment later he started again. "Katya is a Jew! Just look at her! Anybody can see it! Hey, Katya the Jew!"

This time I turned on him. "If you don't stop these insults, I'll complain to the Gestapo!"

He stood there, mouth open, his little eyes glinting. "How could I know you're not?" he said. "With black hair like that, you look just like the Jewish girls in our town."

"Idiot!" I snapped, and we walked on.

In the next few days whispers came to me. The same fellow was spreading stories all over camp that I was a Jewess. I felt sure it was only a guess on his part; he came from nowhere near Hrebenko. But I could not let him go on talking. I had to do something at once, and boldly.

The next day I was called to bring some files to the Gestapo. Herr Mueller greeted me laughingly as always. "Well, well, Katinka, my breath of fresh air!"

And when I had turned over the records to him, I said, "Herr Mueller, there's something personal I'd like to ask you."

Indeed! He was at my service!

And so I told him I was being annoyed by a Polish lout who had taken to crying "Jew" after me. It was insulting and terribly unpleasant. I asked that he be called in and punished.

In a few days I heard that the fellow had indeed been called to the Gestapo and warned not to repeat his insults. After that I did not see him again.

But every day now I felt a greater fear. Tiny incidents that might not have aroused my suspicion became significant to me. For quite some time I had felt almost at rest, I had heard nothing at all about Jews. But now, after the investigation of Nina, and with this nasty incident, the whole subject had been reawakened.

And soon another incident took place. There was a Ukrainian worker who kept crossing my path as if by chance. Only, he was there more and more often. He was an exceptionally tall fellow with a peculiar smile which he always bestowed upon me.

I felt sure that I had seen him somewhere, outside the Hermann Goering works. Perhaps at the movies? At a café? And then I recalled where. I had passed him more than once in the corridors of the Gestapo building.

Our accidental meetings soon happened almost every day. Sometimes more than once a day. He would stop and chat with me now, but it was all in quite a normal manner—a young man trying to get close to a girl, and even putting himself in her path. Perhaps I was oversuspicious; perhaps it was really nothing more than that? I took pains to be nice to him, never to avoid him, indeed even to appear where he might expect to find me. Yet I grew more and more uneasy as our little flirtatious conversations developed. Ukrainians could pick up the slightest irregularity in the use of their language.

He kept inviting me to his room. Finally, laughingly, I agreed. "All right, if I can bring a girl friend."

[ 161 ]

If it had to be that way, he said, then he would invite a friend for her. And which one would I bring? The blonde?

Clearly, he was quite familiar with everything about my life; he knew the girls I went with.

No, I said. The little one.

And so I asked Clava to come along, telling her it was a date with a fellow I didn't much like but couldn't put off.

He had a room in one of the barracks, and with him was another Ukrainian. As we entered, we were overwhelmed by the sight that greeted our eyes—it was a spread such as my good employers the Eberhardts could hardly have managed even at Christmas! A large table was covered with heaped-up platters and unopened bottles. Everything was there—vodka, cherry brandy, wine, French brandy, roast goose—such a feast would have cost an ordinary worker more than a year's wages on the black market. I was certain it had been provided by the Gestapo. I wondered if my genial friend, Herr Mueller, had been the one to order this investigation.

And so I put on my merriest mood. I drank two glasses of vodka at once, and lolled about as though I were already tipsy; I sang, I talked freely.

They went to work immediately. Casual questions about my home, my family, my schooling. I answered as though my mind was a bit fuzzy from alcohol, but still I made sure to answer everything, to give them a complete story, going back and forth, or jumping from one thing to another, as a girl might, if she were utterly unsuspecting. I had a good model to fellow. Clava had got really drunk, in short order, and as she had no idea what was taking place, she was behaving quite naturally, talking about the war, about her husband, even scolding them when they tried to talk politics.

Then they became amorous. A few hugs, a few kisses, had to be permitted. My host's friend complained about Clava. "Oh, this one is no good; she's utterly drunk." And then I said we had to go.

My host objected, in dismay. After all this, weren't we going to stay with them?

"But Clava is drunk," I said, "and I promised her that if she got drunk I'd see that she got home." As for myself, I took refuge behind another excuse: I said I was in love.

And so we said goodbye, with the men assuming that slightly irritated but game look that comes after a defeated effort, while we departed with the virtuous air of girls who had let them take a sporting chance, while promising nothing.


Again, I seemed to have passed inspection. And a quiet interval set in. At long last I received my own room. Herr Lauterman kept his promise and secured me a place entirely apart from the dormitory. It was a room where I would be able to close the door and be my own self, without eternally keeping the face of that lusty, cheerful little Ukrainian girl, Katya. Katya all day in the office, Katya all night in the dormitory.

The room was not even in a barracks, but in a small, separate building close to the entrance to the compound. The front part of my building was the post office, and behind were two separate little chambers. In one of these lived a woman whom I never saw, her work hours were different from mine. She was an old woman, I was told with an air of complete dismissal by Max, the office lover, who insisted on being the first to escort me to my "home." My only contact with this neighbor proved to be late at night, when, if I had visitors, she would knock on the wall for silence.

My room was small, but it had a stove, and a real bed, and a table, and a dresser, and for me it represented the greatest of riches. Even more completely than the garret room at the Eberhardts', this place was mine alone. I had a home. Even Max's obnoxious suggestions didn't trouble me, now that I was in my own place; I laughed loudly and managed to get rid of him, reminding him that there were windows on two sides and that if he, a German, were caught with an *Auslanderin* it would be all up with him.

Then, for days, I reveled. I thought of nothing but fixing up my little house. I traded, I begged, I even ruined myself on the black market. But I acquired a tablecloth, and I managed to get material for curtains. I sewed, I arranged. Nina and Karlus brought gifts, and Karlus put up a shelf, and soon the room was indeed a veritable little house, with colored prints on the walls, one of them even framed, with plates and cups and saucers on the shelf, and a vase with flowers on the table, and a tea kettle humming on the little stove.

My room now became the home of our little band, and each of the girls brought household things, as though to see Katya making a bit of a home was as good as making one for herself.

When I went out from my little house to work, each morning, I had to walk the entire length of the administration area, and on the way I saw something I had not before encountered. Working on the grounds, eternally rebuilding the walks, was a group of prisoners, but of a strange sort. Their heads were shaven, and they wore striped, pajamalike clothing—a uniform I was later to know all too well. An SS guard stood watch over them. I didn't know what these men were. Somehow I felt they were not ordinary prisoners, and, from the first encounter, I felt an obscure connection with them, a tie.

It was then late fall. The whole summer of 1943 had gone by and the second front had not come, and even the Allied attack in Italy, from the little that we could learn, seemed to have been stopped by the Germans. It seemed that this life would be permanent, the only kind of life we would ever know. There were days of cold rain, hail, slush; there were sharp winds. I was well dressed when I walked to work in the morning, wearing the smart zipper boots that Herr Eberhardt had bought me, and a black imitation fur coat that I had bought for myself, with legitimate clothing coupons. It matched the black hat I had made for myself, and when I added a violet scarf, I looked quite modish. I felt heartsick and ashamed each time I passed the prisoners in their flimsy cotton pajamas.

I would say good morning to them, and they would reply in chorus, and with such pitiful joy, that I knew mine was the only human word spoken to them all day. I would toss them cigarettes as I passed. If I crossed the grounds during the day, they would wave to me from wherever they were.

A few mornings, I lingered long enough to exchange a word or two of the most innocent kind—about the weather. But one day the SS guard stopped me. "It is forbidden to talk to them."

After that they didn't even dare say good morning—only with their eyes. But one time when the SS man was a short distance away engaged in conversation, one of the prisoners, bending over his pickax, kept working parallel to me as I walked along. "You cannot know what you mean to us," he said. "We call you our little black star." It was because of the way I was dressed. "Every morning, when we see our little black star in the distance, it's a sunrise for us."

The air raids were increasing. Sometimes they would come twice a day. And there was a peculiar rule in the plant—when the siren sounded, each worker had to carry his tools with him to the shelter. We girls in the office had to carry along our typewriters.

The corridors would become jammed with people bumping into one another, blocking one another, each burdened with some clumsy machine. The typewriters were heavy, and to lug them up and down the stairs at every alarm was almost too much for us.

It was not that we were expected to continue our work in the shelter. On the contrary, a spirit of fun prevailed during the alarms. There would be singing, flirtations—men like Max became insupportable.

Once, during a long raid, we had quite a party. The alarm had come late in the afternoon, and while we were in the shelter the end of our workday came. The all-clear had not yet sounded. We had sandwiches and tea, and some of the men produced flasks of schnapps. Max kept circling around me and whispering, "It's already dark outside. After the all-clear, I'll take you home."

Even Herr Lauterman had unbent. He stood quite close to me, chattering, offering me little compliments, and just then the all-clear sounded. "I'll take you home," he said.

Max was watching us, glowering. Although it was the boss himself who had commandeered me, I was afraid Max would find a way to take revenge. "Someone else was kind enough to offer and is waiting for me," I said to Herr Lauterman.

"Let's give him the slip," said my high-ranking Nazi boss.

"But I have to take my typewriter upstairs."

"Never mind!" And before I knew what was happening, he had seized the machine. Herr Lauterman took the stairs two at a time and arrived, puffing, at my desk. Setting down the machine, he seized my hand and pulled me along, making for the door. We had beat all the others.

It was pitch dark on the grounds. All at once I felt my boss's arm around me. We walked on, came to my quarters. He lingered at the door, again began to pay me compliments. "Katya, are you frightened of me?" "No, please," I said. I returned to the old excuse. "I'm in love." He let me go free. I said, "Good night."

I was frightened of the atmosphere. There seemed to be a kind of contest gathering around Katya, the lively girl with the private room. Who would be coming to her there? Impossible that there should be no one.

They circled and circled around me. I even heard again from Slavek. But I would not let myself see him. Everyone knew that he had taken up with a little French prostitute in Linz.

I found only one escape, on Sundays. There was an elderly translator, a Bulgarian, and we had become quite friendly, chattering a bit each time we met on the grounds. He was a passionate fisherman, and each Sunday he would bring me part of his catch for my little feasts in my room with my friends.

And so one Sunday I went off fishing with Yanko. He brought along some wonderful sausages that he had received in a package from home and a bottle of vodka to keep us warm. And there at the far edge of the factory grounds, where the Danube went by, we sat fishing. I never caught anything, but Yanko always did, and on Sunday nights we would feast until the knocking came on the wall.

So it was until the Christmas holidays. As the men—Nina's Karlus and Clava's Hans the Czech—were going home to Prague for the holidays, we girls began to plan a party for ourselves. It would be on New Year's Day, for my twenty-first birthday. The day on which Alla Blumenfeld and I had always held our twinship parties at home.

This was to be an intimate party for only Nina, Clava, myself, and Anya, who would come to join us. The letters went back and forth, and everything was arranged for Anya to arrive on New Year's Eve.

I wanted to show her that I too could prepare a real feast; we used up our ration tickets, the black market was patronized, and Nina, employing all of her resourcefulness, somehow managed to procure the impossible—a bottle of champagne!

Anya's train arrived, and there was no Anya.

[ 167 ]

It was a disappointment, but a thousand things could have happened to detain her; at the last moment, most likely, she had been required to stay at home with the children on the estate.

Still, she could have sent a telegram.

The three of us had our feast, and it was cheerful enough, the kind of warm, utterly easy time that women can have only when there are no men present. We got a little drunk and began talking frankly, and the girls began insisting that it was high time I ceased being an innocent—so—they were going to teach me to smoke!

As it happened, I had never learned, and with the dreadful time smokers had getting cigarettes, I had been glad that I had never felt the need. But now, yes, I wanted to taste everything, and so I tried to smoke, and choked, and tried again, and choked, and we laughed until I choked more with the laughter than with the cigarette smoke, and my elderly neighbor banged on the wall, but we paid no attention, and finally I smoked an entire cigarette, with tears streaming from my eyes, while Nina said wickedly, "That's how it will be with everything you haven't yet done, Katinka— you'll cry the first time, but you'll like it." And I laughed until I choked again.

The girls slept over. I had hoped Anya would appear the next day. She didn't, nor was there any word from her. I wrote her a long, gay letter about my newest vice. Days passed and there was no reply.

Anya, the well ordered, always answered letters at once, and usually no more than three days passed in an exchange of correspondence. I wrote one more time. When the third letter brought no reply, I felt sure there was real trouble. Perhaps she had fallen seriously ill? Though I had never called her before, I decided to risk a telephone call.

It was her mistress who answered the phone. I asked if I might speak with Anya.

"*Die* Anya is not here," she said.

"Is she sick?" I asked.

She replied, again in the same stiff way, "*Die* Anya is not in the house."

Was it known when she would return?

Again, the same stiff formula, and goodbye.

Now I was terrified. What could I do? Should I go there?

I hurried to consult Nina.

No, she said. Under no circumstances should I put in an appearance, while I had not yet heard from Anya. It was even dangerous to write another letter. I could only wait, in the hope that some sign of life would come.

After several days the situation became unendurable to me. Nina and I discussed every possible approach and decided that the least dangerous move would be to make another phone call. This was less tangible than a letter.

And so I once more reached the mistress. Could I speak to Anya?

"Anya is not here," she said, and instantly hung up.

There could be no further doubt. Anya had been caught.

But how? Where was she?

I kept seeing her under torture. She was being tortured for me, because she would not give me away. No, no, no! she kept crying out to them, and each time there came a heavy slap, so that her head swung sharply under the impact. Or were they beating her with truncheons? Despite my visits to the Gestapo, I did not know exactly how they went about their investigations. I had caught only that one glimpse of men standing against a wall—and surely that was only the beginning. All the dreadful whispered tales I had of course heard, and now I kept seeing such scenes, mingled perhaps with scenes from movies. A girl with her dress torn away from her breast. Let her tell, let her only tell! "Tell, Anya. Don't suffer! Tell!" I would implore her, repeating the words out loud, as though they might reach her. Let her tell! They would in any

[ 169 ]

case know; they would come for me, for hadn't we been registered everywhere together, as far back as Przemyśl, and then again at Kraków, and in Vienna, and hadn't we incessantly visited each other? And even now, there were letters from me to Anya.

My mother seemed to be with me again, saying with such utter grief, Ay, ay, Eva, why didn't you listen, I told you, Eva, you girls must not be together; you must hardly even write to each other.

In the office, I was still the lively, carefree Katya. But how many days were left to me? And perhaps Anya was no longer alive. Perhaps she had already been shot, or sent off in that way of theirs—someone disappeared, and that was all. A death somewhere, in some unknown place, and that left an even darker grief, for you could not even attach a name to it, a place of death, a Belzec, Treblinka, Oswiecim. A death, without even a place of death, was an evaporation, as though the life had never been lived.

And then one day there came a sign of life. In the office, it was I who received and sorted the mail, and as I picked up the letters that morning I at once saw among the neat, typed envelopes with their printed return addresses, a wrinkled, smudged letter. I pulled it out. The letter was addressed to Katarina Leszczyszyn! The name was printed, in pencil, and there was no return address.

I opened it. From Anya! On lined notebook paper, in pencil, she wrote, as though reminiscing romantically, "Here I sit in my little room, with only a ray of light from the high window, and I find myself remembering my childhood days at home, and I think of how we were always together as little girls, since our parents lived next door to each other. We were always in the same class at school, and I remember every Sunday when we went to church to Father Piotr. . . " And she went on and on, with many details about Father Piotr, and his little niece Danusia, and I understood. For we had all become expert in writing our letters in a double language. Anya was telling me that she was in prison, and all these

[ 170 ]

details about our childhood, about the church—these were the details she had given her questioners. It was clear that Anya had denied she was Jewish. They had questioned her about me, and she had denied that I was Jewish, telling them these stories about our families.

Somehow she had managed to smuggle out this letter, to warn me what I must say, if questioned. I felt stronger, through her. Because Anya was still her resourceful self, and she had not given up.

But surely they were now investigating us in the towns we had given as our birthplaces. And as if in deathly perversity, the German retreat had come to an end, their line had solidified again, still short of Hrebenko. So the Gestapo could find out all they needed to know about us.

I was certain now that I was doomed. It was only a matter of time, perhaps a few weeks, at most a month. And a spirit of bitter fatality took hold of me. We could squirm, we could twist in their grip until the last, but they had us. For two years we had tormented ourselves, dissembled, imagined we could outwit them, that we would live through it all. But they were determined that every Jew would be slaughtered, and so every crack and every cranny would be searched and they would find even such as Anya and myself.

Even Nina, too? When they would question me, they would come again upon the subject of Nina. But I would deny and deny. And unless in spring they made their boasted offensive and drove once more into Russia, there was no way they could prove anything about Nina. And even if they drove ahead, surely her city would have been razed, the records destroyed. As to Nina, they could pull out my fingernails one by one, I would only deny!

And in this mood, awaiting the torture to come, I felt that every experience I tasted, every hour of bitter enjoyment, was triumph against them. So if only a short time was left to me, I would know all there was to know of life. I would wait no more.

It should have been Slavek. My whole being kept crying out that it should have been Slavek, and it should have been in other times because I had wanted him so. I had denied that want, because even more than Slavek it should have been the man with whom I would spend my life. With Slavek, I had not been sure. And so I had tried to cling to the belief instilled in me in my childhood, and to wait for my true husband. Oh, Mama, *Mamenu*, I wanted to cry, I tried, I tried. You see how in spite of everything I tried to remain your good Jewish daughter.

But now? Now I wished that I had taken the moment of passion. For over a year now, Slavek and I had been estranged. I had a new friend. Again it was a friend brought by Karlus, and a Czech. He was older than Slavek, in his mid-thirties, and not so brilliantly handsome, not the sort for whom every girl would turn her head. Oh, I wanted no more of those. One had come around, after Slavek—the beau of the Hermann Goering works, a gymnast. Every girl in the plant was eager to be seen with him, but I had said to myself, Not again.

Then Karlus and Nina had come with Hans—yes, another Hans. He was tall, wore glasses, proved a good conversationalist and, like Karlus, he was considerate, attentive, warm. After several movie dates and other excursions together I had told myself, Yes, I was fond of Hans, and it was better to have someone to go out with, so I would not be the odd one in our group. He was married, I knew, and sometimes he would complain to me about his wife, how demanding she was, how he had to send her every penny he earned, and I would laugh and tell him, "Don't complain to me about your wife; she's your wife!"

Now, in my distress, tense with the feeling that I was playing my last cards, I felt more terribly than ever the need of a man close to me. And so, a few times, Hans came without the others, and there were kisses and he would hold me protectively in his arms and know that I was troubled without knowing what troubled me. Hans would not press himself upon me as Slavek had done, and I was thankful for that. I began to tell myself that I was drawn to him.

And then Hans would say, not as a man trying to overwhelm a naïve girl but as one mature person to another, "Katya, why must we deny ourselves?"

And I was grateful that he could not know how these same thoughts were forever pulling on me, for though I had faith in him, and though he was one of us, he was not like Nina and Karlus to me, and he knew nothing.

Things were still that way between us when the call from the Gestapo came for me. It was not the usual call to come to Mueller's office, or even to his section. The name of the man I was to see was unknown to me. And yet, as I went there, I somehow did not feel that this was the visit from which I would not return.

I gave the name at the reception desk and was sent up to the third floor instead of the second. And there I was admitted to an office far more impressive than Mueller's. It was larger, and contained a corner window. There was a conference table, a sofa. Five men were in the room; all of them were in civilian clothes, and I had seen none of them before.

The one behind the desk was of medium build, with rather elongated eyes and straight hair parted on the side. Before him lay the inevitable folder. He opened it. "Do you know Esther Warshawsky?" he asked.

I repeated the name. "Warshawsky? Esther? I really don't remember anyone—Could it be someone I've met in my job? I've met thousands of people."

"Do you know Esther Warshawsky?" he repeated in the same matter-of-fact tone.

"I'm trying to think—perhaps if you tell me where I might have known this person—" I was still afraid to deny outright.

"Try to remember," said one of the men sitting on the sofa.

I waited a moment. "I can't place the name."

"It's a friend of yours."

I smiled. "That can't be. I certainly know the names of my friends."

The chief drew a snapshot from the folder and handed it to me. "This is Esther Warshawsky." It was a picture of Anya, with her braids wound around her head, as she was today; it had surely been taken on the estate, perhaps without her being aware of it.

I studied it a moment, then laughed out loud. "Her name isn't Esther Warshawsky! There must be some mistake! Of course I know her. I know her very well. But what do you mean, Esther Warshawsky? Her name is Anya Ozymok."

Still in his dry tone the chief said, "Her real name is Esther Warshawsky. She is a Jewess."

I burst out indignantly, "Oh, that's a false accusation! Why, I know Anya from childhood, our families lived next door to each other, we went to the same school, we went to confession together to Father Piotr. I even remember a funny pact we made as little girls: when Anya didn't have enough sins to confess I would trade her some of mine." And so I wove in all of the details that had been in Anya's letter, but I tried to mix them in casually, and I added a few things, and changed the order, so that our stories might not seem to have been prepared to jibe. From time to time, I noticed, the chief glanced into his folder; he was certainly checking the names and other items that I mentioned against things that Anya had said.

How could anyone bring such a horrible accusation against Anya? I kept repeating. It must be some intrigue, there on the farm; it must have been done by someone who wanted revenge on her. "You know how it is when a girl is alone, and Anya is very particular about who she goes with. There were a number of men who were always after her, and she would have nothing to do with them. Just for spite, one of them could have done this."

They listened. Then the chief leaned over, took the photograph from my hand, turned it around and gave it back to me. "Read that."

On the reverse side was the stamp of the police office of Hrebenko. In small, neat handwriting, Anya's real history was noted. Her name, the names of her parents, even the fact that she had worked in the post office during the Russian occupation.

I was momentarily taken aback. But there was only one thing to do now: brazen it out. "What a horrible mistake!" I cried. "These stupid provincial police! How can they be so careless with a person's life! But the Polish police are like that. They're idiots; they can't even read. Who knows from what file they copied this nonsense." I became more and more indignant. I was outraged! To risk a person's life on such flimsy evidence as this! I even began to shout—and I caught myself up. "I know I shouldn't be shouting, here, and you can arrest me if you want, but when I see things like this happening to someone I've known all my life—"

I saw that I had impressed them.

Now a few of the others began to put in questions, but my questioners were not antagonistic. I sensed that it counted with them that I was the reliable Katya, a good worker, known here in the Gestapo, a serious girl, never mixed up in anything in the slightest way irregular. And I leaned more and more on this. "I give you my word—I know Anya as I know myself!"

The chief had not taken his eyes off my face. "Katya, we put a good deal of trust in you. It would be very serious if our trust proved mistaken."

"How can I be wrong about my own life?"

We stared at each other. He pushed a package of cigarettes toward me. I had the impulse to take one, but even though nothing

[ 175 ]

might be showing, I felt a trembling inside my body; I was afraid my fingers might tremble in handling the cigarette. So I said I hardly ever smoked.

The photograph was being passed from one to the other; each turned it over and looked at the writing on the back of it. The chief rubbed his chin and said, "In sum, you insist that the police back there in that town are mistaken."

"Yes. That is all I can tell you. You will decide," I said.

He nodded, without taking his eyes from me, and then asked me to go out and wait in the corridor.

I stood there waiting. Was it now the time to run, to run out of the building in some wild hope of escape? But if I did, it would mean the certain end of Anya.

Presently the door opened and I was called back into the room. There were no smiles, nor did my questioners look menacing. In his matter-of-fact voice the chief announced that they had decided to accept my testimony and to recommend the release of Anya Ozymok.

Dazed, I thanked them, trying not to show my impulse to rush away before they could see right through me.

They even joked a bit with me. And then I was out of the building. I felt such triumph. I felt capable of anything—anything! I had fooled the Gestapo. The Gestapo itself! A roomful of them! I had saved Anya! I would never be caught! Oh, these men were not so invincible as all that. Or perhaps there was indeed some good angel watching over me; perhaps there was a special force planted within me. Every cell in my body was excited, everything in me was pulsing, racing. Now I was out in the open battlefield, and I had won. It was as though I had suddenly been pushed onto another plateau of life.

I could not contain my excitement. In the office, everyone saw there was something stirring in me. "What has happened to you, Katya, are you in love?" I hurried to my room, to hide what was written on my face, in my eyes. But I could not remain alone. I walked to Bindermichel. There was even a secret hope in me that somehow, by the same fate that was so good to me, I would encounter Slavek on the way.

At last I was with Nina. But we couldn't talk there, in the barracks. She walked back with me to my place while I told her what had happened. Indeed I felt doubly triumphant; twice I had fooled the Gestapo, once for Nina and now for Anya.

But when I had finished the story I was empty. I found myself saying, "I only hope it's over. That they don't send a photograph of me to Hrebenko."

"No, no, perhaps they won't," said Nina.

And we tried to shut out of our minds what we knew they would do; we tried to cling to our moment of triumph. We decided to go to a movie to celebrate. Karlus and Hans joined us. We went to the Centralkino and afterward we all came back to my room and I offered my friends wine. Hans, of course, did not know anything of what had happened but he sensed the excitement in me. As he and the others were leaving he whispered that he would be back.

Then it would be tonight. I drank more wine to keep myself in the same mood of daring. I had never before taken a drink alone, not from abstemiousness but because the impulse simply had not come to me.

I told myself that I truly cared for him, that he was a mature man, while Slavek had been only a capricious boy. That he was honest, whereas Slavek with his romantic talk would only have been deceiving us both. That the end of my life was probably near, and that I knew now that things did not happen as one wished them to; one must seize life as it offered itself.

[ 177 ]

Then Hans returned; he took me at once in his arms, and I went through with it. I would not let myself feel cheated, feel that the happenings of life had forced me to give up even what I had wanted of this. It was strange to have clung so long to an image, even an image of the unknown one, and now to feel that the man was chosen almost by accident—because he was the man I was fond of at the moment, when I feared that if I waited longer, I would die without having known what it was to be a woman.

He was tender, and even humble, and I succeeded in losing myself in all my senses, reaching for that mysterious ecstasy, that revelation that each girl imagines is to come in the act itself. And he whispered, "You will see! We will still make our life together! My Katinka, my Katya . . ." And the name broke through to me. Who? Who? But he did not even know who I was.

Slavek, Slavek would have known; with him I would have been Eva. And even in this moment I had to be false. All this—it was Katya to whom it was happening, Katya, a lustful Ukrainian peasant girl. Oh, they were freer than we. And for an instant it seemed to me that my mother knew, and grieved.

But so it was, in the world. What I had done I had done. And then I felt only confusion and surprise that it seemed over, that it was nothing more. The next day Nina knew without asking, and I was a naïve, stupid girl, curious about the physical details, not even sure the thing had conclusively taken place.

Nor, in the weeks that we were together, did I ever know that feeling of complete union that was love. I had taken Hans for the experience; now, I told myself, I was mature.

Then why didn't they come and take me? I had finished, I had learned what there was to know in life. Day after day I waited, and each day I thought I would cry out, I would break out. What had they done with Anya? They had said they would recommend her release, but there was no word from her, no sign of life. They had only been teasing me, playing with me. They would hold her while they examined my story, while they investigated Katarina Leszczyszyn in Werchrata, and then it would be over for both of us.

The tension was making me ill, physically ill. Boils erupted under my armpit, on the left side, and they would not heal. Their roots were deep in the flesh, the doctors said, and an operation would be necessary to cut them out.

Feeling unclean, dreadfully unclean, and worn out with sleepless nights, and with endless treatments with boiling water and salves, with the changing of suppurating bandages, I went at last to the hospital in Linz where Slavek had once been. And as the time came for the operation, I saw them preparing to put me under gas.

Then the greatest panic of all came over me. I would talk! Under the ether, I would talk! And in coming awake, too, didn't people always babble? In my delirium, everything would come out! I might even talk in Yiddish! I would give away Anya, if she still had a chance, and I might give away Nina!

I tried to stop the nurses, the doctors, from their preparations. I told them I didn't want to be drugged. I had not known it would be this way; I had thought that only a local anesthetic would be used. But no, the doctor explained, for this particular operation it would be impossible to completely deaden the pain locally, and in general he preferred to work with the patient under ether.

My terror grew. I tried to get out of the operation altogether. I said perhaps some of the salves, the treatments, would still prove sufficient. The surgeon was ready. He was calm, and he took my protest as quite ordinary. Many people, he assured me, were terrified of losing consciousness; it was a normal reaction. But I need not fear. I would be wide awake in a few hours.

And firmly the nurse held the cone over my face. I tried to hold in my breath. With all my power I tried to hold onto my consciousness. And then, as I knew I was going under, I wished for death. I had had enough, enough of this life, and only the worst was before me. Let it all go, I thought; in the end it will in any case be like this, with gas, in Oswiecim. Perhaps it would be best if it happened to me now.

For an instant I wanted to cry. I pitied myself, as if the death were really happening. I thought, not of Slavek, but of that mysterious one, that unmet one who had been destined to be my husband, and who was somewhere in the world. . . . I had betrayed him. No, he was not in the world; if a Jew had been destined to become my husband he was in this world no longer. And did souls meet, who had never met on earth? Did they recognize each other, over there on the other side? Then a tale from childhood came to me, a grandfather's tale, or a tale heard from the Hasidim of our town, a story of a boy's soul and a girl's soul, predestined for each other, wandering and searching for each other in this world and in the after world. . . .


Waking, would I see the Gestapo faces bending over me?

There was only the nurse. Nothing. Everything as before. Nothing.


Then came a good surprise, a letter from Anya! This time it was in the neat envelope of the Steinkeller estate; she was home, she said, and was working at her old job. I must come and visit her.

Of course the letter had to be guarded; nevertheless it could have had some spirit, some warmth. It was good to know that the Gestapo men had kept their word and finally accepted my testimony, and released Anya, but the whole episode was still dreadfully disquieting. At the end of the week I went to see her, and as the train drew into the little station at Leoben, I recognized Anya standing in the same spot as on my very first visit. But she was no longer the same Anya. Her face was pinched, and everything about her seemed to slump. As we embraced, Anya whispered, "Don't talk about anything as yet. I feel I am watched." And so we walked up the mountain, chattering loudly, laughing much, as always before. Could it really be true that we were being watched? Two girls, on this little road in the countryside, so far from the world with its wars and its politics, who were we, what were we, that the energy of men should be wasted to hunt us down, even here? In our artificial way with each other, we were like actors carrying on our role in some empty, darkened theater.

But at last in her room we were ourselves. Keeping her voice low, Anya told me all that had happened. The trouble had come from one of the farmhands, a Pole from back home. She could not recall ever having seen him there, but from the things he talked about it was clear that he came from the region of Hrebenko. A dreadful specimen, the worst type, sly, smelly, squat, a drinker. He had kept after her, following her around the farmyard, pestering her, and finally threatening to expose her. "I know you're Jewish. I know you from Hrebenko. You don't fool me." If she wouldn't yield to him, he would denounce her to the Gestapo. "You're not like the other girls here. Only Jewish girls hold themselves so high!"

What could she say except, "Go ahead, denounce me, idiot!" To yield, even if she could imagine herself doing such a thing, would be an admission. For some weeks he had kept repeating his threats, until she had begun to believe he would never actually carry them out. And then one day the Gestapo had come.

They had taken her to Grumming. She had denied, of course. They had slapped her until she had felt her head was coming off. After putting her in solitary confinement, they had questioned her again, beat her with their fists, thrown her against the wall.

I felt her pain as in my own body. Would I be able to endure it when they did it to me?

Yes, they had questioned her about me. Where had she known me? Why were we always visiting each other? And so she had told those stories about our childhood.

Finally they had left off their questioning and she had remained in the women's prison, not knowing her fate. It was an ordinary jail, with thieves, prostitutes, a few politicals, among them a Russian woman who had become her friend. Two months had passed. The Russian woman had completed her sentence, and through her Anya had sent me the letter that warned me what story to tell.

But how had she been able to endure it when they beat her?

"As long as they beat me I was sure they still didn't know anything. I told them it was all blackmail, that that peasant tried to force me to sleep with him, and then invented the story that I was Jewish. And you know, Katya, they are afraid of one thing. They don't want to make a mistake and condemn a real Christian as a Jew."

Yet even worse, I knew, was their worry that they would let a Jew escape as a Christian. They would go to every length to find out whether our stories were true. No, our affair was not yet over.

I told Anya of my own interview with the Gestapo, and how I had decided to brazen out the story.

"Katya, you haven't changed!"

I couldn't tell her how I had changed. It was all so banal, so unworthy, what I had done even while Anya lay in prison in the face of death. And yet I could not keep from talking of the subject itself, as though wanting her to give me sanction. "Anya, if we are really in danger—they may come for us again, any day—

[ 182 ]

don't you have the feeling sometimes of wanting to know all that there is in life?"

For the first time, tears were in her eyes. "I know, Katya. When I sat there in prison, I thought of it. If there were only someone here I could love." And then she asked, "Are you seeing Slavek?"

"No," I said. "I haven't seen him for a year."

She touched my hand. "Perhaps now, if you really love someone, even if he is a Christian—"

I too was crying. "No, no, Anya." And I couldn't tell her—I was too ashamed—for it had been done without love.

And so the next morning we walked in the springtime fields, trying to appear before everybody's sight as though nothing had happened.


It was only another few weeks before the expected call came for me. One day when I returned from lunch there was the message that the Gestapo had telephoned. I was to come there at two. No further instructions. Only to come to the reception desk.

There, I was given a room number. It was not in the Foreign Workers Section, nor was it the third-floor office where I had been before. I mounted the stairs, found the number, and this time with the premonition of finality opened the door. Another ordinary office occupied by two young men. The one behind the desk demanded curtly, "You are Katarina Leszczyszyn?"

"Yes."

My birthplace, age, other particulars.

I answered.

Abruptly, he snapped, "You are under arrest. You are a Jew, and a spy in the Czech underground apparatus. You wormed your way into the Hermann Goering works in order to obtain military

[ 183 ]

information on secret arms processes, which you passed on to the enemy."

Aghast, I cried, "But I've never even been inside the work-shops!"

The catalogue of my crimes became more and more absurd. What was it all for? If they had caught me as a Jew, what was the rest for?

He was shouting now. "For two whole years you have wound us around your little finger! You completely fooled us about your accomplice, Nina Ilanova."

"No! No!" I screamed. "You can shoot me at once, beat me, cripple me, but the truth is the truth! I am not a spy. I don't know anything of any Czech underground. I never tried to get into the Hermann Goering works. The manager himself requested me and insisted that I come. Why don't you ask him—Herr Lauterman!"

"You are all spies! Your accomplice, Nina Ilanova, is a spy and a Jewess, and her lover, Karlus, is a spy!"

Now a deathly dread came over me. With my being a Jew, with my hiding my Jewishness, I had endangered them all. And in catching me for my Jewishness, they might have got hold of a thread that would lead them on to Karlus, and even to Slavek, and to all those brave men who in spite of the power of the Nazis had somehow been carrying on their underground work right here in the munitions center. Whatever it was they were doing, even if they had only a radio and listened to the foreign broadcasts! But couldn't it be more? Couldn't they be sabotaging the manufacture of shells and guns, so that not all the shells exploded, and not all the guns shot straight? And couldn't they be sending out impor-tant news over their radio? Though I really knew nothing of the mysterious Czech underground, all sorts of things of this kind had been whispered about, in a general way.

Against such important actions, what did it matter if one more Jewess was caught, even if that Jewess was myself? If only their work against the enemy could be protected! And if only Nina could be protected! My luck had already lasted long enough; it had given me nearly two years of life, two extra years. Now it was at an end. Surely they had their information about me, even a picture of me that had been verified in Hrebenko, just as they had had in Anya's case. I felt that my death was certain. I just didn't want to drag down any others.

"I know nothing of spies!" I shouted. "And I told you the truth about Nina! She is no Jew!" In that instant, an impulse came to me. It seemed to me that if I gave myself away, if I admitted the truth about myself even before they produced their proofs, they would then believe what I said about the others. Desperately I cried out, "The only accusation that is not false is that I am Jewish. Yes, I am Jewish. My real name is Eva Korngold."

So it was finished. It seemed to me that the whole time I had known I would be caught, and had really been waiting for this moment. Perhaps, as I think of it now, it was this very feeling that undermined me and brought on my capitulation. For it was like a need to comply with doom.

And perhaps the Gestapo men even knew of this feeling. They knew the game. They played it with many others. I had, in a way, played my game with them twice before. I had felt sure that I could brazen things out. I had been able to face them, as long as I was risking myself for others, but when it came to risking others for myself, I was lost.

And yet, despite my sense of being doomed, when I cried out my real name there came an opposite feeling in me, of victory and of elation. I had declared myself of my own will, proudly, instead of finding myself whimpering after hours of torture that I was a Jew. I was glad for myself that I had managed to do it this way, before they killed me.

But on their side they merely brushed over my admission, my terrible final admission, the end of these years of hiding, of pretense, of dread. "You're still lying! You're lying about the Czech underground; you're lying about Nina!"

Now my strength came back. "If you want to force me to tell lies, you can!" I shouted at them. "I am sure that if you beat me enough you will make me lie. But if you want the truth while I am still able to tell it to you, then it's as I said. I am Jewish. Nina is not."

"So you told the truth about Nina? And about Anya Ozymok? Esther Warshawsky—that was the truth too? The same kind of truth?"

I was silent.

"She's back under arrest, you know. This time we got it out of her. At least half." He laughed. "She admitted she's a Jew, but she claims she's a converted one, a Christian! And that's why she didn't say she was Jewish in the first place!" He roared at me, "Perhaps you have such a pretty story, too?"

"No," I said. Inside me there was only weeping. How they must have tormented her, what they must have done to her to drive her that far. And yet she had still tried to protect me. She had tried to tell her story in such a way that my own testimony about going to church with her would at least not have been contradicted. "No," I said to them, "I am not a Christian convert. I am entirely a Jew."

The questioning went on. Who were the members of the Czech underground? Where did they hold their meetings? Where was their radio?

I could say only that I knew nothing, nothing, nothing. In turns, they shouted the same questions at me. "You know nothing! You were with the Czechs all the time! You go out only with Czechs!" He reeled off their names: Slavek, Karlus, Hans. "Why do you keep company only with Czechs?"

I said I happened to like them. They were more cultured than the other foreign workers as a rule. They were more civilized. These men were my friends, and that was all.

"Just friends! You went to bed with every one of them!"

Let them begin, let them begin with the physical beating! Let them strike me, hurl me against the wall, as they had done with Anya. But still this didn't come, and the waiting for it, while they shouted and cursed at me, seemed even worse. Now they demanded particulars of my family, my real family. I said so far as I knew they had all been killed in the German death camps.

Suddenly both men approached and ordered me to come with them.

In the corridor we passed several people who knew me, who had many times chatted, laughed with Katya. There were no Heil Hitlers now; they passed, their eyes averted. It was certainly over for me. Would I first be stood in that long room, face to the wall? Was it true that the shooting was sometimes done in the basement of this very building?

We were in the Foreign Workers Section. They took me into Herr Mueller's office.

He was standing, waiting. He waited another moment, until they had gone. "Katya, Katya, what have you done?" he burst out. "Why did you admit anything at all?"

I stared at him, crumbling within myself. I had been so clever! I had let them trick me into my admission by their wild accusations, their shouting! All the while, they hadn't really known anything for certain. They had shown me no papers, not even a photograph. They had not even known my real name! And I myself had told them! Perhaps, even now, Hrebenko was no longer in German hands. If not for myself, I would have been safe.

Herr Mueller went on angrily. "If it wasn't for that damned filthy Pole! If not for him, you could have lived here as Katya Leszczyszyn until you were seventy! Katya, if you had only come to me and told me, I might have been able to help you. Surely you knew I would help you!"

How could I have been sure? On this one thing—who we were —how could I know that anyone among them would act humanly?

My voice sounded small. "If that's so," I said, "then can't it be that you don't know anything yet? Let me go out—to the wash-room."

Vague, wild ideas were in my mind. I was on the second floor. I could let myself down from the washroom window, jump to the courtyard, walk out.

"It's too late, Katya," he said. "I can't do anything now."

He told me to sit down, gave me a cigarette. Then, at least, if he felt something for me, perhaps he would tell me my fate? I begged him, "Herr Mueller, can you tell me how it will be? Will they shoot me, or will they hang me?"

Even so, a faint smile came over his face. "Neither the one nor the other, Katya."

"I know that Jews are killed."

"I'll send you to a labor camp," he said.

It was as though there were still a remnant in me of Katarina, and this Katarina had the privilege of asking further about the fate of the Jewess, Eva.

"Can you tell me where?"

"No, I can't."

"If it is for you to decide where I am sent, perhaps I can ask one thing—that it not be to Poland."

"Why?"

"Even while I was still at home, I knew that all those sent to camps in Poland were killed."

"I don't know about that."

"At least then, if it has to be Poland, not to Oswiecim," I said, for even more than Belzec, that had become the name of horror.

Something changed in him; he looked as though he had an impulse to reach out and touch me. "No, no, not there," he said.

And then, coming a step closer, still as though he wanted to touch me but might not, Herr Mueller said, "Don't despair. You'll see—one day the war will end, as all wars have to end. There will be an exchange of prisoners, as there always is. And then, you may even return home. Only try to remain healthy. Try to keep sanitary—that is the main thing in the camps. And let us hope you will come through it all."

That was his farewell, I knew. "Is there anything you want to take along?" he asked. "Your things have been brought here."

Then perhaps they didn't really intend to kill me? Why would they trouble to move my things?

I attempted to test what Herr Mueller really meant. "I don't suppose I'll really need anything." And I looked up into his eyes, recalling, oddly, at that very moment, Herr Eberhardt's complaint that I looked too boldly into the eyes of men. How far away that seemed! Would the Eberhardts hear about their Katya? Surely all of Linz would know.

"Can you imagine! That Katya was a Jewess the whole time!" And the Eberhardts would repeat to all their friends, "Why, she lived with us for nearly a year, and we never suspected!"

"At least, take a change of clothing," Herr Mueller was insisting.

Then perhaps I would live, after all, and if I lived, everything that I had lived through had one day to be known. "There is only one thing I want," I said. "I would like to have my diary."

He didn't seem surprised. Apparently the diary was already known to them. But I had been careful, and put secret things down in symbols know only to myself. "*Yah, yah*, Katya," he said. "We will first have to translate it, and then I will send it to you later."

[ 189 ]

Strangely, I more than half believed him and accepted his words as another sign that I would live.

Now the two Gestapo men returned; they led me to a store-room where I saw all my things spread out, everything that had been in my room—the books, pictures, utensils, my clothing, every single thing of mine, as though I were already effaced from the earth.

Some of the clothing had been thrown into the valise that I had used for my visits to Anya, and other things were in the first satchel I had brought from Hrebenko. The rest was in a heap. I carefully selected my best dress, stockings, shoes, underwear; my guards stepped into the corridor while I put these on. I put a change of clothing in my valise. I was ready.

Entirely silent, the two Gestapo men now took me walking through the town. But for the silence, I might have been out for a stroll with two cavaliers.

A short distance from the Gestapo headquarters was the city jail. There they delivered me, and presently I was in a large cell with a dozen other women. And I was so preoccupied with my fate that I hardly noticed the first time a cell key turned on me.

The girls in the cell talked volubly enough; a newcomer was at least an interruption of the monotony. One was a German girl arrested for consorting with a foreign worker. Others were of the sort who are always in and out of prisons, for thieving, for brawling, for black-marketing. An elderly woman whispered to me to be careful of what I said, as there was an informer in the cell.

A few days later, my escorts called, to take me back to Gestapo headquarters. Would it now be the same as it had been for Anya? They had put her in the jail in Grumming and taken her out for her interrogations and her beatings.

Twice, I was taken out. Each time as they led me out of the cell I tried to strengthen myself. Would I be able to endure what Anya had endured, and more? Even from the way the other women looked at me as I was led out, it seemed to me that they were wondering, What will she look like when she returns? Will she have her teeth? Will her face be misshapen? Will she still walk upright, or will she have to be dragged in, unable to walk?

I tried to make my mind blank, to shut out such imaginings. And at the Gestapo headquarters, I waited, from question to question. The same questions. Who were the members of the Czech underground? Why had I lied about Nina? Did I really imagine I could protect her? She was as Jewish as I was.

But if they knew, would they still be questioning me? So I denied and denied. Herr Mueller's words kept ringing in my ears, "*Ach*, Katya, why did you admit anything at all?"

And for me the awaited blows never came. Perhaps Mueller, doing what little he could for me, had seen to it that I would be spared the beatings. But as the endless repetition of the questions continued, I found myself again praying—if they would only strike me. Strike me, beat me, before I lost my strength!

Then, the third time, they told me to get my things from the matron.

Several of the girls said goodbye. The elderly woman said, "Free?" in a hopeful voice. I shook my head. "Where to?" I lifted my shoulders. And in that instant, even she seemed to recede behind a wall. For who knew what I might be?

And who knew where I was going? They might still put an end to me. This time my cavaliers walked with a peculiar rigidity. There was an odd thing I had noticed in all their handling of me: I never lost my awareness of their awareness that I was a presentable young woman. I knew that this would not prevent anything that had to happen to me, and yet it gave all of our meetings a peculiar quality, almost as though we were admittedly play-acting, as if at any instant they might say to each other, "This is all nonsense; let's take her to a café and have some fun."

I felt this even in their excess of rigidity, their show of indifference. Could there be any moment in which this could serve me? Could I make them more uncomfortable? No, in the end they would shoot me all the same, perhaps with a bit of regret that this equipment for pleasure-giving had to be wasted.

We again reached the Gestapo building, but this time we went in through a side entrance. We walked down a rear corridor; they opened a door, and I saw a stairway leading downward. In the basement, then, it would be done. I took each breath as though it would be my last. Through my body there was a tense, tingling excitement, an anticipation; it was like that night when I had waited for Hans to return to my room, knowing that in a certain instant a part of my life would end. Only here I felt an added anxiety—as if I were actually afraid that I might miss the instant of my death. If a bullet came from behind, on the stairs, I wouldn't even have time to feel it, to know my own death. But, no, it was of the Russians that one heard this story; it was not the method of the Nazis.

On the landing, a keeper waited, and my two guards gave me over to him; they turned, and I heard their tread as they mounted the stairs. The keeper motioned me along a hallway, opened a door, and I barely had time to see the outline of a small cell, in the light reflected from the corridor, when he half pushed me inside and turned the lock.

Was this blindness? There was not a sliver of light, even under the door. I put down my valise slowly, as though it might unexpectedly strike the floor, and I stood there hoping that my eyes might become accustomed enough to the dark so that I might make out the walls. The blackness was complete. I put my hand up to my face, felt it, and holding my hand there directly before my eyes, stared and stared, hoping to see somehow the outlines of my spread fingers. Nothing. I remembered Anya. They hadn't done this to her. Her cell had contained a tiny high window. I moved about cautiously, felt the walls, found a bench, let myself down on it.

Was this the finish of me? Was this my death? I was almost afraid to stretch out on the bench. Presently I was thirsty. I felt my way to the door, called, called. My voice sounded so loud, in the locked room. I beat the door until my fists hurt.

Nothing. Suppose they simply left me here until I was dead of starvation? Why did I keep my eyes open in this blackness? I lay down, closed my eyes. If I could sleep. But on the edge of sleep, long, long intervals passed; once I awoke with a start and told myself I had certainly been asleep. Then it must be morning. A whole night must have passed since I was here. Surely it was morning because I felt such a terribly acute need for my coffee, even the worst watery ersatz, some warm token of the new day. My body was telling me morning had come. I tried to call; I beat again on the door. Nothing. Then I waited, as before.

I tried to summon my family, my close ones, but no image came to me except, over and over, the scene in that room where I had first admitted I was Jewish, as though I could pull the whole scene back to me and do it differently; deny, deny.

Then I became merely apathetic. To feel nothing, to lie in apathy, that would be the best way. That way, I could endure the longest. But why, why prolong this dying?

If I could shut off my life now, would I not do it? And at least cheat them of my final suffering? For now I was certain they had shut me up in this room to die.

And so the time endured in that black cell. I found myself talking to Slavek. Slavek, why had I been so foolish, so contrary? And I lived again through that night of deflowering, as though it were with Slavek. And then I was in the hospital and I longed for the feeling of going adrift, ending, the anesthetic ending, the quietus for all struggles, all fears, as though I had only to let my clenched hands fall open, and life would escape out of them.

And then a sharp anger would arise in me. No, no, I would be stronger even than this! When the allotted time was passed and they opened the door sure to find me dead, I would be alive, alive. I would spring past them with the fierce energy of all that was life! I would reach the open world.

And then out of endlessness I heard a sound. It came down, even piercing the walls of the Gestapo cellar. An air-raid alarm!

There was a double upwelling of joy, of thankfulness in me. The first feeling was one of utterly limitless relief; I was still connected with life. And welling up within this was the feeling of vengeful glory: they were being killed, they were being smashed, they were scurrying into cellars, none so deep, so safe, as this, and in my dreamlike imaginings there was a force in the raid more deadly than any before; there were bombs that would pierce down into all the shelters in all Linz, and the entire Hermann Goering works would be destroyed, shattered, and in the end none would creep out alive from the holocaust, only I. I, from this deep cell, would emerge and live. And I would pass through their dead streets and—And then, in my imagining, a grief struck me: what if it meant Nina too? And Slavek? And Karlus? Would I still call this vengeance down?

A long time later I heard the all-clear.

And then, long afterward, the door opened.

The dim corridor bulb was like a blaze of sunlight. The same two Gestapo men stood there. Instantly I noticed that they carried their topcoats folded over their arms.

"Come," they said.

I started toward them.

"Take your things."

I took my valise, my briefcase.

I followed them up the stairs. We returned to the office where they had first questioned me. A tray with some coffee and bread was on the desk. They motioned me to eat.

[ 194 ]

I didn't know how many days had passed since I had taken food. But though I was ravenous, I made myself eat decently. I tasted the coffee; it was the better grade of ersatz.

Only one curiosity stood at the front of my mind, and it was not even about what was to come, for me. I wanted desperately to know how many days had passed. It was now morning. "What date is it?" I asked.

"The second of May," one of them remarked abstractedly, as though he were really not replying to me.

But surely that was wrong. It would mean I had been only overnight in that cell. And again it was as though they had robbed me of some vital protection; I could no longer even judge the length of time.

The same one announced, "We are now going on a journey. You will not speak to anyone on the way, nor are you permitted to speak with us. When we pass among the public, everything is to appear normal. Do you understand? But don't try to get away." He showed me his revolver. I had scarcely seen him make the movement, but there it was, pointed at me. Both of them held their guns pointed at me for an instant and then put the weapons back into their coats. Momentarily, I had the sense of being in a film, of seeing myself acting on the screen.

"Now come with us."

We went out into the street, to all appearances a well-dressed young woman walking between two friends, one of whom was carrying her valise. I was carrying my briefcase, the one I had usually carried when I went to see Herr Mueller at the Gestapo; now it contained my toilet articles.

We went to the railway station and boarded the Vienna train. There were no other passengers in our compartment, and my companions were silent the entire way, except for occasional remarks to each other.

I thought only of escape. Perhaps in the station in Vienna, if I could run into a crowd, into the stream of people walking from the train, then they couldn't shoot . . .

And why were they taking me to Vienna? Would Anya also be brought there? Was it to execute us together?

In the station, one of them stepped down ahead of me, the other close after. They walked pressed against me on either side. How friendly we must seem. And then I heard someone say, "Hello, Katya!"

It was one of the Czechs from Linz. He smiled; I must have looked quite normal to him, with my two gallants. I said hello to him, and to my surprise he fell in beside us, saying, "Off on a little excursion? A vacation?"

"Yes," I said, not knowing what would come next, as I had been forbidden to speak. My guards nudged me and we turned down another platform.

"Well, goodbye," I said to the Czech, feeling it was my last goodbye in the world.

And he said, in German, *"Auf Wiedersehen."*

THE PLATFORM was deserted. On one side stood a train, as yet completely empty and without a locomotive. We got into one of the second-class cars. We sat down and waited silently. After almost an hour, other passengers began to mount. And again, none entered our compartment. Was it marked in some way? How did they know? Or was it simply chance?

There came a slight bump as the locomotive was attached, and presently the train began to move. What could be its destination? I felt my body was being carried, not I. My body was being carried to a place of execution. But why? Why transport it anywhere? And at such an expense, with these two men occupied to guard me.

It soon became clear I was on an express. I sat, smoking.

I kept seeing a picture of my execution. I would be marched into a small courtyard, behind a building like the Gestapo headquarters in Linz. There would be a firing squad, a small one. I would stand bravely. I would keep my head up. I would even shout out some last words: "Down with Hitler!"

And then I had an obscure feeling: there was something else that I should cry. The *Schma*. The *Schma Yisroael*. That was what Jews cried in their last moment of life. How strange that I was so far removed from my religion that this thought should not come easily to me, and that it took an effort of memory to bring back

the words. *Schma Yisroael, Adonai Elohenu Adonai Echod.*
Would these really be the words of my death cry? But why, from
me?

That which you shouted in your last breath—it was the thing
you were ready to die for. I recalled tales in my Hebrew class,
patriotic legends about the Inquisition, of Jews who in their last
breath, after weeks of hideous torture and as they were tied to
the stake and the fire was lighted, cried out the *Schma*. But was it
that way with me? No one had tried to force me to accept their
faith. The reverse was true. Even those Jews who had tried to
accept another faith, to convert, had been beaten back to their
own race; even those who had changed their names, married
Christians, deliberately forgotten everything Jewish—even they
had had the yellow star pinned on them. There would be nothing
of final defiance in crying out *Schma Yisroael*, as in the days of the
Inquisition. Yet what else would have meaning? Could I cry out,
Murderers! beasts! Could I cry out, You are already defeated! You
can shoot me but your day is near! Or cry simply, I am a Jew, a
Jew, a Jew! until blood stopped my mouth. I am a Jew, and you
will not destroy us! My people will still live! When your cities
are smashed and Hitler is dead and your Nazi Reich is forgotten!

But was that not the same? Was it not the *Schma?*

But mine was a cry of vengeance, and what was the value of a
death cry if it was only a cry of vengeance? Surely that was not
the real meaning of *Schma Yisroael*, and perhaps I did not even
have a right to add a vengeful note to that final cry of affirmation,
for what was vengeance in the face of death?

And was there no meaning to anything I had gone through? I
had tried in my last weeks to seize upon whatever life had to
offer, but in my haste I had been cheated. There could be no haste,
there could be no forcing of life. Perhaps that was the meaning
these tormentors could not learn. Only by living could I have
come to know the rest, to know the feeling of what life was as I

[ 198 ]

lived as a woman and a wife and a mother, with my family growing around me, as my mother had lived.

And so as the train wheels turned I felt that I was at last perhaps touching the meaning, the truth, of all this horror, and of why the Nazis would not be victorious. For they too were trying to force their will on life itself, to rule life and death, and that could not be. For that was God. And just as when I had been a schoolgirl and had found mathematics utterly incomprehensible, and had tried and tried to concentrate and at one moment had felt I caught a glimmer, that I almost saw how fractions were multiplied, so now I felt, concentrating in my mind, that I almost caught the glimmer, that I almost saw God, and that I understood why a Jew might cry out the *Schma*. For this was as close as a man or woman could come to understanding the universe. It was to say that life cannot be forced, that all life was one, a single flowing movement, and it could not be altered, even by the greatest of human schemes and machinations. That was how we understood that God was One.

And so now they would carry my body and do what they would with me. It would not matter so much.

The train seemed to be slowing down. We were in the outskirts of a city. Where? And I suddenly emerged from my reverie and was back as I had been, intent, still feeling the energy of my own will, my own life, feeling the need to take any risk to escape rather than to let myself be carried so to my death.

The train slowed; I arose and said I had to go to the washroom. I walked down the length of the corridor; I could leap from the washroom window. But one of them followed me, and his foot was in the washroom doorway.

Defeated, I returned with him to the compartment. Now the train halted, and two soldiers climbed into our space. They sat opposite us, young, restless, full of spirits. They eyed me, even made audible remarks about the girl. Was she alone? Was she with those two?

I was eager for them to know my situation, but I had been forbidden to speak to anyone. Then one of them addressed me. Did the *Fraulein* mind if he opened the window? I could only smile and shake my head.

Presently the same one thought to offer me a cigarette, and so I turned to my guard and said, "May I accept a cigarette from the soldier?"

In the Gestapo man's eye there was a glint of appreciation at my little maneuver. I had not violated his order. "Very well," he said. But now the soldiers knew my situation.

An awed silence had fallen on them. The cigarette was given, lighted, in silence. Even to each other, they now spoke in subdued voices.

It was a long journey, and covertly they began to communicate with me. When one of my guards was immersed in a newspaper and the other was turned to the window, the more daring of the two soldiers suddenly made a fist at them.

What could the soldiers think? That I had been arrested for black-marketeering, or some other common violation. I wanted them to know the truth. The covert flirtation continued; it was at least a way to pass the time, and who knew, if an opportunity should come, perhaps for the needed instant they would block the way of the guards.

Now I indicated to my guard that I would like to stand in the passageway. He nodded; the train was going at full speed. I went out, just opposite the compartment door, and leaned against the window. Where were we? The landscape seemed to be changing: the wooded hills did not rise so high; everything was flattening out. There was a river, winding sometimes parallel to the tracks; a recognition awakened within me. There were weeping-willow trees along the river. I had seen none in Austria.

Could this be Poland? It was almost as though an echo came in my very flesh. And a mournful sense of appropriateness went through my body. This body was being carried back to the soil that had given it birth. Returned there, for its death.

But why, why carry one little Jewess such a distance? Surely the Germans would not be so wasteful.

And then I caught myself remembering how startled, how desperate I had been on meeting this same disbelief in others. Not long before I had left Hrebenko, after the first *aktione* had already taken place, there had begun to be trains routed through Hrebenko. They were not yet the trains of sealed boxcars that were to flow, soon enough, across Europe; they were still open trains, with a few guards on them. Some consisted of old coaches, and some of boxcars with the big doors still open, and inside sat Jews. They were not in very bad spirits. They were well dressed, they had good luggage, they had taken their best things with them, for they imagined they were being taken east for "resettlement." It was Henig Weiss, whose father had once owned the hotel near the station, who talked with some of them and came with their story. With their last money they had bought expensive luggage and watches and things that they hoped to be able to sell in their new area of settlement. But from the Polish engineers of the trains we had already heard where they would be taken. To Belzec, or to that other camp that was whispered about with the word *death*, to Oswiecim. And Henig was beside himself at their complacency. "We must warn them, we must tell them!" he kept saying. So that perhaps some of them would find some opportunity to jump, to get away from the train—anything! What was there to risk? Then once or twice we ran alongside the trains and called to them, "Jews, Jews, you are being taken to your death!" But when we tried to tell them what awaited them, they replied, "But why would they drag us all this way on a train only to kill us? No, no, if it was for that, they could have killed us at home. It's absurd. The Germans are too practical. They would not waste their trains at a time like this. One thing you must admit, they are practical."

And wasn't I too now giving myself this very excuse? And wasn't I too dressed in my best, hadn't I been told to take my good clothes, my good valise?

But still my mind found another excuse. I was in no mass deportation in a baggage car but was riding in a second-class compartment. Why would they send me in comfort, with two escorts, when, if it was only for that, they could have held me until the next mass transport of Jews passed through Vienna.

Surely a train like this would not take me to Belzec, to Oszwiecim? Would we, I wondered, pass by my own station, at Hrebenko? And then I felt sure that we would. There I had begun my journey, and there would be the end. Perhaps just there I would find a way to leap from the train.

I realized that the soldier was standing beside me. He uttered one word. "Why?"

I had time for one word of reply. "Jew."

I heard a breath from him, a kind of compounded sound of pity, of disapproval, and of separating himself from it all. And then the Gestapo man was on the other side of me.

"Are we already in Poland?" I asked.

"Yes," he said.

And for the first time since my arrest I felt tears. For myself, my fate, and for love of this place where I would drop like an animal in its own forest.

"How much longer until we arrive?" I asked.

"I can't tell you."

I returned to the compartment.


It did not seem very much longer. We had not passed through Hrebenko or any place I knew. The train halted at a small station, and my escorts told me to alight. We were the only ones. I saw the name lettered on the platform: AUSCHWITZ. I had never heard of such a place. Perhaps it was indeed as Herr Mueller had said, and they had sent me to a labor camp.

"Is this the end of our journey?"

We started to walk along a paved road. This time neither of them took my valise.

We walked for quite some distance; on both sides were empty fields, and I saw nothing of any town. It seemed weird. To ride with two guards for hundreds of miles, to get off the train in the middle of nowhere, and simply to walk with my two young men along an empty road.

And then I saw watchtowers and a fence. The high barbed-wire fence stretched endlessly ahead of us on one side, and behind it were rows of low, long barracks, just as in every camp I had seen, except that here they were brownish and were of stone. And this camp was by far the largest I had ever seen.

Then I heard band music.

We approached a gate, with its check post. Behind, I saw a speckless yard, with neatly cut grass, a border of trees, and even some flowers. There stood ranks of prisoners, dressed like those I had seen in the yard of the Hermann Goering works, and to one side stood a band, also of prisoners. Above their heads a huge banner was strung. *Joy through Work*. And another, *Work Makes Life Sweet*.

The prisoners now marched off. They looked strong and well. I felt bewildered and yet relieved. Perhaps this was a sort of reformatory camp, to which Herr Mueller had kindly seen that I be sent? The central yard, with its administration buildings grouped around the lawn, looked almost like a sanatorium. And if it was only a question of my being put to some sort of labor—with music—fine!

And so, with rising spirits, I followed my escorts into a reception office. There sat a pair of SS men, handsome, young, even pleasant. They were having sandwiches and beer.

My escorts greeted them, and all four went into the next room, leaving the door ajar. I saw my traveling companions hand over my papers, and in a moment they came out, passed me, and were gone.

The two SS men went back to their snack. One of them glanced at me and said amicably, "Are you hungry? Want some beer?"

I said no, I had had something on the train.

They finished eating, and then one of them casually opened my folder. He looked at me and laughed. "Are you really Jewish?"

"Yes," I said.

"Impossible!" He laughed again. Then he demanded of the other one, "What do you think?"

The second one studied me and said, "No."

"No, we don't believe it," said the first one.

"But I am," I said. "That's why they brought me." I couldn't quite tell whether or not they were making fun of me. In a grotesque way it was a reversal of that time so far back, in the sorting camp in Kraków, when the two nasty fellows had stalked me, asking each other aloud whether I looked Jewish. Here I didn't know exactly what attitude to take. The world seemed upside down.

"Maybe you're only half Jewish?" the first SS man suggested.

"No. I'm completely Jewish."

"Perhaps there was a little uncertainty somewhere along the line?" He smiled lewdly.

"I'm completely Jewish," I said, "on both sides, my parents and my grandparents as far back as I know."

"Can you imagine that!" he said to his companion as he idly picked up the phone. Presently there arrived another SS man, older, with a huge dog on a leash, and a rifle. "Go with him," I was told.

I walked alongside him. We passed endless lanes of barracks and then were on the road again, between grassless brown fields. On and on, silently. But if it was not among all those barracks that I was to be placed, where was he taking me? Out into some emptiness, to shoot me after all?

A few SS men passed us, going the other way. They greeted my guard. "Who's the beauty? A gypsy? You have all the luck!"

It was true, with my dark complexion, tanned from my last weekend in the country, I could have been taken for a gypsy. And it came to me that I had heard about gypsies, like Jews, being exterminated by the Nazis.

We walked. We had left the barracks far behind us, and I saw that we were now reaching another such area, with the same rows of low stone huts. But here there were no trees, no lawns. And as we reached the buildings, I had my first feeling of unreality.

On the walks between the huts there were prisoners moving about, but they were like none that I had seen in the first camp. Gaunt, ghastly, in misshapen ragged garments, torn shoes, some with only one shoe—were these women? Their heads were shaved or cropped, and they moved with a strange apathetic gait, like ghosts.

We passed among them. The wraiths of women all wore large insignia, patches of different colors on their clothing. Most of them wore the Jewish star, made of a red triangle over a yellow, but some wore different patches of green, black, red, whose meanings I did not know. Some wore striped prison dresses, and among all the ragged creatures these, by contrast, seemed to be clothed. And then I noticed that all the prisoners had numbers tattooed on their arms.

I scarcely had time to adjust my reason, so sudden, so strange, was the contrast between the two camps that were separated by the long barren waste. It was as though a pleasant picture were lifted away from a wall, and behind it maggots crawled. And in that instant a feeling of bitter rage swept through me against those two sleek SS boys, finishing their beer, joking with me, while knowing the next sight that would confront me.

We turned now into a large building that stood amidst the barracks. We came into a hall, with benches around the sides. On the benches sat a number of women whom I deduced to be newly arrived, for once more I was among people who looked like human beings. Though they were thin and sallow, instead of in shining health like myself, they were normally, if shabbily, dressed. My guard with the hound left me.

I looked through the windows. Some distance away, I saw other large brick buildings—factories, I supposed. Several huge smokestacks rose from them.

All of us were quiet, with that curious fear that sometimes comes over a group of people who dare not speak to one another even though they know they are in the same plight. I noticed, now, something in the atmosphere of the room, the very air of the building, that had been penetrating me since I entered this second camp. It was an odor, combined with a density of the air. Outside, I had thought it came from the sickly, malodorous bodies of the prisoners, but the odor pervaded this reception building, too. I could not yet tell what it was.

A few men in striped uniforms moved busily around the reception chamber. One of them approached me and started a conversation. Had I arrived with the others?

No, I said. Alone. Who were they?

A small transport from Terressienstadt, he said, as though the name would mean something to me.

"What's it like, here?" I asked. And, motioning through the window, "Are those the factories where we work?"

A short, ironic laugh escaped him. "Factories? Don't you know where you are?"

"Why—" I said.

"Don't you know what Oswiecim is?"

I would not believe it. "But the sign on the railway platform said Auschwitz."

Even as I uttered the word, I knew. "Oswiecim," he repeated. "In German, Auschwitz." He watched me sharply, a curious light in his eyes, as though he could see everything going on in me. First there was my dazed feeling of betrayal—why had they all fooled me, played with me, amused themselves with a person's last grasping for life? Even Herr Mueller, the fatherly Herr Mueller, he too had played with me, reassuring me, "No, no, not there, not to Oswiecim." And yet, within my bitterness I was still grasping, clawing for some crevice in the wall, to cling to life. Had I not seen many people moving about here? Then it was not true that all were gassed.

"But I thought in Oswiecim everyone was gassed," I said.

"Not all. There is a selection."

"A selection?"

"You didn't come in a transport. In a big transport, as soon as it arrives, there is a selection. Some are selected to work. The others go right into the factory." He glanced out the window at the chimneys in the background. I saw the smoke now, merging into the haze. And still I did not understand, though I wondered whether it was the gas that I had smelled, whether that was the source of the odor that pervaded the air, indoors and out. In all the rumors that had come back to us, the last action had been vague; there had been only the word *gas*. Even now when the chimneys stood before me, I did not comprehend. So hard is it for the human mind to accept what is totally inhuman.

"Now we have the Hungarians," he said. "The Hungarian Jews are going up the chimney." He looked around at the people on the benches. "When there's only a small transport, they sometimes pass without the first selection. Or a special, like you."

"A special?"

"Brought in alone. That's unusual." His eyes glittered as he examined me anew. "But there are selections later on—all the time."

"Later on?"

"Every so often there are selections in the barracks. Or if you fall sick and go to the infirmary." His voice became more intimate. "But you don't have to worry, a girl like you. You look fine. You could pass any selection. And then, you know, it's possible to arrange oneself here. If a girl has sense. After all, some of the men—some of us work on good jobs, in the kitchen, in the warehouses—those of us who have been here longer. Things can be arranged, even here."

I hardly heard his last words. A phrase was still echoing in my mind: *Going up the chimney*. "What did you say they were doing to the Hungarian Jews?"

He looked more closely at me. "Over there. That's where they dispose of those who don't pass the selection. First gas; then they cremate the bodies. It's hygienic."

I could not look at this man who had lived with all this. Something I had felt about him from the first moment, something I had never before felt about any human being, now overwhelmed me, sickened me, as though he himself were a part of the sickening odor, that odor of burning flesh. I asked for the washroom.

He pointed, then walked with me to the door. "Do you want a piece of soap?" he asked. And he went on, "You know, here in Auschwitz-Birkenau we do things for each other. A man will do things for a woman if she will do things for him. I could give you a piece of soap."

I was still dazed. "Speak plainly," I said. "I don't understand."

He told me plainly.

Here, even here. And yet hadn't I myself, when I knew death was near, wanted to grasp at everything?

"No," I said. I had my own soap.

He went away.

[ 208 ]

I came out and found a place on the bench. I talked with a woman from Terressienstadt. It was a special camp, she told me, where Jews from Austria and Germany and Czechoslovakia had been told they would be unmolested. Vast sums had been paid for the privilege of living in this protected camp. But there had been transports out of there, too, despite the promises, and so her turn had come.

Night had fallen. I stretched out on the bench. Slowly my self-possession was coming back in me. I would escape. From this place, I would surely escape! This idea, this conviction, grew until it filled me, crowding out of my mind every ghastly reality. I let myself think only in terms of escape, reviewing in my mind all that I had seen. I had passed such vast empty stretches on the way from the first section of the camp to this one. It was the first part that was Auschwitz proper, I now knew, and this place was Birkenau. Surely it was possible to escape back into that empty in-between area! I clung to this thought, my mind was absorbed in it, nothing else could enter. I let my mind roam to fantastic schemes, I saw myself hiding in trucks, in wagons—people came and went, trains came and went—I would escape.

And so the night passed.

Early in the morning I heard alarms, whistles, shouts of *"Appel!"* The band music began. I went to the washroom, managed to refresh myself, combed my hair. Then I returned to my corner on the bench.

Presently a woman, wearing the striped prison dress, strode into the hall. "Up!" she shouted. "Stand for inspection."

Instantly we were all standing rigid.

Somehow a new word had already been absorbed: *cappo*. This was a cappo, a work commander from among the prisoners themselves.

And now a group of SS officers strode into the room. There were perhaps a dozen of them, of all ages; the older ones seemed of high rank. One of them shouted, "Sit." We sat. The group began to walk around the room. Was this the selection? The decision as to who should live and who should die?

But they made no sign. They simply walked past the benches, hardly ever making a remark, even among themselves. But as they came to me, they halted.

The first, who seemed to be the commanding officer, snapped at me, "Are you Eva Korngold?"

"Yes." Why had they stopped only before me? Why did he know my name? Did it mean that all the others were doomed or that only I was doomed?

The men all stared at me. I recalled the whole series of accusations that the SS had made against me in Linz, the spying, the charges about the Czech underground—all those things must have been included in my papers. They had come to look over this dangerous person, and now I would be taken out and executed.

They marched out.

I waited. Of the SS group, one soldier had remained. He spoke to the cappo; she left, and he stayed with us in the room.

I could no longer endure the uncertainty. Why had I been singled out? And I arose and went up to the SS man, hardly aware of the incredible nature of my act in a place where prisoners were forbidden ever to ask a question, forbidden even to speak to an authority.

"Excuse me," I said. "I'd like to ask something. How is it that the officers stopped before me alone? What is wanted with me?"

He stared at me and began to laugh. "Nothing," he said. "The fellows in the reception office said a beauty of a Jewess came in, so they all wanted to have a look."

I no longer had any way of comprehending. It was as though people talked to you in a language whose words were familiar, but they had secretly reversed the meaning of each word so that what they meant was the opposite of what you understood. Why should men, high officers, trouble to walk over to see if a girl was pretty before they sent her to be gassed?

As for the compliment itself, I knew what took their eyes. I was smartly dressed; I still had the air of "someone." My hair was sparkling black, worn long. I looked around the benches; among the women from Terressienstadt there were a number with faces more beautiful than mine. Yet all of them already had that lack-luster appearance, that look of absence of life, that seemed to include them in the same unliving world as the wretches I had seen in the yard. They were already on the way to becoming like the others. But I—I would never let myself become like that!

And I wondered at myself, at the sense, still so strong in me, of being inextinguishable. How could I imagine, how could I still believe, that I would succeed in maintaining myself, where all the others failed? Yet, wasn't there some special fortune in my life? Wasn't it indeed as though I were always singled out? Even in the way I had been brought here, alone, in comfort in a second-class compartment! And before that—I had suffered no beatings, nothing. I had even been caught only by a mistake of my own rather than by some act of bad fortune. No. If I trusted to my good luck, I would live! Even if all the others were destined to die, even though my heart was torn for them, even though I was ashamed of my selfishness, still I would make a special fate for myself, and escape, and live!

And then the process began with us. First our hair. In a side room we took our turns on a row of chairs attended by prison women wielding shears and clippers. What was done seemed to depend on the whim of the cutter. Some heads were clipped entirely bald. Others were left with a feathery cut, not too different from the boyish coiffures that were to become the mode after the war. So mine was done.

Then we were marched to another building, told to leave whatever baggage we had, and to undress for the showers. Instantly a panic spread. Was this the last moment?

The women from Terressienstadt had heard what took place in the death camps. They said it was the way of the shower. When all were naked in the shower room, the door would be locked and deadly gas, instead of water, would pour through the nozzles.

And so the whispering grew, and there was a hesitancy as to who would be the first to enter. Angrily the cappo shoved those nearest her into the room. We heard water. And one by one we entered, still uncertain, for surely they could still, at any moment, lock the door and change from water to gas.

But we were alive. From moment to moment the belief grew that we would live.

And so we emerged into a room at the farther end. A pile of garments lay there, wrinkled, torn, and a pile of shoes, lopsided, scuffed, wretched.

"Cover yourselves."

We pulled whatever we could from the heap of clothing. These were the remnants from the dead, after whatever was good had been removed, just as our own clothes had now been taken away. I found a brown, shapeless dress in my hands and I pulled it on. It hung loosely on me. I hunted through the pile of rags for a belt of some sort, found a bit of rope, tied it around my waist, and somehow felt as though I had retrieved a tiny hold on myself.

In the other women too I could see a distress, a shame before one another; we had lost what we were. Some joked about their shaven heads, but underneath it all was shame.

And so we were now herded back to the main hall for the final detail of the transformation into other than human creatures. There, again, stood a number of women in prison-striped dresses, and in our rags the feeling came that we were less than they. Each of them held a tattoo needle, and we stood in line for the numbering. Some of them were rough; they seized the arms of their victims and brutally forced down the needle, making large, prominent numerals on the wrist. But I found my arm taken gently by a stolid woman whose hair had partly grown back, with streaks of white. I could scarcely feel the needle as she swiftly wrote small, neat numbers on my forearm, close to the elbow: 81332. If I escaped, I told myself, these numbers could easily be covered. And so once more there came this unreasonable, almost insane feeling that—even here—I was somehow lucky.

And this distorted optimism remained in me as we were marched down to the rows of barracks. At Block 9, five other women and I were taken inside. The fetid odor stopped my breath.

I saw the long dim room with shelves on either side, three high. On these shelves lay creatures, even worse than what I had seen outdoors, haggard, skeletal, all eyes, ghastly. My heart seemed to die. But no, no, I would never become like that!

In a partitioned corner near the door was the nook of the "Block Eldest," who ruled the barracks. She emerged, a squat, piggish-looking woman with a strong, angry face. Marta. A Slovene, I could tell by her accent. It was hard for me to believe that she was Jewish.

She indicated our places, a section of the top shelf for all six. Each received a tin receptacle for food, a spoon—and if we lost it, she snapped, we would get no other.

And so we clambered up against the ceiling. On the lower shelves, forms of women lay, exhausted from the day's work. It was difficult to avoid stepping on a hand, or kicking against a body, a face, and curses greeted our clumsiness. We tried to find places on the boards, but there was hardly space enough for each to lie prone; some would have to lie on their sides. We had not yet fitted ourselves in, or understood the way of it, when the entire block was shaken by a consorted, guttural cry, an utterly animal sound, of aggression, of fear, and at the same time there was a turbulent movement, all the women flinging themselves together in a single pack, clawing and thrusting.

The ration had come.

I waited, saddened, sickened. This they would never make out of me. I might starve, but I would not become such an animal.

I lay on my upper shelf waiting for things to become a little quieter. Suddenly a raucous voice struck me. "The Lady, does she expect to be served?"

It was one of those who wore a striped dress; I now knew I must not answer back, but tumbled down and crowded in for my ration. "Perhaps the Lady is accustomed to servants, but here you will be like everyone else!" she shrieked at me.

I was soon enough to learn who she was—Elsa, the Room Eldest, assistant to the Block Eldest. Always angry, always on the lookout, Elsa was the quickest to strike a blow if a prisoner was slow to answer the *appel* in the morning, Elsa was the surest to catch a girl if she tried to creep out at night to the toilet.

I received my two slices of bread, a bit of margarine, a cup of greenish fluid called tea. There was a stirring around in the remote corners of the barracks as some of the women furtively exchanged bits of food, and others crept onto their shelves to hide away part of their ration or to take something out of their secret stores among the rags on their sleeping space.

Only a few of the women ate together; even in that crowded space each creature somehow huddled to herself like an animal. At the same time there was a division between the two sides of the room. On our side, I noticed, all wore the Jewish star. On the other side, the women wore a variety of patches. A bit timorously I asked one of the older women what the different colors of the patches represented. Some were politicals, and others were ordinary criminals such as thieves and murderesses, she said, and among the men there was a special patch for homosexuals. She became talkative, and warned me about Elsa, and especially about going out at night to the toilet, for Elsa slept in a strategic spot where she could catch the slightest movement. It was a bottom shelf, not far from the door, and, as a Room Eldest, Elsa occupied a space usually given over to six. She had blankets, too, and other amenities. Besides Elsa, she warned me to beware of the clerk, who kept the barracks records, a woman with eyes behind her head, and shifty eyes too, and then there were the cappos, each in charge of a work commando. Tomorrow I would see, for, at the *appel*, I would be assigned to a commando.

As I started to eat my second slice of bread she warned me, "Put it away. You'll get no more until tomorrow night." I put it away, under my dress.

Where had I been caught? she asked, and I told her. She nodded; this explained my healthy appearance. I had not been taken in a ghetto, and I had not yet been in any of the other concentration camps. As for herself, she had been a year in Ravensbruck—she spoke the name as though I should know it, just as I should have known of Terressienstadt. In Ravensbruck one learned the ways of the camps, of cappos. But there, she said, there was no gas chamber. When she was sent to Auschwitz, she had been sure she was being transported only to be gassed. "We are now in the quarantine section," she told me. "Here we will be kept for three or four weeks." She had been there two weeks already. As the woman spoke, I looked at her more closely, for by her voice, by her intonation, she seemed to me younger than I had thought. Her face was wrinkled, the skin lifeless, and her gums were shriveled. Sensing what was in my mind, she asked, "How old do you think I am?"

I put it even lower than seemed possible. "In your thirties." She shook her head, without changing her expression. She was twenty-four, only a few years older than myself.

[ 215 ]

We were permitted to move about in our section of the compound until nine o'clock. Some went to the neighboring barracks, or stood on the walks, talking. I struck up conversations with one and another, trying to find someone from home, but none were from the region of Hrebenko. And then, I could speak only about the one subject on my mind. Had anyone ever escaped from here?

They looked at me as though I were insane. Didn't I know the fence was electrified?

What of the empty field between the two camps? I asked.

Some said there was still another, outer fence that enclosed the whole vast area, both Auschwitz and Birkenau with the grounds between them.

Did anyone know this for sure? I kept asking. When I persisted, they would stare at me in a different way, even with a kind of fear, and they would end the conversation. No one ever thought of the electric fences, except as a way of putting an end to himself. Then a prisoner would walk to the fence.

I roamed the section restlessly, going near the edges. As soon as I got out of quarantine, into the larger compound, I would explore the limits.

And so, at nine, the light was out and we lay on our platform. It was impossible to turn from one side to the other unless the next girl turned. An arm was always in the way, or a leg, crossing, entangling. And almost immediately there began the dreadful sounds of night: coughing, groaning, snoring, sudden angry curses, whimpering, growled whispers, as each woman tried to find a position of ease. As the night deepened, the stench became unbearable. There were women with diarrhea, there were women with disordered bladders. One could hear them trying to relieve themselves in their tin cups. One could hear dripping sounds. At least, I told myself, I was on the top layer.

All night my mind fevered with fantasies of escape. Every thought, every memory, was driven out, while I tried to focus on

[ 216 ]

that broad empty area between Auschwitz and Birkenau. And I saw myself, one night, hurrying across that area, into a woods. An arm was flung across my face. I lifted it off, tried to turn. There was an angry snarl, I tried to lie utterly motionless. My mind burned. No rest came. Then my bladder began to torture me. I feared I wouldn't be able to control myself until morning. I tried to turn on my face; perhaps I would feel it less. I even thought of using my tin cup, but the revolting thought made my pain and need even more acute. As I heard others relieving themselves, the torment increased. And all the time I kept repeating to myself, Sleep, sleep. I must sleep or I'll have no strength to work and I'll be sent to the furnace.

And then came the horror image of the furnace itself. And then a thought so dreadful that I nearly screamed aloud. Suppose they didn't trouble to use gas at all? And it seemed to me that two huge executioners were seizing me, naked, and flinging me through the open door of a furnace, and for one eternal moment before death I was consumed in such unimaginable, total pain . . .

But I was alive. I forced myself again to think of escape.

When the grayish light began to filter into the room, the *appel* gong sounded. Up! Up!

Instantly, I slid from the shelf, to be the first to run to the toilet, but already there was a line. One small toilet building served for several barracks. The floor was slimy, intolerable, and filth was everywhere, from those who had somehow managed to slip out during the night.

In another structure was the washroom, with only a few taps for nearly a thousand of us. The water dripped weakly while the women, ill-tempered, half-awake, fought to reach the taps.

Whistles shrieked continuously. When I came back into the block, the cappos and the barracks aides were shouting, cursing; here or there a woman had been slow to rise—a whack, a kick, threats: "To the oven with you!" Until, half dazed, all were out the door, forming up in front of the block. Down the length of the row of barracks, the women stood in their ranks.

And so we stood until the SS women came, with their hounds on leash, their boots and belts glittering, and they strode past us, making their inspection. Here was mortal danger. If an expression displeased, there would be instant punishment—blows, or disappearance.

So we stood while the count was made, the inspection completed. And at last into the barracks for breakfast. The same bitter greenish fluid. Some ate their bread, saved from the night before. And then each cappo marched off her detail.

There were large commandos of forty or fifty women together, and there were also smaller groups for special tasks—toilet cleaning or fetching the rations.

With a score of women, I marched to the edge of the quarantine section. There we received pickaxes, spades. We dug ditches on the two sides of the main road that passed through the camp.

And so I labored, as did the other women, not too hard but careful never to be seen idle. Nevertheless it was work such as I had never done, and my hands were soon blistered. The great dread of infection gripped me. It was impossible to keep sanitary here. I tried to shift the spade in my hands. I somehow managed until noon.

We were marched back to our block, and once more there came the wild, fierce lunging as the soup was brought in. I felt Elsa's eyes on me. Worst of all, I knew, was to be constantly noticed. So I pressed into the crowd, but still I claimed my ration only when the ravenous fighting had abated.

It was a watery soup, gray, with some remote taste of vegetables. I had finished my bread in the morning. Always a hearty eater, a big eater for a girl, I knew I would soon suffer here. The soup only half filled me.

Then we were back at work. Until five.

In the first days, I tried to discover how to save my strength, how to keep from wasting a single ounce of energy in disputes, and how to save it in our labor. When we had finished the ditch we were put to moving a pile of stones from one side of the road to the other. Some of the women said we were putting them back to the place from which they had been moved the week before. The ditches we had dug would be filled again, and dug again.

Though I was determined to give Elsa no excuse to strike me, though I hurried from my shelf at the first sound of the *appel* and was always among the first in line, there came a morning when I had diarrhea and was compelled to run back a second time to the toilet. When I came to the line-up, I was among the last. Elsa caught me slipping into a rear row. She marched up to me. "The Lady likes to sleep late?" And her hand struck me on both cheeks, while her shoes kicked at my legs. I stood still. I could only do what all prisoners did: vow blindly in my heart, against every probability, that one day, if I lived, if we got out of here, if we met . . . And in circumstances that I could not then have imagined, that day was to come.

I had been in the block for a week. Already there were newer girls than I, and I felt myself habituated. There were Hungarian girls, a few of them in our block, and a neighboring block was filled with them. They clung together, sometimes two sisters together, or girls who had gone to the same schools, or a whole group from a village, and sometimes there were even daughters and mothers. But few mothers had passed the selection.

It had come on the train platform. They could not yet talk of it much. Some had believed, and still tried to believe, that the selection was only a sorting out for different camp areas. But they knew, they knew that the other group had gone to the area of the camp that was sealed, and from which no one ever emerged. Yet they were still too dazed from their own narrow escape to understand it fully, and the strength of each one was pulled into her need to find out how to live in these new conditions.

And I too found that all my strength was drained into this task. Even from those who wanted to talk, I didn't want to hear. I didn't want to hear of the *aktione* in which they had been taken, I didn't want to hear of the packed transports. I knew, I knew; it was Hrebenko, the same. I could not let myself become obsessed with it; I had to live.

Then one day after work I saw three women brought into our block. I paid no special attention. But one of them shrieked, "Katya!"

For the first instant, the name did not strike me. Already, I was only Eva. But the voice struck me. It was Anya. I looked down and could scarcely recognize her. Without her thick braids wound around her head, her face was so different. And her mouth had become pinched, small. We clutched each other. We trembled together.

"So we end our journey together after all!" she cried.

"No, no, it is not ended! Even here, it's possible to live!" I told her. It would be all right. She'd see. If we were only careful, we could survive. And as an old habitué, I helped arrange everything for her. I warned her of Elsa, I told her in a rush all that had happened to me, I told her I was sure I would escape from here, I babbled, I overflowed. Until she came, I had not known how alone I was.

Yes, on the second arrest they had beat her worse than before, and, unable to endure it, she had told that story about being a convert, hoping it would still not damage me, but there had been no way to warn me of the change in her story.

No, no, I told her, she must not blame herself for my arrest; we had already been too far entangled and it was inevitable that we would be caught. But still the two years of hiding might prove to have saved us, for if we had been sent directly to Belzec we would long ago have been dead. Now, if we could only do our work here, and remain in health, if we could only hold out—the war was turning, turning. And perhaps we would even escape.

Escape? Surely I was losing my mind. No one ever escaped from here!

Day after day I talked of nothing else, and Anya tolerated my talk, considering it a madness. Even the electrified fence, I insisted, how did we know it was really electrified? The Germans were so strict about the smallest waste of electricity; would they really keep the power going in such a long, endless fence? Suppose it was not electrified at all? Or only at certain hours? Suppose they counted on no one's daring to try it?

Each evening we walked close to the fence. I would feel an urge to stretch out my hand. The current was said to be so powerful that death was instantaneous. Anya, frightened, would pull me away. "Don't walk so close! With you, one never knows!"

One morning there were sirens, alarms, and we were ordered to form up instantly for the count. Word spread: someone had attempted to escape. Who? Where? No one knew. But we stood in line hour after hour. Each unit was counted, but not until the entire camp had been checked would the order be given to return to our barracks for breakfast.

The cappos were in their most violent mood. Kicks, blows, on all sides. Some girls wavered as they stood and were held upright by their companions. It was almost noon when the dismissal was given.

Whispers, rumors, all day. It had been two together, a man and a woman. The man had a teamster's job that gave him the run of the entire camp, and thus he had been able to contact his sweetheart in the women's compound. He had tried to hide her in the wagon, and to break through the gate, but after a short chase they had been caught and shot down like dogs.

Another story was entirely different. It was a woman alone. She had tried to dig under the electric fence. Bloodhounds had found her.

Not long afterward, our entire block was punished because one of the women tried to hide, so as not to go out to work. Too feeble, too death-weary, to face the day's labor, she had burrowed, like some animal, under the platform at a far corner. But they had dragged her out from her hole, Elsa grabbing her by the feet, cursing and kicking at her, and then our entire barracks had been punished. In a row, in front of the hut, on our knees, each with her hands raised palms upward, with a stone on each palm. So we remained for an eternity while the cappos walked back and forth to make sure that no arm was lowered. I heard stones fall; through the corners of my eyes I saw, down the row, a woman pitch forward; none budged to help her. A cappo marched up to her, kicked hard, and suddenly the woman's head jerked; she pulled herself up, took her stones. The cappo moved on. On each side of the woman who had fallen, her neighbors moved on their knees, closer to her, to hold her up.

The weeks passed; my hunger became deep, constant, a condition like a burn that never stopped paining. Yet I knew I would survive. Only disease held me in terror. One day I noticed a boil forming near my shoulder. In terror I recalled the infection that had gone so deep in my side as to make an operation necessary. I squeezed and squeezed the boil. But within a few days there was a second sore. Each night as I lay on my shelf I squeezed until the blood came. I did not dare ask to be sent to the infirmary, for fear of the selections that took place among the sick. I pinched so hard that the pits in my skin remained visible for years.

Then one day came an order for showers. This order came once each month, the habitués said, but as the group in quarantine changed each month, no one was certain how much time had passed since the last order for showers. The yearning to be for once entirely clean, to be rid of our layers of grime, was balanced against the great, pervasive fear of the gas chambers. A panic spread; some girls tried to hide. The fear of the shower was even worse than what I had seen on my day of admission.

When we entered the shower block, there was an anguished hush. Could we in any way find out before the final moment? Did our Block Eldest know to what she was leading us? Some of the girls began to argue about what date it was. We were in May 1944. Some tried to reckon the month by their period, but a woman's calendar was of no use here. This I had already learned. My period had not come, and the veterans said to me, "Oh, don't worry, you won't be troubled with that." If I had spent time in Ravensbruck I would have known, they said. Something in the food, perhaps the tea. They didn't want to talk about it too much, as though ashamed, or possessed of some darker fear that even if they lived they would never again be women.

Nevertheless we returned from the showers. And then, my time in quarantine was ended. I had to leave Anya there. Even to go across the border to some other section of the camp was a fearsome step; I had forgotten the sense of being alone. She would come in a week to the other side, but surely not again to the same barracks as I; we would have no such good fortune a second time.

My new barracks was identical to Block 9. Only, from the moment I entered, I became aware of the next stage in deterioration that threatened me. For among the "normal" prisoners, the emaciated but yet enduring, there were a number of skeletal beings with faces of a peculiar kind, faces in which the light of the spirit was entirely absent; only a kind of existing remnant of the body

[ 223 ]

was there, of an organism not yet dead. There was a look in their eyes—or, rather, a vacancy. Of all that I had seen until then, these faces brought the deepest despair to me. These, I knew, were the creatures called mussulmans, the creatures in the last stage, when they reacted only as brute animals. Sometimes they could cling to existence for months in this state, before dying.

Yet, in Block 13, there were others who seemed entirely intact. Almost on the first day I met Fanny. Somehow in the crush for rations she jogged me, and I heard her say, "Excuse me." I replied automatically, "It's nothing," and then I realized that this was the first time since I had come to Auschwitz that I had heard a polite word.

All the courtesy of normal life had dropped away from us, as though we had consented to be what the Nazis wanted to make of us. Yet in each block there were a few women who tried not to succumb. I turned to look at the girl; she was slight, dark, with heavy eyebrows, and she looked somehow a little cleaner, a little neater than the others. But more important was the feeling which came from her, that here was still an intact being, a person.

We began to talk, and there was an instant rapport. It was as sometimes happens between schoolgirls who become immediate friends and cannot for one instant part from each other. We stood side by side the next morning for *appel*, we managed to trade sleeping places so that we could bunk next to each other, and we began at once to look out for each other's interests, to make sure of each other's place in the washroom, to guard each other from a cappo's wrath.

And as it had been with Anya, as it had been with Nina, the moment I had a friend I was revived. It was as though this too were achieved in spite of our tormentors, who wanted to dehumanize us; even this was a victory. There were evenings when we sat on our "top story" and sang. Fanny had a good voice, and I too loved to sing, and soon others would join us, and there would be a little center of life, of spirit, in the block. We sang all sorts of songs—love songs mostly—in Polish, Russian, and German.

Fanny had been in the camp for almost a year; she had been taken in the Sosnowitz ghetto. She had lost a sister. Hers had been lost here in this camp, after the first months. Her sister had been taken ill, had gone to the infirmary, and been caught in a selection.

With Fanny, I was able to talk of our fate. She told me how things had closed in around the Jews. The open ghettos such as we had had in Hrebenko had later become enclosed with barbed wire, and some of them even with walls. People had dug hiding places deep in the earth, but still they had been dragged to the transports. There were tales of partisans, but there were also tales of Jewish partisans who had been slaughtered by Ukrainians and Poles.

She had been brought in a transport with her mother, father, two brothers and her sister. Through the men who sometimes attended to jobs in the women's camp, she had tried and tried to find out whether her brothers might still be alive, on the other side. But they were not known. Still, they might have been sent off on a labor transport to some of the other concentration camps, even to Germany.

Yes, I said, to give her hope, I myself had seen slave workers in Germany.

Fanny knew the ways of the camp; she was adept at trading for food. Some of the girls had extra bread. A number of them had good jobs; a few even worked in the clothing warehouse where valuables could be found in the seams of the clothing of the dead. If a girl managed to find a bit of money or a jewel, and managed to hide it, she could use it to buy bread from a cappo or even from an SS woman. And there were some girls who received gifts from men friends who were well placed on the other side, friends from their own town, or relatives, or even, in one or two lucky cases, from husbands or lovers who managed to send their gifts through the even luckier men whose jobs took them into the women's section.

In trading with these girls, Fanny and I would offer our margarine ration or the bit of horsemeat sausage that sometimes replaced the margarine. A slice of bread was more filling than a few bites of bad sausage. Fanny knew just which girl had a bread supply; we would bargain, and then share our food equally.

So, little by little, she showed me the ways of the camp. To get a steady job on a good commando, such as the clothing commando or, even better, the kitchen commando, was everyone's ambition. But there was intrigue, there were favorites, and sometimes it was only a question of good luck. Most envied of all were the commandos whose tasks took them outside the camp gates. To me, with my constant obsession to escape, an assignment to such a commando became an all-consuming objective. I intrigued, I plotted, I begged, and one morning it came by a stroke of luck.

Fanny and I found ourselves counted off into a commando of about twenty girls, assembled for some unknown task. Presently we were marched through the main gate. We were going outside the grounds!

Heavily guarded by SS men with their hounds, our little group passed onto the road to the town of Auschwitz itself. It was as though I had attained complete freedom. We marched beyond the brown, barren earth of the camp area, and suddenly I beheld a green field. My breath caught. "Fanny! Fanny!" I squeezed her hand. "Grass!" So strong was my hunger for a sight of growing things that for years afterward almost everything I wore was green.

We marched a few miles and entered Auschwitz. The town seemed like Hrebenko, with its central business street and its courthouse square. A military hospital was being built there, and our task was to scrub the floors, wash the windows, make the building ready for occupancy.

To see ordinary people, civilians—even if they scarcely dared glance in our direction—was a happiness. To find ourselves in an empty room with space around us! And then, to find ourselves alone! For our SS man supervised several workers on the same floor, and from time to time stepped out of the room, leaving Fanny and myself momentarily unwatched. There could be no question of escape, for the building was heavily guarded. But to be alone! We scrubbed away, singing.

And one day there came an act of kindness, as though to remind us that there was still humanity in the world. Some of the civilian workmen were still in the building—carpenters, painters, electricians. One day, leaving a room just as we arrived to clean it, a carpenter pointed to a pile of shavings. As soon as the SS man went out for a moment, we tore the shavings apart, and there we discovered a sandwich and a boiled egg. Half weeping, we shared the food. I told Fanny how, in the Hermann Goering works, I had each day passed a group of slave workers on the grounds and had sometimes dropped cigarettes for them. I did not want to think of this as repayment, and yet how could one avoid such a thought?

One day the two of us were scrubbing the floor of a large room, probably intended for a ward. We were singing a Polish song that Fanny had taught me, a nonsensical song about five sailors coming off a ship, one dark, one blond, one redheaded, when suddenly we felt the presence of our SS guard. We fell silent, scrubbed harder. He was known as a brute, rather older than the other men, heavy, and bad-tempered.

"Why did you stop?" he demanded. "What are you frightened of?"

We knew enough not to answer back even if the remark was made in the form of a question. But he repeated, "What are you afraid of? Sing!"

We couldn't. We only scrubbed.

"I order you!" he shouted. "Sing!"

We tried, but the sounds were feeble.

[ 227 ]

"Not like that! Like before!"

We tried to sing louder. It was hopeless. Soon the boot would strike.

But instead he turned and walked out.

For nearly two weeks we worked in the hospital building. Now that we were going outside each day I was constantly on the alert for the escape opportunity I so dreamed about. But not for an instant, on the way to and from the hospital, were we more than a few steps away from an SS man walking alongside the column. And once in the building, we were locked up as effectively as in a prison.

And then the task was finished and we were once more back inside the camp, standing each morning on *appel*, to be assigned to jobs inside the grounds.

In our block itself, things were comparatively decent. We considered ourselves lucky in our Block Eldest. Lotta was strict enough in her way, but not a devil; she did not look for faults. And if someone had to be punished, she punished her within the block; she didn't turn girls over to the SS women.

Still, no matter how decent a Block Eldest was, there were times when she had to strike, to beat. So many of the prisoners had been reduced to an animal level, they understood nothing else. There were the cunning ones, and the evil ones, the bread thieves, and the thieves who would snatch anything, a spoon, a comb. There were the half-crazed ones, and the ones from whom the last vestige of human training had disappeared so that they were as helplessly filthy as babies.

If there was a row, Lotta would stride in from her lair, administer a few slaps, confiscate things. She was about thirty, squat and strong, also a Slovene. The Slovenes had a monopoly on the good jobs. But at least she was not a sadist. Her beatings were short and to the purpose. Of the other kind, the sadistic, we had at least one—a girl of seventeen, a Jewish girl who had become the aide of a cappo. When she struck, she would become excited and would strike and strike until she drew blood.

And yet despite the brutality, despite the hunger, despite our exhaustion, despite the stringent rules, a secret inner life existed in the barracks. And with this Lotta did not interfere. It was a life of smuggled messages of love.

Strange love affairs would develop: love affairs between men and women who had never seen each other. The intermediaries were the drivers or the repairmen who could move about the camp. Our entire barracks would follow the growth of such a love affair, hungrily sharing in every line that the loved woman read out from her letters, for it was as though the missiles belonged to all of us. And when Lotta saw a group of us huddled around a girl who was reading something, she let us be, even though every message was a mortal violation of the camp rules.

There was in our block a girl from Lódź; one day she mentioned her home place, in a brief conversation with a passing driver. She hoped to get news of her father, who had worked in a textile factory. "Lódź," said the driver. "I have a friend in my block who was a textile worker in Lódź." Though the man turned out to have worked in a different factory from her father, this contact was enough, this feeling that their lives had somewhere touched. A burning, devoted correspondence began.

When the driver would smuggle through a letter to Sonya, we would gather around her. "Read! Read!" And she would read ahead a few lines, treasuring certain words to herself, and then she would read aloud to us, "My Only One, I feel as if I know you so well, to the very depths of your soul, and I want to help you, if there is anything I can make easier for you, for my beloved—" And she would read us part of what she wrote to him, admonishing him if he truly loved her to take care of himself, to guard his precious life. Half blushing, she would even read us the lines where she told him that her thoughts were of him when she lay all night on her bunk. And she would tell him not to deprive himself for her, not to send her his bread but to keep it for his own strength, to save himself for her, to live. . . .

So people reached each other. And there were even extreme achievements, times when men and women, within that hell, managed to meet and touch hands, to embrace for a moment behind some wall. These triumphs came to us like tales of some underground defiance—whispers that the Jews of the Warsaw ghetto had actually risen with guns in their hands and killed a number of Germans; that there was even contact between emissaries from Palestine and the Jews in the concentration camps. All this was impossible, but if a man could still meet a woman, in Auschwitz itself, then anything might be true! And so every one of us gained strength from the few who even here had triumphed over our condition, and loved.

One morning, on *appel*, I was told that the Block Eldest wanted to see me. I went. Lotta greeted me pleasantly. Her cubbyhole was cozy, with a real cot, real bedding, porcelain dishes, even a few pictures on the wall. "Eva," she said, "there is a new section of the camp being opened for the Hungarians. Block Eldests are needed. You are strong, you have character." In short, she could get such a post for me. I would have a room like this, a bed, food; I would have first pick when a heap of clothing came for the block. Did I want the job?

It would mean that I would be virtually assured of life. And yet, it would mean that I would be separated from the rest of the women. No matter how decently she behaved, a Block Eldest was, like a cappo, on the other side. No matter how lenient was her nature, there were times when she had to strike, to punish.

"I don't think I have a strong enough character." I said. "I may give the impression, but I don't think I would be equal to the task."

"I think you would," she said. She wanted me to reflect, and to give her an answer in the morning.

On this, Fanny would give me no advice. I sought out Anya, who was now in a block not far from ours. What should I do? Should I accept?

And Anya too said she could not advise me. Then I saw. Even by asking the question I was already on the other side. I could not take the post.

But soon, a different opportunity came. As we lined up one morning Lotta appeared to make an announcement. All those who were able to translate from Polish into German, and who knew how to type, could leave their names with her if they wished to volunteer for a special commando.

The moment the roll call was over, there was an intense buzzing. What commando? What was it for? All she could tell us, Lotta said, was that a commando was being organized to work in the city of Katowitz, in the prison.

To work in Katowitz? To leave the camp? "I'm the first," I announced to Fanny.

"Wait. Find out more about it," she advised.

"But as soon as I am in Katowitz—"

She shook her head soberly. "How do you even know it will be Katowitz? Just because they say so?"

All day there were endless speculations about the strange announcement. Some said it was a ruse. They wanted to take out the

[ 231 ]

best girls in the block, the most educated. Why? Who knows why they do things? Can anyone ever reason why?

"You'll see," one girl predicted. "If there is ever a history written of this place, it will be noted that there was a certain Katowitz commando—they marched out from here and were buried alive." And tales were told of other groups that had vanished without a trace. And there were rumors, even more macabre, of victims used for medical experiments.

No, others said. The commando was surely for a house of prostitution.

But why girls who could type?

Not one of us signed. The next morning, the Block Eldest repeated her request. No one budged. She became angry. "I managed to get this for the women of my block!" she shouted. "If you don't sign, I'll let it go elsewhere!"

That day the discussion veered. Perhaps it was indeed something good. Lotta wouldn't knowingly betray us. Then one by one those of us who were qualified put down our names.

Fanny couldn't type.

I said I wouldn't go.

This was not only an expression of our unity; I was afraid to go out and be alone again. But she insisted that I go. If it turned out to be something very good, she did not want to feel that I would have missed it because of her. Finding out that there were not enough qualified girls in our block to fill the commando, and that some girls from other blocks would be taken, we hurried and told Anya. Now I would not be alone.

Within a few days, all the applicants were assembled and marched to a separate barracks. Anya was not there. Typhoid had broken out in her block, and the inmates were quarantined.

We sat in the barracks, waiting, day after day. Oddly, we were not sent out to work. Our whole time was spent in spinning new stories, repeating rumors to one another. There were nearly a hundred of us. How could they possibly need so many translators and typists in a prison in Katowitz? No, it was all too strange; perhaps, after all, we had been fooled.

And as always, I found a new friend. It was an absolute need with me, and surely it did not change my loyalty to those I had lost. Lola was short, with a round, baby face, a puckered mouth, a look sometimes of childish helplessness; yet she had survived more than a year of Auschwitz.

On the very first day of the new commando we became intimate friends, talking and talking, always finding something more to tell each other. And as with Fanny, I shared with Lola completely. Sometimes at night I would wake with an aching hunger. Should I take part of tomorrow's bread? I would poke her awake, "Lola, maybe we should eat just a little of tomorrow's bread? You eat too, then I will."

In spite of her long experience in Auschwitz, Lola was sometimes strangely diffident, even shy about approaching others. Perhaps it was already the creeping up of apathy. At times this passivity of hers irritated me. When for several days I had gone from one girl to another to do our bread trading, I told her she ought to do it once. Not that I minded the task of bargaining so much, but I wondered what it was that held her back, for she kept saying she didn't feel like approaching anyone. "Why? What's the matter?" I asked.

"I don't know," she answered. "I know I should take my turn, but I can't. I don't even know how it is that I got myself to volunteer for this commando."

One day we were notified that examinations were about to take place. In an adjoining barracks an office had been arranged, with a few typewriters on a table. Three SS men conducted the examination. Each of us was given a page to translate from Polish into German, and our typing was timed.

Fifty girls passed the test, Lola and I among them. The rest were sent back to their former barracks.

Next came the medical test. Again, the naked line. But we were a select group, and we had had several days of rest. Most of us stood well, and color had come back into our cheeks. Mine were flaming red again.

As the line advanced, the doctor suddenly turned one girl aside, announcing to the whole group, "No one will be accepted who has been in the lager less than three months."

At this, one of the Hungarian girls stepped out of the line. Although I knew I was a week short, I decided to remain for my turn.

It came. The doctor glanced at my number. "Why didn't you step out of line?"

I held myself erect. He was looking at me, up and down. I said nothing, but in that moment I felt a faint echo of what it was to be a woman. Somehow, in the world, being a woman could always help. The doctor gave a little snort and said to the nurse, "She's not bad, eh? All right, take her anyway."

Now we received fresh clothing—the striped prison uniforms—clean, new! We were a little nearer to our destiny, whatever it might be. Presently we were marched out, under close guard. And I saw that we were marching along that same road between the two camps on which I had traveled on my first day in Auschwitz. Now I was returning across the barren mud flats to the front camp.

And there, we were marched to a new section where we saw a row of two-story buildings, not all of them complete. Into the first of these we were led, and up to the second floor. Clean! New! A long clean room. With sleeping platforms, it was true, but only two levels of them instead of three! And never before touched, with the wood still smelling fresh!

And there was an inside washroom, with plenty of faucets, with clean toilets. It was as though we had been ushered into a luxurious hotel. We ran back and forth, each showing the conveniences to the other. We made the water flow; it didn't drip, drop by drop; it flowed in plenty! And no one was shouting at us! We had no cappo! Where was the Block Eldest? Were we suddenly free?

Then one of the girls who had gone down the stairway, exploring, came running in, her face pale. "Do you know who lives downstairs?" she gasped. "The prostitute commando."

There could be no question of it. She had just seen a group of them going out to work. Painted, with high heels and tight skirts, loud, ghastly. They were surely on their way to a special place in the camp, where men could come to them.

Some of the girls began to run about the room, hysterical. Yes, yes, we had been warned; the wise ones had warned us! Others sat mute. One ran to a window and had to be pulled back. She kept screaming that we must all kill ourselves. Several took up the cry. Yes, all, together! We would join hands and run against the electrified fence.

And still, many sat quiet, their faces apathetic, their eyes vacant.

I sat with Lola, and we talked in whispers. All the while, fantastic images were going through my mind, but of these imaginings I did not want to tell her. Things from dim childhood, tales from my mother, warnings—if someone offers to take you on a journey, beware, never go, even if it is a woman who offers it. Tales of girls falsely married and sold into white slavery.

Every woman at some time has surely pictured to herself these dreaded things, and girls have always whispered them to each other, "Suppose you were stolen, and sold into white slavery . . ." And then there always comes a blank wall to the story. You could picture the abducted girl—yourself—being locked in a room, a slave. And then? Men entered. And then?

And then always it became shadowy. There always stood the question, Would I do it if I were forced to? Or would I somehow die? Die of the thing itself.

And now, would I walk to the electric wire, would I run toward the sentinel posts until the bullets struck me from behind? I could not reach that far to know myself. I had so wanted to live. I had done so much, endured so much. What would my body do? It was no longer I, about whom such things could be imagined. It was not Eva, it was not even Katya, but the body that had number 81332 stamped on it.

The panic had subsided somewhat. There was a slightly older woman among us, Erna, a German Jewess of forty, well educated, an expert linguist; she had once worked in a consulate in Berlin. Gradually the girls gathered around Erna. Why should we believe such a thing? she asked. What would they want with her, for example? Why should they have given us an examination in typing? And if the Nazis wanted girls for prostitution, they had only to take them, without subterfuge. Indeed, they would surely find enough volunteers, for hadn't they arrested hundreds of professional prostitutes?

It was probably true that there was a house of prostitution in the camp. We had all heard such rumors. It was said to be reserved for the use of the SS and a special category of German prisoners, though sometimes, it was rumored, other men who were wise in the ways of the camp managed to make use of the place. But no one had ever heard of any Jewish girls being placed there. Perhaps, Erna said, the girls downstairs were indeed prostitutes employed in the camp. We could have nothing against them. And it did not mean that everyone else in the barracks would be forced to do the same work. We must wait.

And so we waited. The first joy of our new surroundings was gone. Glum and fearful, we waited.

Then later in the day another commando moved in, downstairs. These were sturdy, healthy-looking girls, and we learned that they worked in the vegetable gardens. And presently we heard that there was an additional commando of office girls living in the building, girls who worked in the political section, where the records of the inmates were catalogued. They were quartered downstairs, too. The first floor was to be for Christian girls, the second floor for Jewesses.

And presently our Block Eldest appeared. She looked sharp, businesslike. Her name was Maria, and she was German, a Communist. Surprised to find us already in residence, with bunks already chosen, she remarked that we had been brought in early, but no matter. Since we had already settled in our places we could keep them. She wanted strict order. If we obeyed the rules we would have no trouble.

The anxiety had diminished, though many of the girls were still uncertain and suspicious. What had been the meaning of all that talk about Katowitz? Why hadn't we been sent to Katowitz? But the water flowed, and, feeling clean, in new clothes, we were able to sleep as we had not slept since entering the camp.

In the morning the *appel* sounded; an SS woman appeared and marched us to our fate.

We didn't go far: through the gate to another section, occupied by administration buildings. And here, again in a new structure, we found ourselves in a long room with two rows of small tables, and on each table a typewriter!

An SS man appeared with a pile of folders. He looked irritated, as though his task were disagreeable. These were records from the Katowitz courts, he announced. We would find marked passages. Such passages were to be translated, typed.

So it had all, in a way, been true!

Our new chief continued. He expected a certain norm of work from each typist and would not tolerate less. Bad work would have to be done over. Understood?

His voice was high pitched, and like all SS men he did not talk, he shouted. To work, then!

Lola and I had taken tables side by side, and we exchanged delighted looks. It was a moment as happy as that when we had walked into the clean new barracks. I suddenly recalled the instant, only a few days before, when despite my being disqualified by the three-month rule, something had made me stay in line. Yes, surely there was good fortune upon me. And yet, none of us could have known what awaited us; they could really have marched us to a brothel. Now here we sat in a clean room, typing.

The task itself appeared utterly meaningless. There seemed to be no rhyme or reason in the passages selected for translation from the interminable records of the Polish court. But we hoped that the task would indeed turn out to be endless, and that we would not, on some dark day, suddenly be marched back to Birkenau.

So our lives became regulated. Only one thing was unchanged, and that was hunger. Our rations were, as always, the bitter tea, the watery soup at noon, bread and tea at night, with a bit of margarine or sausage. One day at my desk I fainted from hunger. Lola and Erna hurried me into the washroom. Fortunately, the SS man had not seen me; he had his own little office and appeared only when he had work to give out.

I remained most of that day in the washroom. That was our haven. If a cigarette was to be smoked, it was in the washroom; two puffs each, down to the last shred held between the fingernails. If messages were to be sent, it was through the washroom. We had discovered an air space between our toilets and the men's toilets, which were directly behind. That part of the building was still unfinished, and it was possible for almost anyone to go into it on one pretext or another. Through the air space, love letters, gifts of food, clothing, cigarettes—things of all sorts—were passed. For from the first days our threads of contact had been woven.

Here in the front camp of Auschwitz were the men with the longest skill at managing things, and so they soon found the way to us.

Only about a month after our arrival, we began our knitting. Fall was coming, winds would blow. The men smuggled woolen things in to us, sometimes a knitted dress, or a sweater, taken from the clothing warehouse. We would unravel these garments and wind the wool. They brought us knitting needles. And we would knit them things for the oncoming cold weather—gloves, scarves, and earlaps. For ourselves, we knitted knee-length hose, gloves, shawls.

The knitting was done in snatches, between our translation tasks, for we managed to set a modest pace of work. Our SS officer, Piotruch, suspected us, we knew, but he had not yet caught us, and besides we soon learned that he was one of those who would scream and curse but would not turn us in to his superiors. The chief of our project was a higher officer who sat in an office across the hallway and was never seen. Everything was communicated through Piotruch. Perhaps Piotruch did not want it to be suspected that he had difficulty handling a group of women; perhaps he even retained a touch of humanity; but we felt quite sure that he knew about our knitting and would not turn us in. And so sometimes half the commando would be sitting there knitting away, knitting things for our men outside, and we would feel as though we had restored ourselves to the human world.

One day we heard a whistle, and a message came flying through the window. "For Eva!" cried the girl who had picked it up. She gave it to me, while others hurried to the window and reported that it was a driver, a young man, who had tossed the message.

The note was from Anya. She had been assigned to work in the gypsy section of Birkenau, in the kitchen! She would try to send me food!

I ran to the window and asked the young man to take back an answer. He couldn't remain there outside so we pantomimed for him to go around to the unfinished side of our building. We would knock on the wall and he would hear us.

Hurriedly, I wrote the note to Anya, telling her how well

things had turned out, how I longed to have her with me, but perhaps in a kitchen she was better off! I would knit a vest for her.

I ran to pass the note, but on the landing stood the big boss himself. He had just emerged from his office. "What have you there?" He snatched the note from my hand. Now, surely, I had come to the end. Such strictly forbidden acts were not lightly punished. I would disappear.

"Who was to receive this note?" the officer demanded.

"It was for a friend," I said.

"How was it to be sent?"

I had seen someone out there, I said, and hoped to send the note through him; I didn't know who he was. The officer pulled me into his room, strode to the window. The messenger had of course already fled. Didn't I know, the officer shrieked, what a terrible breach I had committed?

I knew, I said. I awaited my punishment.

"It will come," he promised, and sent me back to my work.

Day after day I waited. Surely this time I could not escape. A few days later, three high-ranking SS officers strode into the room. "Who is Eva Korngold?" one of them demanded.

I rose.

"Come here."

I went.

"You're the one that understands Ukrainian?"

"Yes."

He handed me a printed leaflet to translate. I began to do it, out loud. "Soon you will see your German masters fleeing—"

"Not so loud!" he growled.

It was a war leaflet that must have been dropped from a plane by the Russians! I read the whole thing, softly, keeping any expression out of my voice, yet wanting almost to sing the lines. That I should have lived to enjoy this moment! If no more, it would be enough! That I should stand before three SS officers and read out loud to them words such as, "Soon you will see your German masters fleeing before the mighty offensive of the Soviet army. We are your avengers! Already we have liberated your cousins and your brothers, in the greatest part of the Ukraine! Help us! Prepare the way!"

If this could happen, perhaps the day would even come for us!

We knew nothing of what was happening in the war, not even that the Allies had several months before landed in France, that Paris had been liberated. Only vaguely, we knew that things were not going well for the Germans on the Russian front.

The three officers left. I hurried back to my work, whispered to the girls what the leaflet had said. The very air of the room seemed to be filled with silent jubilation. All day, sudden titters could be heard.


And not too long afterward we did learn great news. We received a newspaper! It came from the hand of a German soldier who had already become a person of unique importance to us. He was elderly, a man who looked about fifty, rather small, with a puckered face. The barracks next to ours had been completed— indeed, there were four more in the row. A fence had been built around ours. The others were occupied by German soldiers.

Every morning they would march out to their mess just as we were being marched to work. Several times, as their lines passed close to ours, this elderly soldier had managed to whisper words of encouragement. "Have patience, children. Don't despair."

We talked and talked of him. As we did not even know his name, we called him Grandpop.

The toilet in his barracks was opposite our washroom; he would appear there and make signs to us. There could be no possible motive for his risking himself in this way, except the purest goodness of heart. And of this we became certain when he sent us the newspaper, flinging it over our fence very early one morning, wrapped around a stone.

The paper carried the news of the attempt on Hitler's life.

All that day, after we got to the office, we were unable to contain our excitement and our joy. Girls kept running back and forth to the toilet, sometimes eight of us at a time, just to hug each other, jump up and down, weep, and repeat the news over and over. Perhaps Hitler was even now dead! Perhaps all these walls around us would suddenly collapse! Oh, God's punishment would yet come on all of them!

In our block that night we never stopped talking, singing. And we discovered that we were not the only ones to have had the news. Our barracks was filled now; on our floor there were four hundred girls, most of them from the textile-plant commando. Mysteriously, through space itself, the great news had spread. In the sudden spirit of festivity, all those who had food hidden away brought it out, shared it, and we talked of what we would do as if we were certain now we would live.

Then things became quiet again. We typed. We knitted. We hungered. Yet we hungered with spirit.

In our commando there were three girls all named Fella. Fella the First, from a wealthy home in Kraków, had a gift for mimicry. Perhaps hers were the same jokes that appear wherever there is privation, and it is true that some mornings we wanted to choke her for them, but most times we would laugh and feel in better humor when she imitated a lofty English butler inquiring how we would like our eggs. Or else Fella the First would become a twittery hostess, wanting to make sure that the coffee wasn't too strong, or too weak, that the omelet was properly seasoned, insisting on sending back to the kitchen a plate that was soiled by a speck of grease, and apologizing for the untrained help one had to make do with these days because of the war.

Fella the Second entertained us too, but in a quite different way. She had been married and divorced, and she would talk for hours about the most intimate details of her married life, describing the prowess of her ex-husband, the little peculiarities of his sex habits—everything. Some of the girls were shocked. "*Ach*," Fella the Second would say, "if we live, we'll never see one another again, but most likely we'll all be killed even if this place is ever liberated, and so everything that I say here will die anyway."

Fella the Third also made her contribution. She was a cosmetician. Soon we were again doing our fingernails, begging her for facial massages, even finding ways to stain our lips!

But the liveliest spirit among us was Tosca, a Parisienne. A pianist, a composer, she even wrote a marching song for us, with sadly comical verses about our yearnings for bread and cigarettes and men. Going to and from work, we sang her song. In the evenings, Tosca organized entire programs, with recitations, imitations, and chorals. If I ever came to Paris, she promised, she would train my voice.

The communal spirit among us had grown so strong that it even brought about a tiny betterment in our food situation. There were several girls who had connections for extra rations and hardly ever troubled to finish their soup. More than once, they were seen throwing their portions away! A central soup tureen was organized, and the unused soup was shared out equally; there were many days when my ravenous hunger was stilled by the extra cupful.

And once we even received a spread from downstairs, from the "powder-puff commando." The prostitutes had more food than they could eat, all sorts of delicacies, gifts from their well-placed clients. And almost every day they would set out their superfluous food in the corridor; the package would immediately be snatched by their first-floor neighbors.

We had little contact with the powder-puff commando, perhaps still from that fear that lingers in almost every woman: fear of what she might herself be capable of. But also, they were really strangers to us, with their garish ways, their loud make-up, worn even here in Auschwitz! There was one girl, however, who looked rather sensitive. We had long suspected that she might be Jewish. One day Tosca struck up a conversation with her. Our suspicion was true. But she had not been arrested as a Jew. She had been passing as a Christian, in Brussels, and there she had been forced to take to prostitution to survive; she had been arrested in a raid and had ended here, still keeping her Jewishness secret for fear that discovery would mean death.

Soon after Tosca's talk with the girl, we found a large parcel of food from downstairs on our landing.



Our Block Eldest, Maria, counted on us to maintain our own discipline. Occasionally she would stride into the room. "I smell smoke. The smoking must stop at once." She would not try to find the individual law-breaker but would march back to her quarters. And at once we would descend on the girl who had been so foolish as to try to smoke outside the lavatory. We would confiscate the precious cigarette.

If there was too much noise, if there was quarreling, Maria used the same method. Nothing more was needed, and we were grateful to her. But if Maria was decent, she had an intimate friend, a cappo named Edit, who made up for it. Edit was in charge of the girls who kept the records of politicals. With a snaky head and restless, darting eyes, she was everywhere, she saw everything. What made the two friends we did not know, unless it was true

[ 244 ]

that Edit and Maria were lovers. By temperament they were opposite: Maria, stolid, yet with a base of fair-mindedness, Edit, filled with intrigue and venom.

Though she had no authority over us, one day Lola and I received a severe beating because of her. We were walking in the yard after work, and we strolled close to the fence. On the other side, from among the administration buildings, two men appeared —prisoners. They saw us, called, and we approached to snatch a few moments of conversation.

Before we knew what was happening, an SS woman was belaboring us, using her belt and her heels. We glimpsed Edit walking away. She had pointed us out.

The blows fell on our heads, on our breasts; her strap beat us to the ground; bloodied, on all fours, we tried to crawl back to the barracks, and the whole way she continued to beat us, to kick at us.

Every girl in the block vowed not to forget Edit.

At work, too, we were to learn that we had become overconfident. Our Piotruch had taken to leaving us pretty much alone; finding it bothersome to come in at frequent intervals to apportion our tasks, he had asked us to appoint a cappo. To appoint our own cappo! This was unheard of! By acclaim, we appointed Erna. She saw that all the work was properly done, and yet we had plenty of time for our knitting.

Knitting had now become a mania with us. The use of the things we knitted no longer mattered. The knitting itself was like a drug, a medicine. I felt, as I knit, a restored womanliness; at moments I could almost forget where I was and imagine I was at peace, a girl with her ball of yarn in her lap, her friends around her, gossiping. By some desperate illusion our surroundings fell away, and we were a group of Jewish girls, a circle of good friends, close, close, loyal to one another. We were the girls of Hrebenko.

Though we still lived in daily fear, our existence was bearable, as it had been even when the Nazis ruled in Hrebenko as long as our family was able to stay together. For the worst time of all seemed to me that time of tense, lonely terror in Linz before Nina and I made our secrets known to each other and became close, that terror of someone's pointing to me and crying out, "You are not one of us! You are a Jewess!"

And what had become of Nina? At least I had not heard of her appearing in Auschwitz. Somehow I felt that if she had been sent here, I would know.

So I would sit among the other girls and type a while, and knit. We could not take our material home with us to the barracks, where there might at any time be a search. And so we had found a way to hide everything in the office. Under each table top, a closed space had been constructed. We had given the measurements to the men who worked in the carpentry shop, and they had cut the boards and passed them to us through our toilet communication system. We fastened the boards in place, and there, each night, we deposited our knitting.

One morning we arrived to find the hidden boards removed. On each table lay the contraband wool. Piotruch strode in. "I know who is responsible for this!" he screamed. "That red-cheeked one, Eva Korngold. And I know where the whole traffic is carried on! Through the washroom! Half of you are in the toilet more than in this room! It will stop! All this, I will confiscate!" Hereafter, he decreed, no more than three women could be out of the room at any one time visiting the toilet.

Again, we had got off easily. Erna gathered us together. She read us a lecture. We were toying here like naughty schoolgirls,

[ 246 ]

with our rule-breaking, but had we forgotten where we were? In Auschwitz, five minutes from the gas chambers!

We were sobered. We decided to make sure that Piotruch's new regulation was rigorously obeyed, and it was I who was given the responsibility to see that no more than three girls at any one time were missing from the room.

And yet, our perversity returned. Perhaps there was something hysterical in our behavior, in our need to tempt fate. Perhaps without this we could not have survived mentally. In every kind of prison, among every group of prisoners, it is considered a triumph to circumvent the rules, to deride the authorities, and so we soon were laughing at our misadventure. The girls made an arm band for me and pronounced me Cappo of the Water Closet. And at night, in the barracks, we made up songs, a whole comic opera about the incident, in preparation for a full evening of entertainment that we were planning, on Tosca's birthday, when we would invite all the eight hundred girls in our barracks, even the powder-puff commando!

The party was not held. Altogether, tension was increasing; the war, we could feel, was approaching a crisis. Air raids were more frequent. They came at night, and at dawn. The entire population of our barracks, all the eight hundred girls, would run in panic, crowding into the basement shelter. There was not even room to stand. If the raid was a long one, ill-tempered fights would break out. In the morning, exhausted, we would still march to our work.

There was then only one element of cheer for us. Each time we passed our friend, the elderly German soldier, he whispered a few words of sympathy.

One night the air raid was heavier than ever before and closer to the camp. The planes came shrieking down as if we ourselves were the target. Surely they could tell from the endless rows of barracks that tens of thousands of prisoners were on these grounds!

And yet, there were military barracks, too, and there were

munitions plants in the area. We realized that the bombing had to take place.

The entire yard quaked as the bombs exploded. Even if this was to bring our own death, we still exulted. Smash them! Smash them! We felt as though each bomb had been released with our own hands. Yet we clustered together, seized each other at every tremblement of the earth, and several girls moaned and cried in hysteria. Erna and Tosca tried to gather the frightened girls still closer, to soothe them. One of the most terrified was Mandarinka, a girl of only seventeen, whose family, oddly enough, had lived in the very town of Auschwitz. Perhaps this was in some way the reason for her hysteria.

"The bombs won't hurt us," Erna kept saying. "You'll see, none of us will be hurt. The fliers are aiming; they're aiming only for the factories."

An instant later we were in the center of an earthquake; shrieks, and breaking walls, and we were one heap of beings clinging together. From the far end of the barracks came a gust of cold wind. The side wall of the building had collapsed, splitting all the way down to the cellar. There was no light. Each felt around for her friends, called out names. It seemed that we of the typing commando were all alive, unhurt.

Finally the raid was over, the anti-aircraft fire slackened and stopped, and there came a whole new series of sounds: fire engines, sirens, shouting. We were told to go upstairs, and not to budge from the barracks.

We saw the damage then, the wall split and half fallen into a crater. One girl had been crushed to death. She was from the commando working in the political office; she had been standing on the stairs, unable to endure the crowded shelter.

But then we saw the real destruction. Beyond our barracks, but in the very same row as ours, every building was destroyed. All those were the German army barracks. Under the masses of ruins lay hundreds of dead, SS men, Wehrmacht, and from those who were not yet dead ungodly screams reached out.

Our awe was so great that we could hardly speak to one another about what had happened. Surely no Allied bombardier could have known that ours was the only slave barracks among the five buildings. Surely no one could have aimed so closely.

I could no longer tell what I believed. We had wondered at the ways of the Nazis—on the one hand burning to ashes millions of us, and on the other hand ordering us down to air-raid shelters. I did not dare to face the same irony in the Almighty. Why, why? When it had been allowed that all our families be carried to the gas chambers, why now this seeming act of divine intervention, with the German barracks utterly destroyed, and our own, spared?

But an act of God even stranger than this was to be manifested.

Clustered at our gaping windows, from which the glass had been broken out, we stood watching German soldiers and a commando of prisoners working in the debris. We saw them carrying mutilated, smashed bodies, in shreds of uniform, and placing the dead in rows on the ground. We saw the sudden urgent activity when one was found still alive—the running with stretchers, the wheeling of ambulances. A few men even came staggering out by themselves, the dust and rubble falling from them, while plaster clung to their hair and covered their faces and arms.

We dared not speak of Grandpop. He too must be dead under the rubble.

Then suddenly we saw a familiar form emerge, small, compact. The man shook the white powder from his head, and there was white hair underneath.

In one voice, our entire commando cheered.

We wept, we embraced, we crowded the windows, waving. "Grandpop is alive! He's alive!"

One of the girls said, "You see, there is a God."

Outside, below, none of them could know exactly what had ex-

cited us. Grandpop made no sign. But the next morning a note fell
into our washroom. It bore one line: "God helps the righteous."

We never saw our friend again. The German soldiers were
moved to another part of the camp. But we used to talk about
Grandpop, saying if we only knew his name, if only we could
find him, after the war.


Each day now, we could feel the end drawing nearer. Why had
God waited so long? And then, one day, a story spread through
the camp like a radiance, making the day almost as bright as that
day of the attempt on Hitler's life. One of the death chimneys had
been blown up! Jews had done it! Right here in Auschwitz-
Birkenau, there was an active underground!

The story came to us from one of the drivers, but swiftly he was
gone, and then, over the entire concentration camp, there came
a nervous silence.

Among ourselves we whispered, we marveled at the incredible
deed. We imagined the towering smokestack crumbling to the
ground. We were too far from Birkenau to have heard the explo-
sion, but how the prisoners must have exulted when they heard the
great blast and saw the chimney toppling!

"The chimney," we said, and "One of the chimneys," yet even
now we could not bring ourselves to speak of its use. Who had
really ever seen what happened there? Living within its very atmosphere, we had still been unable completely to feel the reality
of the crematorium. What was said, what was known, was too
vast to be accepted. It was as though a thing so monstrous could
not be taking place so close to us without somehow manifesting
itself; it was as though so many millions of souls put out of life
would somehow make themselves felt, would thicken the air. It
was true, people vanished into that closed area. The mystery was

the mystery of death itself. You could not believe in it until the instant when it touched you.

And all day we whispered of the fallen chimney as though death itself had been cut down.

Who had done it? How had it been done?

Nothing more reached us.

But the next day, when our work was over, we were not returned to our barracks. Instead, Piotruch himself marched us toward the center of the camp. The whole area was still silent, deserted. Was the revenge for the deed coming now? One chimney was down, but the ovens still burned. Would they have done with all of us, for revenge?

On the whole way, we saw not a soul. Then suddenly as we turned into the central square of the Auschwitz camp, we saw the prisoners in their ranks, thousands and thousands, men and women, standing at attention. In the center of the square was a gallows.

On the loud-speaker came a brief announcement. Criminal conspirators had blown up an installation. Powder for this plot had been supplied by saboteurs in the munitions plant. As an example, their execution would be a public one. Let no prisoner take his eyes from this example, lest the same punishment be visited on him.

A prisoner's number was called out, and a name. Achusia was the name, and I took it into me, to keep. A young girl was led up to the platform, a small, frail girl.

The band played a military air.

If I had still been there in Birkenau among them, if I had been sent to work in the munitions plant, could I have done this that she had done? Achusia. What a moment it must have been for her, to see her work being accomplished, to watch the chimney crumbling.

[ 251 ]

She stood quietly under the noose. The SS women scanned us row by row to make sure that no face was averted.

The music had stopped. We could hear the tread of the hangman on the boards. Could I make my eyes unseeing? How was it that one death could be so much more unbearable than the knowledge of millions of deaths? How was it that our masters knew that such a death could strike us with force, even though we had seen so many, such countless corpses, skin and bones, breasts shriveled and dried? Even though so many around us had disappeared?

For an instant I saw the body hanging there; my eyes turned downward as though scalded.

Then a second girl was hung.

The music resumed and we were marched to our barracks. For the workers on the night shift in the factories, two more were hung. And for those in Birkenau, too, there had been hangings. There, the tale went, it was the man who had been led to the gallows, a young man who had been in love with Achusia, and for their love she had stolen the dynamite with which to blow up the chimney of death.



Now it was winter. The ground was either mud or dirtied snow. Within the barracks, so long as the windows were tightly closed, the body warmth of the four hundred women on our floor kept the air from freezing. But then the atmosphere became unbreathable. If we opened the windows, cold winds struck those who were nearest. The slightest cold might mean the infirmary, the gas chamber.

No matter how much we knitted, we did not have enough to keep us warm. My knees and thighs were always blue. Between the barracks and the office, we ran. Lola and I would keep our blood circulating by standing back to back, linking elbows, and swaying each other forward and backward.

The short period of exhilaration had passed and we were again in the gray endless world of the endless war. It seemed that nothing was happening. Without Grandpop, without his occasional thrown newspaper, even if it was German news, we had to depend on the vaguest rumors. The Russians appeared to have been halted again. Of the West, we dared not hope. The Allies were too far away to save us.

And so our morale began to fall. I caught cold, and despite all my fears I had to go to the infirmary. But after two days I got up and returned to work.

As I returned, Lola pulled me aside and slipped into my hand something small and warm. I looked. It was a piece of chocolate candy! Had the world come to an end? Yes, it had, she said, for our master, Piotruch, had come into the room yesterday with a box of candy and distributed chocolates to all the girls! She had saved my piece for me.

"The time of Messiah has arrived!" said Fella the Second.

Was it a sign? Was our master worried about how we would speak of him if we were liberated? But we dared not hope. Before such an event, the Germans would surely massacre every inmate of the camp.

Still, why had he done it?

One day not long afterward, having finished our noontime soup, we sat in our block waiting for the *appel*. It did not sound. Presently an SS woman appeared and ordered us to remain in barracks.

Were there to be more hangings? Was it a selection? Hours passed. Nothing like this had ever happened. We tried desperately to find things to talk about; we even made an effort to gather and sing. But each time we found ourselves separated into little groups, waiting. Fella the Second had even stopped telling of her married days. We waited in silence.

Then suddenly a rumor spread. Someone had been downstairs and the girls there knew. In Birkenau, they said, squads were entering each block and machine-gunning everyone to death. . . . No, on the contrary. A Red Cross inspection team from Switzerland was touring the camp. . . .

And then at five the *appel* sounded. We rushed out, forming our line more quickly than ever before. It was snowing. Twilight had alread come, gray, eerie. We were counted. The bread ration was given out. Then the command came: "Go back into your block and do not stir out of it, under pain of death."

In one instant, the entire yard was empty.

Some said they were going to blow us up. Others said no, we would be burned to death in our barracks. A number of the women sat rocking back and forth, reciting prayers, brokenly, half remembering. Others, from more religious homes, remembered by rote, and they kept reciting over and over, "*Rebbono Shel Olom*—Master of the Universe, save us, rescue us . . . "

And then Mandarinka of Auschwitz, peering out the window into the dusk, said, "There's no guard outside."

That couldn't be true. I hurried to the window. Out there, the snow was untouched. More snow continued to fall on the trackless yard. And where the guards always marched, along the fences, and where the guards always stood, by the gate, there was no one.

Was it the moment now to flee?

"No, no!" Lola cried. "It's a trick. They want us to run out and they'll mow us down."

We stood by the window, staring into the half dark at this strange sight. Now the spotlights had gone on, and they showed us only the bare yard, the snow.

[ 254 ]

Some said, "They're getting ready to blow us up. That's why all the guards are withdrawn. They don't want any of their own men to get hurt. It's a sure sign."

Then should we run in a mass rather than wait to be massacred? A few might somehow survive.

"No, no, if the searchlights are on, the electric fence is still alive!"

Then Lola said, "I hear shooting."

The whole barracks became one ear. Yes, from far off, explosions. Distant guns. From the east. Yes, yes, the Russians. They were surely advancing. That was why Piotruch had given us the candy.

We listened intently. Each called on her experience of the war, and we tried to guess how far away the Russians might be. Had I not heard Russian guns before, at Hrebenko? And German guns. And in all this time they had never stopped.

If the end was really coming, would it be liberation or death? And gradually we all came to agree that it could only be death. The Germans would never allow a single witness to live, to tell of what had happened here.

And we stared into the yard as if certain to see that death approaching. But why wait so passively if we were doomed? In anguish, our argument was resumed, until we were nearly ready to tear at one another. We must get out . . . we must wait . . . no, we must get out. . . .

Tosca proposed that we place a watch at each window. If any German was seen approaching the building to set explosives—if anything suspicious was seen—then, yes, we must use our last moment of energy; we must break out, try.

So we stood watch, changing each half hour. We stared at the untouched snow.

Was the shooting coming nearer? Could any of us really tell a Russian from a German cannon?

Hours passed.

[ 255 ]

And then, at ten o'clock, all the whistles shrieked. In the same instant, SS troops marched into the yard.

So it was too late. We had missed our time to run.

*Appel! Appel!* SS women pounded up and down the stairs. *"Raus! Raus!"*

We obeyed from habit, hurrying down to form our line. All through the camp as far as we could see, columns were forming, columns were already standing, thousands and thousands, women prisoners and, dimly beyond, men prisoners. And here, outdoors, the sound of the cannon was louder, nearer. . . .

Now they would mow us down as we stood.

The SS were everywhere, their dogs barking; here and there around the yard short bursts of gunfire sounded. So some were trying to run, and meeting their end at once.

"Not yet, not yet," I said out loud. Lola was beside me. We gripped hands. It was bitter cold; we shifted from foot to foot in the snow.

Beyond us, we saw a column in movement. But where to? A long, endless column. We stamped our legs, swung our arms; we tried warming each other back to back. Perhaps two hours had passed. The movement in the yard constantly increased; it seemed that thousands and thousands were coming from the direction of Birkenau.

And then came the order: "March!" It must have been just after midnight.

Our column joined onto the long column proceeding through the camp. Where to? In the ranks, panic increased. It was certain now. They would massacre us. Not a witness would be left. Hear, hear the shooting? It's the massacre. It's from Birkenau. It's from the woods, before you come to the town of Auschwitz. No, it's from the Russians, coming closer. We'll be killed by our rescuers themselves!

And then wailing arose. From among us, from behind us, the

wails arose and wove together into one constant cry: "*Rebbono Shel Olom*—Master of the Universe; save us, rescue us!" The shrieking became infectious, and arms were raised to the sky, with cries of "*Schma Yisroael!*" "*Gotenu, Gotenu.*" And the screams. "*Schma Yisroael.*" And from the Christians, "Jesus! Maria!" And bursts of gunfire, and the dogs howling, and the raucous cursing of the SS men. And over all this, the snow fell.

We marched, and then I saw that we were approaching the electrified fence. And the gate. The last gate! And we marched through the gate. And as we did so, I felt an elation shivering through my entire body, through every limb and nerve, an intense thrill such as I had never known. Insanely, in contrariness and defiance to all that was happening, to reason itself, I felt a seething joy. I was released! Free! I would not die in the camp! And the absolute certainty swept me; I would not die, I would live!

I began to sing. In a wild, ecstatic voice, above their shrieks of "*Gotenu!*" above their wails, their calling to Maria, above the yelling and the curses and the shouting, I sang.

"Eva! Eva!" Lola gasped, as though I had finally gone completely insane.

"We're free! Lola, we're out of there! Now we'll escape, as I always said we would!"

And I heard them around me: "Eva's lost her mind."

But the ecstasy boiled in my blood. I sang a song that had come to me from years before, when the Russians had been in our village, a song from some Russian film, a girl's song as she left her village to go out into the big world.

> *Oh, now my feet are light!*
> *I could fly halfway round the world!*
> *No place is too far for me to reach—*
> *Don't laugh! I'm out the door, and the whole world lies*
> *    before me!*

They were wailing, they were sobbing, and Lola clutched my arm and tried to hush me, but I shouted the words of the song:

> *The moment the door was opened*
> *I was out, I was afraid of nothing!*
> *Don't laugh!*
> *I have such strength now!*
> *I don't advise anyone to stand in my way!*
> *Don't try to stop me!*
> *I'm free! And the whole world lies before me!*

Then something made me look back. Everyone else turned at the same instant, as though a throb of emptiness had come from the air itself, as though the sky behind us had lifted.

It was red. The night was red, and a brilliant pillar of fire rose from Birkenau. The entire camp was aflame! Birkenau, Birkenau was burning. It was as though the cover had been lifted from hell itself, where so many millions were consumed. Birkenau was aflame. The remaining chimneys would topple into the fires. All the evil of that place would feed the flames higher. Let it burn; let it burn forever!

For a moment, the entire column halted. Even the SS guns were silent before the spectacle. We turned our faces and looked at Birkenau burning, and a sound arose from the entire mass of prisoners, a sound such as I had never heard before on earth, of horror and woe and grief and vengeful exaltation, mournful vengeful exaltation, a groan and a roar that wavered up and down the endless column. And again triumph seethed in my blood, and I sang; I stood and sang at the top of my voice. "Free! Free! The whole world lies before me!" and all around me the women stood and stared at my madness.

THEN WE MARCHED on. With each moment, as we marched
farther, and Birkenau flamed behind us, I felt more certain
of my life.

The SS strode all along the column, and from their guns spo-
radic bursts of shooting continued, but I knew I would choose the
right time. If they meant to slaughter us *en masse* they would have
done so already. No. They were taking us somewhere, to some
other prison, but before we got there I would run. There would
be forests along the road. The SS could not watch each one of us
each minute. I began to explain this to Lola. We must choose the
right moment, then run. "It's night. In the woods, we'll have a
chance. After they've passed, we'll find some peasants, beg them
to help us; at least we'll have a chance."

"The dogs will find us. They'll tear us to pieces. Eva, we can't.
I'm afraid."

"We must."

"The peasants themselves will kill us. Jews."

"No. we'll manage."

All along the line the SS kept yelling, "Faster! Faster!" The
tempo of the march quickened. They shouted, "Anyone falling
behind will be shot!"

We stumbled on in the black night, trying not to lose those
ahead of us. Lola was having trouble. I pulled her along. Then

under the slush our feet struck something less hard than the road. We were walking over bodies.

There was no stopping to pull out the fallen. We stumbled over them, walked over them. And if we fell, those behind would march over us. Endlessly behind us as before us, the column stretched. And again and again there came to my mind—"Anya." Where was Anya in this column? She must not fall. Oh, God, if Anya was under our feet in the snow!

Along the sides of the road, too, there were bodies. Some tried to step out on the sides, so they would not be trampled over, so they might catch their breaths, and the short bursts sounded and they lay on the roadside and in the ditches, and in the dim reflected light of the snow we could see their forms.

And Lola and I were slipping back in the ranks. Lola couldn't keep up with the pace; we slipped behind and behind, and if we came to the end of our column the bursts would sound and we would lie there.

"Lola," I whispered, "we must try it now. We can't keep up. We'll fall behind and be shot. As soon as we come to a dark place, where the woods are thick on both sides, we'll roll into the ditch. We'll lie there as though dead until the column has passed."

She gripped my arm in terror. "Eva, I can't. You go alone. You do it. Save yourself. I'll only bring you to death."

I knew she could not survive if I left her. Death was pulling her down. I knew, I could understand, I felt death pulling on me. We came to a place that was just right: dark woods on one side, and on the other side, not too far away, on some hill above the trees, I could see the outlines of a tiny village, with the low thatched huts so sharp against the snow, just such a village as we used to stop in for black bread and sour milk when we were children, going on our summer hikes.

"Lola. Now!"

She drew away from me, whimpering. And just then a rattle of shots rang out. Others had thought of it.

We went on. All feeling of our bodies was gone. It was as though we were clinging to the column as to a rope that pulled us along, and if for an instant we lost our hold we were doomed.

Here and there an anxious cry was heard, only a name: "Blumeh! Blumeh!" Or a call: "Malka, are you alive? Malka? Malka?" And sometimes even an answer: "I'm alive!" And sometimes a shriek as a loved comrade fell, was lost. "Gita! Oh, God! Gita, get up!" And in our own little group, our commando, our forty-six girls who had lived together these months, and had even been able to laugh, and had triumphed with our knitting, a name would be passed along. "Tosca. Is Tosca all right?" "Erna has dropped behind." "No, she is still here." "Erna, are you there?" And then, a half-gasped response: "Yes, all right!" Her voice would give us life, draw us all somehow closer together, holding one another up.

Fantasies passed through my mind. I seemed to hear Tauba's voice. "Eva! Eva, are you alive?" And then a whole dream, like a film. Tauba had been caught once more, in a partisan battle, and she had been taken to a camp, to Birkenau itself, and almost, almost, we had met, on a walk in Birkenau, and now, in this last moment—oh, horror, horror, she was under my feet! Tauba!

Then, much much farther, as though a long dark area had rushed past on the screen and it was another film, I saw Tauba still with the partisans. They would burst out of the woods at the next clump of trees; the partisans would rush onto the road and the SS men would fall, fall like mowed-down grain, and we would be freed. Tauba would come running toward me calling, "Eva! Eva!"

"I'm here!"

And she'd take my hand.

Then nothing. Nothing. Walking, walking in a column, walking, and all around me close to me they were walking, and then it was as some blurred, vague, eternal endlessness in my memory, a memory that existed in my limbs, in my body, so always it had been for us, so I had always done, from far back, from the time of Moses in Egypt, on the sands, in the snow. . . .

So through the length of the night. And we felt dawn coming, that first feeling of something less dark behind the sky. The column was entering a town. We marched directly through the main street. Empty. The town hushed. Surely they were awake, watching us from behind their shutters, behind their doors, watching us in our flimsy prison dresses, our broken prison shoes; surely they heard the stumbling rhythm of our feet, and the boots of the SS, and the shouts, and the shooting. Was all the world dead?

We came to the end of the town. Again the road, snow. What was that place?

And there came the voice of Mandarinka, who was from this region, from Auschwitz itself. "Plecz," she said.

Someone asked, "How far is it from Auschwitz?"

She said, "Thirty kilometers."

We had walked thirty kilometers. Through the night, without a stop, without food or water.

Then again, the outlines of a village. The neighing of a horse. And as the sun rose we were strengthened a little. We kept walking, walking, still another kilometer, still another, as in a half-wakened trance. All at once we felt something along the whole line, like a shudder. A shiver to a halt. Yes, halt. The SS men had cried, "Halt!" We stood before a farmyard. "Find places and rest."

The yard was black with women prisoners dropping where they stood. We crept over them to reach the barn. Straw there, and already covered with bodies. We crept among them, found a crevice for ourselves, against the hay. Dry, almost warm. Instantly we were in exhausted sleep.

Yet even within that instant, as I dropped to the ground, something in me had insisted, Not now, don't sleep now; now is the time to escape. And I had answered as though begging of myself, Only for a few moments, only let me rest a little. But the urging continued, within my sleep, Eva, Eva, don't sleep now; now is the time to escape. At last the command was strong enough to rouse me. I had rested a few hours.

I managed to get to my feet. All around me the women lay, in positions of exhaustion as they had fallen, each as though she had been too tired to unbend a knee, to untwist her back from a position that would give her agony when she rose again.

In the yard a few moved about dazedly seeking food, water; their hunger had awakened them. My legs were so stiff from the cold that I felt myself walking as on stilts, and with each step a pain shot up into my thighs. Clutching the walls for support, I made my way around the barn. Behind, not more than a hundred yards distant, was a dense forest. In the center of the farmyard our guards had built themselves a huge campfire, and they were sprawled around it, most of them asleep, a few of them sitting on logs, eating, drinking. Surely this was our moment.

My energy returned. Excited, I no longer felt the pains in my legs. I hurried back, crouched down beside Lola, and woke her. "Lola," I whispered, "I've looked around. It's only a few steps to the woods. This is the place. We've got to do it here. We can hide easily. After they leave, we'll come out."

Lola could barely summon her breath. "Eva, I can't move. Eva, you must go. I can't get up again. Let them kill me here."

"No, no, Lola. What are you saying? It's only stiffness. I felt it too, but as soon as I got up, moved a bit, my blood began to flow again." But I could see that her legs were dreadfully swollen, her ankles were doubled in size. Under her torn stockings, I could see the skin, all blue. Her face was ghastly; this was no longer the soft, pouting Lola but a waxen-faced mummy. I knew that she

[ 263 ]

would never be able to move out on the next phase of the march. What she said was true; she would die here, unless I could find a hiding place.

I got up and went into the yard. Where could we hide? The haystack was out of the question; they would search it thoroughly. The barn, the wagon shed, the few outbuildings. If only the earth itself would open and hide us for a few hours!

Then, in the yard, I saw two civilians standing, talking. They were not far from the farmhouse and not too near the SS. I moved toward them, and as I came close, hovered as though dazed and not yet fully awake, so that if the SS saw me it might not seem as if I had sought conversation with the Poles. Sidewise I pleaded, under my breath, "Help us. My comrade will die if she has to go on from here. Save us, I beg you; help us to get away from them."

The men did not turn their heads or utter a sound. But one of them moved a finger of his hand. It pointed toward the house.

He must be the farmer here, I thought. In his house, we are saved! I hurried back to Lola and told her what had happened. "Lola, you don't have to walk far—only to the house. Get up, get up." She stared at me and closed her eyes. The will to live seemed to have left her. I seized her arm, tried to pull her up. How much time remained to us? At any moment the whistle might blow. Under my breath I begged her, then I began to curse at her like a cappo. "Up, up, or you'll never get up again. Up! Instantly! You lazy bitch, up!"

Her eyes opened and she looked at me as if trying to recognize where she was. Her limbs began to twitch. I put her arm around my shoulder and tried to lift her. We staggered to our feet. She could not move her legs. I pulled her forward a step. Then the pain came in her legs, I could see, a thousand times worse than in mine; a cry, a half-stifled babyish whine broke from her, and she pitched forward. Somehow I caught her, brought her back to balance. And so, step by step, I got Lola out of the barn. I tried

[ 264 ]

rubbing snow on her legs, I pleaded with her, begged her. She was trying hard now. She took her arm from around me and made a few steps by herself. So we moved around the yard, on the other side from the campfire, moving toward the house. We watched for a safe moment. Lola looked one way, I the other. Only a few prisoners were stirring around the yard. A single SS guard, near the barn, had his back to us. "Now, Lola!" I yanked at her hand. We walked along as though going past the farmhouse; we were under its shadow; there was a door; we darted in.

We had entered a hallway, with doors on each side; a stair rose before us. Without hesitation we hurried up the stair, trying to keep our steps from resounding. We came to a landing. There were again two doors; perhaps these were bedrooms, perhaps people still slept there. We ran up the next flight of steps, opened the single door on the landing and found ourselves in the garret. The concrete floor was ice cold. There was a litter of broken, disused things: chairs without bottoms, empty picture frames, a few boxes packed with old dishes, pots. Where could we hide?

A high, half-rusted metal wardrobe stood there. In the bottom part of it, drawers were missing, leaving the lower area open and visible. If we stood in this wardrobe, our legs would show. Unless we turned it around.

We had to turn it to the wall, but to budge it seemed beyond our strength. If we pushed instead of lifting, the metal would scrape on the concrete floor; surely we would be heard. We must lift, lift, and turn it bit by bit.

How we did it we could not tell. But at last, when we were weeping with the hopelessness of our effort, when all our strength seemed pulled out of us, the wardrobe moved. And at last we had placed it toward the wall, leaving only space enough to squeeze ourselves inside.

There was just room. We were packed so close that we could not move. We stood, waiting. From all our efforts, from the dust, we had become dreadfully thirsty, although we felt no hunger. At moments I saw myself breaking out from that iron coffin, clamoring as I hurled myself down the stairs, "A drink! Water! For God's sake!" And I could hear water pouring from the tap, I could see the man, the owner who had stood in the yard, handing me a cup. No, I would rush and put my head under the tap. . . .

We waited. During that time, our consciousness must have lapsed again and again. For I would start up, feeling that I had perhaps slept. For how long? Could the column have been formed again, while I slept? Perhaps everyone had marched out. I would strain my ears, to catch sounds from outdoors. There were voices; yes, there was movement.

It must have been past noon when we heard whistles, and the familiar shouting: "Up, up, in line! Up!" The commotion grew; there were a few shots. We heard orders given: "Hunt them out! Dig them out! Tear apart that haystack! Some of them must have sneaked into the woods, the Jew bitches! The column doesn't move until every last one is accounted for, either in the ranks or a stinking corpse!"

But how could our ranks be counted when so many had died on the road?

And then there were noises inside the house. Doors banged. The pounding boots of SS men were on the stairs. They yelled, "Out! Out! Come out of there!" It was as though they knew and were yelling directly to us. They reached the floor just below. A door slammed. "No one here."

And now they were coming up the last flight, to our landing. They flung open the attic door. "Out, out! Who is in here? Come out!"

We held our breaths. They kicked over something—a chair—and then stamped out and down the stairs.

Still we didn't dare move.

Outside, the running about, the yelling, continued. Were we

the only missing ones? Were all the women being made to stand, lined up, counted, only for us? Then it was as though I were pleading with the girls of our commando, and I could hear their answers. "Yes, Eva, do it, do it; good luck to you!" "Eva, Lola, don't worry for us! Do it!"

Or were some of them angry? "Eva, with her mad ideas of escape! She has brought all this on us, and she'll only have herself killed in the end. And Lola too. Eva must have dragged Lola into it."

It was as though I were asking them, one by one. Erna? "Yes," she would say, "in such a case, yes. Even if it brings hours of hardship on the others. It is no harder for us to stand than to march." And Tosca? "Yes, with my blessing," she would say. "Come and see me in Paris." And Fella the cosmetician? And Fella the talker? "If you've already done it, then don't fail."

And so we stood still. From the amount of light that came through the small, dirty window, I judged it to be the middle of the day. And at last, at last, we heard the whistles again, the order to march. And the spread-out sound of their marching away, for a long time, until the yelling had an echo of distance. There seemed less shooting. Perhaps by day the march would be easier for the girls. But where were they taking them? For how long? And Tosca, Fella, Fella, Mandarinka, would each ever reach her home? And suddenly the wry thought came to me that Mandarinka, if she wanted to see her home again, would have to return to Auschwitz itself.

A quiet, the quiet of a farm in winter, had settled back on the house and over the yard. The sounds of the animals came from time to time. In the house below us, nothing. Only the creaking of the boards, like bones stiff from the cold.

Did we dare emerge? Suppose some SS men had been left behind for such as us, to catch us as we crept from our hiding places? Surely that farmer who had signaled to me had been aware that we got into his house. Surely he would come looking for us now, if things were safe. If he did not come, it meant that things were not yet safe.

But there was not a sound below us.

Lola's body had long ago slumped against the cold metal wall. The end of my own endurance had come. I tried to stretch it another moment.

I'll wait until I count one hundred. But I couldn't finish the count. No, no, I had to get out. If I gave way, my consciousness would never return; I would freeze in this iron box.

And so I stirred Lola, and we tried to get out. But our legs had become utterly numb. I tried lifting mine, half stooping to lift my leg with my hands. I stirred it, I scratched it. I could feel nothing, until suddenly there came the excruciating stab. With agony, the legs returned to life. I somehow twisted myself out of the metal wardrobe. Lola, too.

We tottered on the floor, leaning against each other. No, no, we must not yet go downstairs; we must wait for the farmer to come to us. As one, we sank to the floor. We were done for, unless help came. The strength to remain awake, even if it meant to remain alive, was gone.

The concrete floor was so cold it shocked us alert for an instant. A caution reared itself in me. If we lay on this floor our bodies would stiffen and we could never again move. On our knees, we searched among the debris, found the remains of an old quilt, spread it and rolled onto it and lost consciousness.

We seemed to have awakened together. Perhaps there is some last mechanism in the body that gives its alarm at the moment before death. All was dark. I turned my head to the window; outside it was dark. I whispered, "Lola," and she still answered, "Eva."

My body felt as though it had been sucked into the cold concrete. The quilt had given us its little help, but the cold had penetrated the shreds of cotton, penetrated our poor flesh, filled every bone. Even our pains had been numbed, frozen. If we should sleep again we would never awake.

"Lola, Lola, shake me." We rolled feebly against each other, trying to get to our hands and knees. Why hadn't the peasant come? Perhaps after all he had not seen us going into his house. It no longer mattered. We were at the end. We had to reveal ourselves.

So we crept on hands and knees to the door and raised ourselves against the door jamb, steadied ourselves somehow, and managed, clinging to each other, to stumble down to the next landing. We listened. Not a sound. How late was it? Were people awake? Asleep? Was this a bedroom?

I tapped on the door. A woman's voice came, alarmed. "Who's there?"

At least, a woman. Surely the farmer's wife. "We," I said. "Open. For God's sake, open."

"Who are you?" she asked, but we heard her steps. The door opened a crack. In the lamplight from within the room we could see a middle-aged woman, fat, short, in broad peasant skirts. A shriek came out of her. "Go away! Go away!" and she ran back into the room.

I pleaded, "Please help us! Your husband—"

She had seized a lamp and was coming back toward us. Then, directly behind her, I saw the SS man.

Lola gasped, "It's finished."

"Out! Get out!" he yelled in the raucous voice of his kind. Yet in that same instant I knew it was not finished. If he hadn't at once shot us, he wouldn't shoot us.

Lola was crying, whimpering like a child in a nightmare.

"He's going to kill us."

The SS man kept yelling, "What are you doing here? Get out of here!"

And I heard myself pleading, pleading even with him. "Tell us

[ 269 ]

where to go. Where can we go? Just let us stay a while in the straw in the barn. Give us a drink of water, a bit of bread."

Still he did not shoot. And each time he replied, even to curse us, I felt safer. "Out of the question!" he shouted. "You think you are the only ones? There were some before you and there will be some after you. Do you want me to get killed—for you?"

"Just let us gather our strength. Give us only a little bread and water."

He glanced at the woman. And then he blurted angrily, "There's a village near by. Go there. Maybe someone will take you in. I can't give you help. Transports stop here all the time. Soon there'll be another."

"Where is the village?" I begged.

"I'll tell you where to go, but don't tell anyone who told you, do you hear?" He glared at us.

"No, no," we gasped.

Then he told us the name of the village, Laaka. "There's a man there named Pavel Schlachta. Go to him. He may help you." And he gave us directions. We must cross the main road. Carefully. Troops and transports of prisoners were constantly passing. Across the road was a forest. We must go straight on until we saw a path to the right. "Take it. You'll come to a small wooden bridge. Cross it. You hear? On the other side, you'll see an isolated house. Avoid it. Go around it. Understand? And keep on, to the village. The second house on the left is Pavel Schlachta's. Now get out of here!"

He put his hand to his revolver.

We hurried down the stairs. The door opened onto a smooth yard of snow. Every sign of our transport's passing had been covered. While we slept, it must have snowed again.

Only the sky was unquiet, filled with bursts of fire. Back there from where we had come, shelling could be heard, powerful bursts, and shorter, nervous bursts. Beams scanned the sky. The

[ 270 ]

war had really come to us. And the Germans were really in flight.

Should we follow the SS man's directions? Suppose he had sent us straight into the lion's mouth? Should we perhaps rather go the opposite way? No, we had no strength to roam the forest. We had to chance everything on what the SS man had said.

We scooped some snow and put it to our lips. At the edge of the road, we paused. But all was still. We ran across. Safe. Among the trees were a few wagon ruts, lines dented in the snow, leading into the forest. We followed them. Now must come the path to the right. The trees were thick. But perhaps the path would be trodden.

So we walked, peering, searching for the path to the right. We couldn't find any such path. Perhaps he had made up nonsensical directions only to get rid of us.

Or we might have missed the path, dim in the snow. We went back to where we had entered the forest. If he had only told us how far we would have to go before we came to that path! Surely he meant soon. We started again, carefully, staring at the ground on our right. After some distance, we were in despair. We were going in the direction of the shooting. If we went straight on we would run into the German army.

Once more we returned to our starting point. Once more we hunted for the path, almost weeping with hopelessness. Then Lola saw a path on the left. Perhaps we had heard him wrong? He was yelling so, and we were so terrified. In our excitement, perhaps we had mixed it all up, or perhaps he himself had mixed it up? We would try. We took the path; we went quite a distance. Where was the bridge? He had said, "Soon." "Soon you will come to a little bridge." If we kept on, we would get lost altogether and wander in the forest until we dropped.

Could we go back to the farmhouse? Impossible. Dazed, beginning to bicker, we stumbled once more to the wagon ruts and followed them down, even toward the shooting, going farther than at any time before. And then, together, we saw the path on the right! A distinct, trodden path! Exhausted as we were, we almost ran along it. Within a few hundred yards we came to the little wooden bridge. And just as he had said, on the other side was an isolated house.

And then we saw two forms, men, coming toward us.

We hid among the trees. They neared. They were civilians. Should we reveal ourselves? Take our last chance with them? No, everything the SS man had said so far had proven true. Perhaps he had truly sent us to someone friendly.

We waited; the two men passed, going the way we had come. We moved out again. A light burned in the isolated, forbidden house; we took a long way around it, across a field, and at last we were at the entrance to the village. But the houses were scattered in such a way that it was impossible to tell which was the first, which the second from the left.

The street was deserted. The houses were dark. How late was it, in the night?

We stared at the houses, arguing nervously. No, this one; no, that one. I thought of the moment with Anya long ago when we had just left Hrebenko and were standing before the door of the Arbeitsamt in Przemyśl.

The step had to be taken. I walked up to the door of what seemed to be the second house, if one counted a house set a way back from the street. I knocked.

Again, a woman's voice. "Who's there?"

"Open, please."

"Who are you?"

"We're two girls. We escaped from the Auschwitz transport."

"Go away!" her voice came, terrified. "Leave! Leave me! I have six children. Go away, go away. They'll burn the house; they'll kill us all!"

We pleaded, " A bit of bread. Only bread."

[ 272 ]

"There are Germans all over the village. Go away."

Should we ask for Pavel Schlachta? I was afraid to speak the name, through a closed door to someone unknown.

We backed away, and we were afraid to risk another door. Suppose German soldiers were quartered inside? We crept along the village street. At the top of a rise, we heard voices. Some women had come out into the night; they were watching the shelling. And they were discussing whether to stay or to flee. If the Russians came, would it be worse? Better?

We approached. There were three of them. "Please," I began.

From under their shawls they peered at us. In the eerie light reflected from the snow, in our striped prison dresses, we must have seemed ghostly.

"What are you doing here? Get out, get out; there are still Germans in the village!"

"Take us in. Hide us."

"No. They make searches."

Then I ventured—with our last hope—"Do you know the house of Pavel Schlachta?"

"Schlachta?" One of the women peered more closely at us. But she did not ask how we had come by the name. "Follow me."

She walked rapidly. We hurried after her, down the street, to a house close to the one where we had knocked. She went to the door, called, "Pavel!" The door opened. There stood the same man who had moved his finger, pointing to the farmhouse! Then it hadn't been his own house.

And now, after one glance at us, he shouted, "Escaped prisoners! Get out! Get out! Not here!"

"But I was told—" I began.

"I don't hide prisoners!" he screamed. "You are endangering my family! Get away!" And he slammed the door.

The woman who had guided us had vanished.

We hurried away, as though lashed by his voice. There was

nothing left for us but to creep into some corner, in some shed, in some barn, and wait for the Germans to find us—perhaps only our frozen bodies.

Then, as we wandered, we heard footsteps running behind us. If we tried to flee we'd be shot. We turned to face our death.

It was the same man, Pavel Schlachta. He had caught up with us. "Quick, quick," he whispered, already between us, dragging us back with him. "I couldn't take you in, before that woman. She's the biggest gossip in the village. By morning everyone would know. Quick, quick." And he led us to his house and opened the door.

Warmth and light embraced us.

A woman came from the kitchen—his wife, in nightclothes. Another, a tiny old one, came behind her. "Bring them food, something warm, quickly," the man said. But first the grandmother came up and put her arms around each of us. Then both women were hurrying back and forth—tea, vodka, hot water to bathe our legs, bread with bacon fat. I felt I was swooning with happiness, but I must not drop away, I must feel, feel the goodness, feel how people were good.

And the man, Pavel Schlachta, was telling us he had indeed seen us go into that farmhouse. It was his brother-in-law's house, and the SS man inside was a cousin. Schlachta had thought it best not to say anything to the inhabitants. But just now he had sent two men back there to look for us—hadn't we passed two men in the woods?

Yes! Yes! The two men from whom we had hidden, behind the trees!

Then Schlachta asked, with his shrewd yet sympathetic smile, "Jewish girls?"

"Yes," I said.

"No matter," said Schlachta. "They had many of our girls, too." And after an instant, "But how did you know my name?"

I explained to him that it was the SS man, and how we had promised never to reveal his help.

The same shrewd smile appeared, and now even with a twinkle. "He has always been ashamed that he joined them. Maybe now he sees it is going to go badly, he tries to have someone to vouch for him." Pavel Schlachta chuckled.

And then for the first time I understood that we had become persons of value. Again, the world was turning upside down. Our lives, our despised lives, in another day, another week, might become treasures to an SS man who could claim that he had saved two slaves from Auschwitz.

As if adding another point in favor of their misguided relative, Schlachta's wife said, "And he told you to avoid the house near the bridge?"

"Yes," I said. "There was a light in it, so we went across a field to be far away."

"My mother and father live there," she said quietly. "They have German officers quartered with them. My father is the head of this village."

Now Schlachta's old mother said, "Enough, enough. They need sleep, the little daughters need sleep. Come with me, little daughters."

There was a hasty, half-whispered conference, but the tiny old woman insisted, "No, no. They will sleep in my bed." Hearing this, we begged her to let us sleep in the barn, in the straw—anywhere would be heaven to us—but she took hold of us, each by the arm—what strength there was in her old dry fingers. And she drew us along to her room.

There, with the walls covered with pictures of saints, and ancient family photographs, and amidst all the crowded little furnishings of a woman's life, there stood a high bed; layer on layer of goose-feather quilts surmounted it, and a mountain of pillows. She put us to bed like little girls. The quilts melted around us; it was as though we had fallen asleep in God's warm arms.

And so we slept. Until I sensed a presence: the little grandmother was beside me, in all her ample skirts, and, half awake, I knew I was actually there, safe in that room, and yet I knew it was all a vision, and I touched Lola, telling myself, even if she awakes and says it is real, it will still be a vision for both of us.

"I've brought you some warm milk borsht, children," said the grandmother. "I woke you only to nourish you a little. Drink, drink, and sleep again. You have time, time."

And it was as when a child, drowsy and thirsty, and really still asleep, drinks down a glass of milk in the middle of the night and sinks back on the bed, not having fully awakened. So we drank the milk borsht—*zur*, it was called—and it spread all through our bodies, into each vein, and we slept again.

It was high morning when we awoke, and the little grandmother was there with the three children of the Schlachtas, who were quietly looking at us. Two girls and a boy. The boy, the youngest, perhaps seven, was telling his sisters that they must never say who we were. The mother now came, bringing coffee and eggs, bread and butter, and as we ate, Pavel Schlachta also came in. He already had his plan.

We would have to be dressed as village girls, of course, and he would say we were two nieces who had fled before the fighting. We were from a village near Katowitz, for Katowitz had just fallen into Russian hands. Katowitz, already! Yes, that was what all the bombardment had been, the skies lighted all night long.

It was generally known in Laaka that the Schlachtas had relatives near Katowitz, yet his nieces had never been here, so nobody knew what they looked like. And in these days people did not question too much. But though we must not give the appearance of being in hiding, it would be as well to keep to the house as much as possible, not to run about in the village.

Now to transform us. The women began to whirl around, bringing skirts, petticoats, the voluminous garments of the peasant girls. Again, I would be Katya.

And again, what to do about our hair? We could tie kerchiefs around our heads, but still our clipped curls sprang out, looking strange, as the village girls all had their hair pulled straight back from their foreheads, and braided. My own hair had grown back enough to be combed away from my forehead, but Lola's was curlier and shorter, and no matter what we did, kept peeping out from beneath her kerchief. Well, so it would have to be.

We put on layer after layer of skirts, with the little tie strings, and aprons on top. When we were dressed, Pavel Schlachta was called in again, to behold his nieces. Ah, excellent, he declared! He was ready to believe the story himself!

Then his eye fell on our bedraggled, striped prison garments. "Can we burn them?" I asked.

"No, no," he insisted, "you must not destroy them. You must keep them."

"What for?" Lola gasped.

He had a peasant's caution. "One never knows what will be useful." Schlachta went out into the courtyard and dug a little hole. Then we buried our two bundles of striped cloth, as though burying there the deaths that might have been ours.

In a day or two we had settled in as part of the household. We tried to help with the work, the cleaning, the washing; we tried to get the little grandmother to take back her own bed, but she insisted on sleeping in the big family bedroom of the Schlachtas.

On the second day, Schlachta told us that another Jewish girl had saved herself from the march and was hidden in the village. Did we want to meet her?

We went with him, at dusk. There were German soldiers everywhere in the street. Their army was falling back; heavy guns, vehicles of all sorts, filled the village. As Laaka was off the main road, it was clear, Schlachta said, that these vehicles were taking up their station here to continue the battle. We would soon become part of the front.

The soldiers looked utterly weary. They went heavily about their tasks, setting up a field hospital, setting up their kitchens. In many of the village houses, they were requisitioning space.

They did not particularly look at us.

As we came to the other house we wondered whether we would recognize the girl as Jewish. Would she know us, in our disguise?

She was in the kitchen. At the first glance I told myself, No, I would not have known. And she said the same to us. She would never have known. And all of us felt safer.

Gita had marched a day before us, from Birkenau, and she had hidden in the woods. The SS had combed the woods with their dogs—she had heard them—but they had not come as far as her hiding place.

In Birkenau? I asked. In what commando had she worked?

A kitchen commando.

Then could she have known Anya? Esther Warshawsky?

Anya! Yes! Everyone had still called her Anya.

Was Anya alive? Had she come this far?

Yes, yes! And she had been calling for me, for Eva! On the road, she had called my name whenever they encountered another group of women—at the rest halt—yes, at that farm—Eva, Eva! she had called. And so I was that Eva, Anya's Eva! Alive!

That far at least, Anya had not fallen.

We talked a while. Gita too asked names, names. But we did not know any of them. Then we agreed that it would be best not to be seen together while we remained in Laaka.

Day by day, the army thickened there. And now officers came to Pavel Schlachta too, and one day several of them moved into the living room, where beds and couches were put up. And they wanted the Schlachtas to prepare meals for a little group of officers—decent meals instead of their army rations—and so we cooked and served for them. Yet, they seemed not to see us, glancing at us only in the way people do at waiters and servants, hardly looking at us as people. They were busy, and weary, and we kept out of their way as much as we could.

But one morning as I was sitting on the back stoop peeling potatoes, one of the officers stopped and watched me. Suddenly he said, "That's not the way a village girl peels potatoes."

It was true enough. My peelings were thick. The peasants peel with tiny, rapid strokes, and the peelings are so thin that nothing is wasted. One has to be born with this knack.

I kept on working, as though I hadn't understood what he meant. After a moment he went off. Frightened, I hurried to Pavel Schlachta, told him of the incident. He nodded, worried. But we could do nothing. Perhaps nothing would come of it.

The next night the officers had a party in the house. All day long we labored, preparing the feast. Tables were put together; dishes, utensils, were borrowed. Presently, captains, lieutenants, even higher officers crowded the house. The front room was filled with them. Drinking began early. Schlachta himself drank heartily; each time he carried a platter from the kitchen he had to stop for a schnapps, and soon I saw that he was becoming quite merry, and unsteady. His wife and his mother were busy over the stove. It was left for Lola and myself to serve the dinner.

And now the officers began to notice us. Again and again, one would stretch out an arm, catch hold. A squeeze, a tap, a merry remark. Then presently they began to discuss us. One said, "You know, they don't look like farm girls to me. They're a little too refined."

Another agreed. "They don't talk like peasant girls either. They're more educated."

And a sort of game began. The first one, holding Lola around the waist, gazed at her with half-closed eyes and said, "Look at her. She doesn't look like a peasant girl. She looks like a town girl."

Then there was a remark from the one who had noticed my potato peeling. "Look at the way she serves." He asked Lola, "Where did you learn to serve so correctly?"

"At home," Lola replied.

Again his observation was exact. A peasant girl would simply have put everything on the table, helter-skelter. We had been serving them properly.

Now Lola's first admirer leveled his eyes on me. "You, you with the red cheeks—you know what I see in you? In my imagination, I see you as a student, with a knapsack, on a hiking expedition."

A third officer now joined the game. He studied Lola. "No," he said. "This one—I don't see her as an outdoor girl. I see her in evening clothes, with high-heeled shoes, in an elegant bar."

She pulled herself away, laughing, saying she had no time for the bar tonight, but perhaps another night. And she hurried to the kitchen. But the game did not stop. One of them said he saw me as an office girl, dressed in a smartly tailored suit. I shivered.

And the worst was the silent one. Just as in that strange examination by the scientists in Vienna, there sat a silent one, here, too. An officer of about forty, with a seamed, brooding face, he had not taken his eyes off me, following me wherever I went.

Even in the most normal times a girl feels an uneasiness when a man sets his eyes on her. You move about, and he sits there staring at you because you are a girl; you are reduced to nothing more than flesh. Among soldiers, it is even worse. To your uneasiness, fear is added. Who knows what a brutalized soldier may do? And for me, that night, it was still more frightening. For suppose it was not so much desire as suspicion that was behind his stare?

I gathered up empty plates and hurried back to the kitchen. I pleaded with Frau Schlachta, "I can't go out there again. Someone else has to serve them." But before we could decide on anything, the silent officer was there in the kitchen, still staring at me. He was utterly sober.

"Come out with me." He indicated the courtyard.

The way he said it made me hope it was still only a case of a man trying to get hold of a girl. "I'm busy," I said, smiling. "I have to wait on your friends."

"They're all drunk," he said curtly. "Come on out. I've something to tell you."

He was not to be refused. Picking up a shawl, I followed him out to the yard. It was cold there. He seized me by the shoulders, his seamed face came close to mine, his eyes, deep, black, penetrated me. "Who are you?" he demanded.

"What do you mean, who am I? I'm Katya."

"Who are you?" he insisted.

I laughed, as one might to a tipsy man. "But I'm called Katya. That's who I am."

Suddenly, with a quick sweep, he pulled off my kerchief. He stared at my cropped head. "I knew it," he said. Then he seized my arm and yanked up my sleeve. The number was bared.

"So that's it. From the first moment, I knew it."

My whole body trembled uncontrollably. After a moment, as though in satisfying his curiosity he had not noticed what was going on with me, he just as abruptly drew me into an embrace. "Don't be afraid. Don't be frightened. I won't do you any harm. I didn't call you out here to frighten you, only to warn you." Smothered against him, still limp, still trembling, I heard him go on. "They've become too curious about you; they talk too much about you and your friend. Who you are, what you are. It's dangerous. It needs only one of them to make an inqury, and he will shoot you down like a dog. From me, you're in no danger."

[ 281 ]

And he began to tell me about himself. He had been a political prisoner in Germany. Then there had come a time when prisoners were given a chance to volunteer for the army as shock troops. He had volunteered. At Stalingrad he had been badly wounded. After months in a hospital he had been sent again to the front. He had distinguished himself and been made an officer. But still he was not certain what his fate would be, should the war end. He had a wife and two children in Hanover. And he had a premonition that he would never get back to them.

All at once, the officer took a scrap of paper from his pocket and wrote a note. "Do me a favor. My name is Helmuth Winter. Here is my address. When the war ends, go there and give this to my wife. Tell her you saw me. Tell her I thought always of her and the children." I took the note. I felt somehow that this was an assurance that I would live.

Now he added, "The Russians will be here in a few days. Their army is only a few kilometers away. Then you will be safe. You have only a few more days to worry about. But you must be more careful. You must be very careful because it is near the end."

And so we returned inside. By now, a number of the officers were snoring, half sprawled over the table. Their party was over.

All night, Lola and I whispered together. Should we again flee? Where to? As soon as Pavel Schlachta was awake, I told him of the German officer's warning, and he agreed that we must somehow get out of the way. But every house in the village was filled with Germans. At least, Schlachta decided, the two of us should be separated; in that way we would perhaps not stand out so prominently. And besides, if one remained in the house, they would not start wondering what had become of us.

So Lola would remain with the Schlachtas. And I would be sent to the big, isolated house by the bridge, to Frau Schlachta's parents. I would work in the kitchen and try to keep out of the way of the Germans.

I went. Her mother and father took me in and were like angels to me. A day and another day passed. Still the Russians did not come. Instead, more Germans arrived, more cannon. The village was now ringed with huge guns. And then the house was turned into a headquarters, with telephones and radio, and motorcyclists coming and going, and staff cars, all day long.

Laaka was in the battle zone now, and the Germans were too busy and desperate to have a thought for the villagers around them. I passed unnoticed. In Laaka itself the inhabitants had taken to the cellars. Some piled their families onto wagons and fled. Shells fell day and night.

And in the headquarters, I heard everything. Message after message shouted into the telephones, always begging for munitions, for men. They couldn't hold.

Why didn't the Russians know this? Why didn't they come? I hurried to Schlachta's. Wasn't there some way to let the Russians know? They were only a few kilometers away; they were already in Plecz, the town we had walked through on that ghastly night of the evacuation. Had it been only last week?

Couldn't I slip through the German line and go to the Russians? At night, perhaps? Schlachta laughed at me gently. "There is not only one line, there is line after line in such a war." It would be certain death. I must wait, wait. Only a few days more. The Russian shelling too had become lighter; perhaps the Russians themselves were waiting for ammunition.

And so several more days passed. We were like prisoners who have been told their sentence is ended but who are still waiting for the order for their release.

Then one night the Russian shelling became intense. All night long, incessantly, the bombardment continued, while we crouched in the cellar of the big house by the bridge. And above us, the Germans were packing. Outside, despite the shelling, their huge trucks stood with motors running.

They kept up their firing, but sporadically. Their machine guns could be heard, and a few cannon around us, but in the yard their motors roared, and their command cars and their supply cars and their armored cars pulled backward.

In the morning we saw only a scattered few of their soldiers. The house was empty of them. We cleaned. The whole day was quiet. And I remembered Hrebenko, on the day between the armies; only then it had been the reverse, the Russians had fled and the Germans had come. And yes, Bistray had said, "We'll be back. We'll be back, and we'll break their heads." My throat was filled with joy.

As the day wore on, uneasiness, even panic, grew among the villagers. Wild tales spread. The Russians soldiers would rape all the women. All the men would be shot for having dealt with the Germans.

In the market place, the villagers clustered in little knots, holding hurried consultations; a knot would break up, but the same people would stop again, farther on, to consult with others. To stay? To flee?

I went to the Schlachtas. The family was gathered in the courtyard and Schlachta too was worrying. "Stay, stay," I said. And I told him that from everything I had seen, in Hrebenko, those who stayed were the better off. At least they could protect their homes. Those who fled, suffered. Besides, Lola and I would tell the Russians that he had rescued us from the Nazis.

Suddenly he made up his mind. Taking his spade, Schlachta dug open the hole where he had buried our clothing. And Lola and I went into the house, removed our peasant aprons, our skirts and our petticoats, and once more we wore the striped Auschwitz garments.

Soon the Schlachta boy came running from the fields. He had seen a Russian on a horse! The Russian had galloped close to the town, looked around, and galloped away.

The night passed.

And in the morning we saw them coming, first the troop of horsemen, and after them the soldiers, marching in ranks of threes, and cannon pulled by trucks, and cannon pulled by horses —endless lines of cannon. We ran out to meet them, Lola and I in our prison dresses; we wanted to embrace the whole Russian army. They had finished the war for us! Now, in this morning, with their cannon around us, we were free of the Germans, free!

The soldiers were busy and paid little attention to us. They planted their cannon all through the town and around the town. They hunted through every house, every hayloft, for Germans. Their officers moved into the house by the bridge where the German headquarters had been, and there they too set up their radios and their telephones.

And now Schlachta's kitchen was busy cooking for the Russians, and I hurried to put food on the table for them, babbling all the while to whomever would listen; Lola worked beside me, smiling, her mouth open, but she couldn't speak Russian and left it all to me, to tell our story.

Only, strangely, they hardly seemed to respond. At first, I knew they had their tasks to perform, and they were weary. But soon I began to hear a few remarks, to be asked a few questions, and the tone was not warm at all. How was it that we had got away from the Germans? asked one of them—a tall one, wearing glasses. No one else had got away, he said. They had not seen a single Jew escaped alive from Auschwitz.

And in his eyes I could see his suspicion. Perhaps we had been left behind as spies.

Would it never end? What was there to de done? How could we convince them? Would no one ever accept us as friends? How

I had wanted, only a day ago, to run through fields of fire to tell the Russians of the German weakness!

A soldier drew me aside. In an undertone, he began to speak in Yiddish. Yet even he seemed suspicious. He kept asking questions —how was it that the Germans hadn't arrested us if, as we said, we had been in this house during the whole of the past week?

As he kept staring at me, at my clothes, it suddenly came over me that the simplest thing hadn't been understood. "But of course we weren't dressed like this! We were dressed as Polish peasant girls!"

Still, he was suspicious. Yes, of course he was a Jew, but that was of no significance; he was Russian. And suddenly more friendly, he gave us advice. Not to stay too much around the army. To go to the rear, the sooner the better.

We would have gone at once, except that we now felt we owed a debt to the Schlachtas and should remain and help them until the army had passed on. The Russians too demanded feasts, vodka; they roistered incessantly.

The German counterattack had begun, shelling and shelling. As they knew each important house in the village where their own officers had stayed, they assumed the Russians had taken over the same places, and they seemed to aim constantly at Schlachta's. Yet the Russians were slow to take shelter. They hung around the yard, drank, sang, talked. I couldn't bear it. I kept begging them to come down into the basement. Once, as I stood on the stairs calling to a soldier, a shell struck, falling into the yard, close to the house. The soldier, the horses in the yard, were one mess of dying flesh.

But the danger seemed to drive them only to wilder drinking. That night it was the turn of one of the Russians to pester me as I served. When I bent to set his plate in front of him, he caught me around the waist, pulled my head down, kissed me on the mouth. This one meant to have what he wanted. I got loose and rushed to the kitchen: Schlachta's wife motioned to the barn. I ran, climbed into the hayloft.

I heard the Russian pounding into the kitchen, roaring. Where was that Katya? She would be produced! She would be sent to his room! If not, he would burn down the house. We were spies, the lot of us!

He didn't burn down the house, nor did he shoot Schlachta. But in the morning, though sobered, he was still shouting that there were spies in the house.

The Jewish soldier sought us out. The situation was dangerous, he insisted; we had better leave. "This is an army. There are no investigations, no trials. It's enough for one officer to cry, Spy! and suddenly everyone will be saying it, and suddenly you will be seized and shot. Go, go to the rear."

Early the next morning we sat with the Schlachtas and wrote out our testimonials for them—how at the risk of their lives they had hidden us, sheltering us from the Germans. As two former inmates of Auschwitz, we asked that every consideration be given them.

And then, in our prison dresses, with little bundles of clothing and food that the Schlachtas pressed on us—bread, some boiled eggs—we were ready. They walked with us to the edge of the broad field at the end of Laaka. We would cross the field to pick up the main road back to Plecz, the road of our night march from Auschwitz.

We pressed their hands. The old grandmother, too, had come out into the field; she kissed us, called us her little daughters, and prayed that we would be safe.

Again we embraced each one. How good they had been to us. Then we watched them start back toward their village. Good Christians.

And then we turned to our way, to the open field. The snow had been trampled away by two armies, so that it was firm-crusted earth on which we walked. The cannon were out of sight. There were no more fences. The whole world seemed open and clear, in front of us.

And as we stood there in the February wind in our prison shifts, we turned to each other and saw in each other's eyes the same question—Where? To whom? In all our great world, to whom?

THEN CAME A TIME of wandering, of grasping everywhere for some connection to life. I felt I had already lost so much time in my life, I must quickly begin. Everything in me pressed for a regular existence, a home, a house with a husband and a kitchen and sheets on the bed and children to watch.

Lola and I had walked only a kilometer or two when we saw on the road a group of civilians, under Russian guard. And as they came up to us the soldiers motioned with their rifles—we too were under arrest. Was it to begin all over again? I explained, I pleaded with them in Russian, but I met only the stolid, stubborn faces of soldiers carrying out an order.

And so we were led with the others to a command post where each person was examined. "What are you?" the officer said to me.

"Jews. Jews escaped from Oswiecim."

"Jews? But what are you?" He stared at me, hard, as though he were weighing the disguise of the striped prison dress, of the very flesh on my face. What was I?

What was I? And I saw in his eyes what he was looking for. Was I Polish? Was I Ukrainian? And what was I, as a Pole or as a Ukrainian? Was I connected with some underground nationalist group? Perhaps the AKA, the Polish terrorist group who wanted to restore a nationalist regime? Already, even in the village of Laaka, I had heard this name, heard of these underground struggles.

But I was only a Jewish girl from Hrebenko, and my friend was from Kielce, I said.

And in Hrebenko, what had I been?

Now I knew. Under the Soviets, I had worked in the notary's office, I said, and gone to school at night, I had been active in the singing society and our choral group had won the regional competition. Indeed I myself had won the regional secretarial competition, for my work in the notary's office.

He nodded, nodded. And what had my father been?

During the Russian occupation, a night watchman, I said.

And before that?

A shopkeeper.

He nodded, and finally took his eyes off me. Yes, Jews. Well, I was free; I could go.

With Lola it was the same.

So we were back in the world.

We continued on the main road to Plecz and found the town deserted; the inhabitants had fled, the armies had passed through. The streets stood empty, the shops gutted, the houses, apartments, open to whomever might come.

And wandering about we encountered a few other women, a few men, who had escaped from the Auschwitz death march and had momentarily settled in some abandoned apartment. "Come, stay with us," the girls said.

Already there had begun the special comradeship that was to be encountered all over Europe in the months to come, in the D.P. camps in Austria and Germany and Italy, and in every city where we stayed. Wherever there were veterans of the concentration camps, we gathered and lived together, feeling strange to all those in the world who had not touched our experience. In any town you might reach, if you encountered a concentration camp survivor, if he had a lodging, you could share it, and if he had food, you could share it. Men and women, you could sleep in the same room without a thought; it was as though we had reached a wholly different understanding of the essentials of life, and our ways were our own.

And so we settled down for the time in Plecz, and all at once the whole weight of our years of tension broke on us. An immeasurable exhaustion pervaded us. For days we drifted about the vacant little town, unable to move on from there. We talked of what we would do. And at last it became clear to me that I had two things to do before I could begin to build my life. First I had to find out for certain what had happened to my family. Second was the need for revenge.

I must go to Hrebenko. But on our second day in Plecz we encountered a Jew, a survivor from Auschwitz like ourselves, a bald, older-looking man, brooding and silent, who threw out a word here and there as though tearing out for us a part of his bitter knowledge. He had already been in those regions. Around Lwów there was shooting, shooting behind the Russian lines. The Ukrainians were in revolt. The Ukrainians would kill a Jew as quickly as the Nazis. It was not yet time to go there. And why go at all; there was nothing, nothing there, nothing, not a Jew left in the whole region. Not even in Lwów, much less Hrebenko. I would find no one.

Then I talked of going to Palestine to find my brother. But didn't I know? The way was closed. The British barred the way. No Jew could enter Palestine. Some Jews had tried to go there in a ship, and the ports had been closed to them, and they had sunk themselves in their ship and drowned in the Mediterranean Sea.

There was nowhere, nowhere, for a Jew to go, he told us. And the next day he had vanished from Plecz.

The Russian soldiers had begun to annoy us; they had discovered the flat we had taken over—several girls together—and every night they would come and pound on the door, and we would have to barricade ourselves. Lola and I decided to go on our way. We would go to her city, to Kielce, since it was not too far away.

In Kielce, Lola showed me a whole street of buildings once owned by her father; she led me to a modern apartment building, much finer than the house my father had built in Hrebenko. Lola rang at a door. A well-dressed Polish woman opened, asking, "What do you want?"

"I used to live here," Lola said. "Can I just go inside and look?"

The woman stared at us. "I'm all alone in the house," she said. But then she let us in.

"The furniture is all changed," Lola said. She opened a bedroom door and stood on the threshold, weeping. "This was my room, where I grew up."

We turned and left.


Now where would we go? We wandered about the streets for a while, and then an elderly man approached us, asking, "You're Jewish girls?" He told us a committee was taking down the names of those who had returned. And so we went there. The committee consisted of two brothers who had been hidden on a farm. They had a large copybook in which only five names had been written thus far. We put down our names. "Where will you be staying?" they asked. We didn't know. Perhaps we would go on.

"Stay here for a while, then." The younger one was named Marek and the older one, Zev. They made tea, they found us things to eat, they talked and talked. They were going to Palestine.

"But the way is closed," I said.

"No! No!" Zev insisted, excitedly, like a conspirator. "We are making a way. Underground. We will go." And they would take us with them.

Again to struggle, again to hide, to be hunted—no, I had no

[ 292 ]

strength for it. And I could not go yet; I could not leave this land, for the tale of Tauba haunted me more and more; perhaps she would yet appear from the Russian side, writing her name in copybooks such as Zev's, seeking her sister Eva. Perhaps, perhaps by some miracle even Yaacov had escaped. Perhaps Belzec had been a camp not too different from Auschwitz, where in spite of everything a few could survive. I could not go on until there remained no more to find out.

We lingered, and one morning in the street I saw someone I believed I knew. He was quite old, with a sunken mouth, and dreadfully stooped, but I knew him—yes, it was Dr. Appel, from Hrebenko, once erect, fine-looking—he had even been a member of our Judenrat! I cried out to him and he peered at me. "Eva Korngold!"

Yes he had been in Hrebenko, he came only now from Hrebenko, he had been the whole time in Hrebenko, hidden in a cellar, a schoolteacher's cellar, alone, after an *aktione* in which his entire family had been seized. And when he had come out, there was not a Jew left in Hrebenko, and so he was wandering, seeking. . . . He had had three brothers, once, here in Kielce.

And of my family? Had he heard anything?

He had heard. In that fourth *aktione*, it had happened. When his own family had been taken. After the raid appeared to be over, and all was quiet, Klein's deputy, Mayert, had walked through the Jewish streets. Standing in front of the Blumenfeld house where our family was hidden, he had cried out in Yiddish to my mother, "Mrs. Korngold! Come out! Come out!" And not knowing his voice, and thinking a Jew needed her, my mother had come out of the cellar into the hands of the murderers.

And my father? And Yaacov?

Later, in another *aktione*. All, all, even the members of the Judenrat had been taken. All, all, to Belzec.

Then I begged to know, was Belzec perhaps like Auschwitz,

where a few, where a strong boy like Yaacov, might survive? We were still standing there in the street, two passers-by who had met and were quietly talking.

"Belzec," he said, "there no one survived. No one. There was no labor there. Nothing. And before the Russians came the whole place was razed to the ground. Nothing remains. Nothing."

But still haunting me was the story of Tauba. Perhaps a few had escaped. I begged. Had there not once been a partisan attack on Belzec?

He peered at me with the ghost of a smile, tender and pitying. Ah, he had heard this legend, even while he was still in the Judenrat.

But couldn't it have happened? And I told of Tauba's letter. As I spoke, the little smile vanished and his mouth, his whole body, seemed even more sunken. Yes, he had heard of such letters. Dr. Appel's hand moved and touched my arm. "My child, strange things happened in the ghetto, as time went on." About such letters—there had always been money connected with the delivery of the letters. Even large sums of money. Strangers had appeared in the ghetto, Jews, from where, who knew? Strange things had been done. And there had been tales of such letters, heavily paid for. And then, such people had vanished.

"But my mother even wrote that the letter was in Tauba's own handwriting."

The pained little smile returned. Handwriting could be copied. And when people wanted to believe something—who knew?

But could one be absolutely certain there had been no partisan attack on Belzec? I asked. Perhaps Tauba was in the interior of Russia somewhere. Perhaps she had even been sent to Siberia. Perhaps she had lost her memory. One day she might come wandering back to Hrebenko. . . .

He had listened, as one listens to the obsessed, without stirring, without changing his expression.

[ 294 ]

And so I asked about the others. Of all my friends, had none escaped? Alla, and her sister Freda, and Milla, and Rita Mayer?

"After you went," he said, "a few other girls tried to go the same way. "Alla and Freda had gone out, posing as Ukrainians. Then perhaps they lived! And did he know of the others? Rita?

A strange thing happened with Rita. She had worked in a construction office for the Germans and one of their officers had fallen in love with her and, it was said, had helped her to escape.

And pretty Rachel Schwartz, who had got me my false papers?

Rachel had been seized in an *aktione,* and so had Feigheh Segal, and Lucia Kuner, the dentist's daughter, had been taken, and all of our boys had been taken—all.

We seemed to have no more to say to each other. As we were parting I remarked, "Still, I thought one day I should go back."

He touched my arm again. There was a hoarseness in his voice. "Don't go, Eva. Don't go. If anyone is alive, it isn't there that you will find them. Not there. Don't go."

And so we separated.

I wrote to the city authorities in Hrebenko. If anyone should ever inquire for the Korngold family I could be found—where? In the end I put down the address of the Committee of Jewish Survivors of Kielce.


Only vengeance remained.

One day we encountered a girl from our own commando, Carola. In Katowitz, she told us, the Poles were arresting collaborators, spies, even cappos from the concentration camps. On this commission, translators were needed. There we could strike back at our tormentors.

And so we hurried to Katowitz. In a heavily guarded building was the U.B., the Polish counterpart of the Russian NKVD. We were interviewed by a young woman. Yes, translators, secretaries, were needed. She examined my qualifications. Since I knew Russian, too, I might be just the person to help the prosecuting attorney.

Yes, yes, I felt, at last I would strike back, I would confront the enemy, I would catch them in their lies as they tried to squirm out of their murderous deeds. Then the young woman fixed me with a stern look. "One thing I must tell you. If you enter this service, you cannot leave of your own free will. You will leave only if we dismiss you, or if you die."

Without a moment's hesitation, I said I was ready to accept this condition. For after everything I had been through, I was thinking, no force would be able to keep me where I didn't want to be. Hadn't I even escaped from the Auschwitz death march? And here was my opportunity to have revenge, and no rule would keep me from it.

The young woman pressed her lips together. We must think about the condition at least overnight, she said, before making our decision.

Lola decided not to go into that service. But I returned the next day and was at once assigned to the chief investigator, a Russian working in the Polish U.B. His name was Stashek. Quite tall, with an impatient, tense manner, he looked me over, asked my name, repeated it—"Eva. Eva Korngold"—and said it would not do. To be known as a Jew would be dangerous for me, especially in this service. He set the matter forth plainly, factually. Of course, in Poland now, as in the Soviet Union, anti-Semitism was outlawed. But in Poland much education was needed on this subject. And meanwhile the AKA, the violent nationalist party, was conducting widespread assassinations. Jews came first. His service was engaged in a bloody, bitter, underground battle with the AKA. A Jew in this service would be marked. Yes, even a secretary. It would be inviting assassination for me to be known as Eva Korngold.

I already knew—I would go back to being Katya. Katya Leszczyszyn. And why not? Nothing was left of that other life. There was nowhere for Eva to go; there was no one left who knew her. And perhaps I should remain Katya forever. Why change and change again? Why not have done with Eva and forget her? I had survived, but the enemy had won after all, for the Jewess could not survive; she had to disappear.

And what did I have to live for, the I who had survived, Katya or Eva, what did I have to live for except revenge against the enemy? Here was my work before me. Eva, Katya—only revenge mattered.

At once I was swept into that work, into Stashek's life, for the prosecutor never stopped working. He worked with passion—to get them, to catch the spies and the saboteurs and the terrorists, to pull their information out of them, convict them and punish them! All those who had killed and tormented!

Everywhere, I soon learned, Nazis had been left behind, dug in among the population. They connived with the nationalists, the same reactionaries who had collaborated with them during the German regime. We had to root them out. Yes, it seemed to me, this was my new life here, in the land of my birth, in Poland. A whole new life would arise, a strong life for the young, a life in which all would be equal, in which Jew-hatred, or any other kind of hatred, couldn't exist. Hadn't there been a bright sweep of life, for the young, when the Russians came to Hrebenko? This would be our way! We would build the new world! Some day, after my work with the prosecutor, I might even be singled out to go to Warsaw, to Moscow, to study law, I might yet fulfill my girlhood dream of becoming a lawyer! I would develop, I would yet make something of myself!

And I fell into the work with passion. I saw the parade of the arrested. I knew the room with locked doors where the questioning took place, and I had no pity; everything was necessary to build the new world.

And day by day, with the headlong rapidity of those days, I formed a life with Stashek. Working together, striking back at the enemy, making the new world secure. And soon I was doing all the womanly things—taking care of his clothes, putting food before him when he forgot himself in his work, and putting him to bed when he got roaring drunk at the perennial parties.

For there were parties every night. Vodka, mountains of good food, dancing, and boisterous friendship. The U.B. occupied a special group of buildings, with flats for the officers. The whole block was shut off from ten at night to six in the morning; even the surrounding streets were shut off by security police.

I was living outside the area with Lola, and Stashek was reluctant to let me go home after the parties. "You are known. It's dangerous to go about in the dark."

Soon enough, I knew how true this was. More than one U.B. agent had vanished. Hardly a night passed without exchanges of shots in the streets of the closed-off area.

But it was not until Lola left that my real terror grew. Lola had found an aunt alive in Belgium, and she begged me to go there with her, to leave this dark country once and for all. I couldn't leave. I was emotionally bound to my work, and already emotionally bound to Stashek. And so I parted from Lola.

Then it became impossible for me to live alone, outside the U.B. enclave. Stashek had given me a revolver, and as I entered my apartment—a fine one, requisitioned from an arrested collaborator— I would hold the revolver at ready, in my hand. Switching on the lights, I would hurry through each room, gun in hand, until I felt sure the place had not been visited. I would turn the radio on, loud, and keep it on all night.

In the streets, I walked swiftly, with the expectation at every moment that I would be shot from behind. And at last I gave up and lived almost entirely in the enclave.

Stashek and I became dear to each other. We felt so strongly that we were building the life of the whole people and that we would build our own lives together, too. We would have a home, a family. For the first time in my life I was with a man who truly wanted all this with me, and soon, soon, that real life would begin.

Meanwhile we were busy with revenge; even when Stashek slept his mind was working: not one collaborator, not one tool of the Nazis must escape. And one day I knew the feeling in my own hands.

There came a call for me, from the railway station. It was Carola. "Katya!" she cried, "Do you know whom I've just caught at the station? Edit! The cappo! She's still with our Block Eldest, Maria."

Edit, who had pointed me out, that time by the fence, with Lola, when an SS woman had nearly beaten us to death!

"We've caught a cappo," I told Stashek. He ordered Edit brought in, but her friend Maria was to be sent off on a train. Word flew through the building that a cappo had been caught, and the women began to gather. Edit was led in, her small eyes darting about, her body already hunched together, tight. As she saw who was waiting for her, she wrenched so hard that she nearly pulled herself from the grip of the U.B. men.

Something utterly animal took hold of me. I tore at her, all of us tore at her, with our nails, our teeth; had the men not pulled us away from her we would have torn her to shreds. "Leave her alive until I have her indicted," Stashek pleaded. "I can't indict a corpse."

And so that was one.

When I had calmed and returned to my typing, I found I was without feeling about what I had done. Neither happy, nor relieved, nor ashamed—it was like some pressing bodily function, released.

That night Stashek said, "I never believed you had it in you! A Jewish girl, too!"

There was something in the way he made the remark—only another Jew would have said it that way. I had long felt that Stashek was Jewish, and now I brought it up to him. "Stashek, I know you are Jewish yourself. I feel it. It's part of what draws us together. Why don't you admit it? Why don't you acknowledge it at least with me?"

Why didn't he admit it? Why, then, if it was so important to me—yes, his parents were Jewish. But why make a problem of it? For expedience, in the service, especially here in Poland where anti-Semitism was still rife, he preferred not to have it known. And, in any case, he remarked offhandedly, he wasn't even circumcised; these barbaric rites were practiced less and less among the descendants of Jews in the Soviet Union, and in a few generations the whole question of Judaism would be liquidated.

I listened. I knew. I had heard these same ideas long ago from Bistray, in Hrebenko. I had never been quite sure I knew what was meant. As for the Jewish religion, which I myself had never practiced, perhaps in a way it would die out. But then, what about being Jewish, in itself?

Stashek laughed. Being Jewish. What did that mean? What was it? In time, Jews would be absorbed, assimilated; they would merge with the others. What good was there in keeping alive this separatism? It had brought only agony, and mass murder, and bestiality. For what? For an outmoded religion, a cult in which no enlightened person believed? The Jews had contributed their share to history; long ago they had ended their usefulness as a single unit to the cause of human advancement, and now let them disappear.

But then what of Palestine? I asked. I did not mean to dispute with him, but a puzzled feeling had come over me, and a strong memory of the Zionist atmosphere of my childhood. And I had a half-brother there!

Palestine? Let those Jews who wanted to try to revive nationalism continue their efforts there, he said tolerantly. He was certain that they were historically doomed; they had attached themselves to the capitalist imperialist cause. But even if they should by some twist of history succeed in establishing themselves, what would that matter to the descendants of Jews in other lands? It would be even more reason for them to disappear as Jews.

I didn't argue with Stashek. I no longer felt that I knew, for myself. Perhaps I was finally Katya.

And then one day everything was solved for me.

We were at work. Stashek was called out of the office. Someone was waiting for him downstairs, just outside. It was a name he knew. He hurried out, but I noticed he hadn't picked up his pistol and cap; it was forbidden for an officer to leave the building without them. I took the things and ran after him. I had barely reached the top of the stairway when the shots were heard. Stashek fell, there by the entrance to the building, assassinated.

I heard a fanatic scream: "Yid!"

ONLY THEN, for the first time, after all I had been through, was I no longer interested in living. Why? For whom? Apathetic, I sat at home, no longer even afraid of assassins.

And at last one morning, like a voice making itself heard again, came the thought: But I have a brother in Palestine.

Why had I gone again among a strange people? I would leave now, to find my own. What of my pledge to the service, with its blood-soaked secrets? Even the U.B. could not stop me!

And so once more I mounted a train, to steal my way across a border. I had no papers. But I had dressed like a Russian army girl, and I sat with a group of them and laughingly put one of their caps on my head, and when the control officer passed through he only glanced at us, and so I arrived in Prague.

There was only one being I wanted to see before going on my way. If Nina had survived, I was certain she would be with Karlus. The search proved easy. There was a central directory—so many people were seeking people. I gave Karlus' name, received an address at once, went there, rang, and in a moment was in Nina's arms.

"We knew you would live! We knew it!" Karlus was there, holding my head between his hands as he kissed my forehead, my cheeks. And then came the recitations of the fates. Ah, Clava. She had gone to Berlin to visit her sister, had been caught in an air raid and killed.

Slavek? I waited for them to bring up the name, not knowing, myself, how I felt. But Karlus said, "He never deserved you, Katya." The last they knew, he had gone off to France with some girl.

After my arrest the Gestapo had again questioned Nina, telling her that I had admitted she was Jewish. And then Nina had recalled my warning—she was to deny and deny. She had denied, and been returned to her job, and there in Bindermichel she had waited out the war.

The next day, when Karlus went to work, Nina and I had a long talk. Here she was happy. She had her man, her home; she was pregnant. Why shouldn't I stay? The Czechs were not like the Poles; she scarcely felt anything about being a Jew any more.

"But what will your children be?" I asked.

"Why, nothing. We're not religious."

And she kept on—why shouldn't I remain with them? Stay here, marry, have children. She knew a fine man, a Czech.

I had come to feel that if I fell in love with a man it wouldn't matter what he was, Jew or not. And so I understood this in Nina. But still, perhaps things were different for her, since she, like Stashek, had been raised with the feeling that Jews would in the end disappear. No, I told myself, it wasn't any care in me for keeping the Jewish people alive, it wasn't any kind of patriotism, nationalism, whatever they called it with their endless arguments. It was only that my heart yearned for a relationship where there would be no questions, no problems, where we would be the same kind of people, and each would know what the other felt, as though knowing it through everything that had happened in the lives of our people all the way back to the beginning. It was only for my own comfort. I wanted to live with a Jew, not a lost Jew like Stashek, and I did not want to be a lost Jew like Nina.

All that was finished. The whole question—finished. Surely people had a right to be their own selves in the world. If not, all the turmoil, the strife, the war, the victory, had been for nothing.

And so I told her. I loved her and Karlus. I would love them as long as I lived. But I must leave their land and be on my way.


The time of confusion began. I became a Displaced Person. I gravitated to Munich; it seemed I lived in a different place every week, for I would not go to a camp, I would rather starve than live once more in a barracks. From Poland I had brought a watch, a ring, a fountain pen; when these had been sold, I found bits of work. I haunted all the D.P. centers. I put my name on every list of survivors, at UNRRA, the Red Cross, the Joint Distribution Committee. In every office, I sent through inquiries for my brother's address in Palestine. And there was no response. I made contact with the underground immigration that the two men, Marek and Zev, had spoken about, in Kielce. But the list of Jews waiting to be taken across the borders, to board illegal ships, was a long one; it would take a year for my turn to come.

And in my wandering, as I had been told by Dr. Appel on the street in Kielce, I began to meet those from Hrebenko who had survived.

In Munich there were dances for the D.P.s, and one night I saw Alla dancing! I screamed. The dance stopped. People stared as we flew to each other. Alla, my twin! Born on the same day as I! Alla Blumenfeld, from whose house I had left, on my journey! And so we talked into the night. My mother had convinced her mother to let the girls follow me, and Alla and Freda had reached Vienna and found places as Ukrainian maids. But Freda had worried and worried for those at home. She had been unable to bear the silence. "I know, I know," I said. And Alla said, "She kept telling me she had to go back. And one day when I went to see her she was gone."

So Freda had vanished.

Soon after finding Alla, I found trace of my brother in Palestine. One night at curfew I returned to my room; I was cold and pulled the blanket from the bed to wrap around myself while I sat reading. A piece of paper fluttered down. It was a note left by an acquaintance, a D.P. He had a letter for me from my brother!

In the morning, holding the note, I rushed to the tram. My face must have been ablaze with happiness, for a German on the tram remarked, "But what are you laughing about, Fraulein, so early in the morning?"

I found the D.P. In a moment, Nahum's letter was in my hands. He had met Esther! Esther was already in Palestine! She had survived the death march and been liberated in Bergen Belsen. Through some chain of D.P.s it had been heard that I was in Munich. I must cable him. He was well, he was married, he had a little girl, he had managed to study law and was completing his apprenticeship in Jerusalem.

Now I had to be on my way more quickly. I rushed from camp to camp, wherever I heard a rumor that a group was leaving. One day I was told there would be a movement from a camp near Munich. I packed my things and went to the camp. When night came, though I was not on the list, I mingled with the crowd and slipped into the last truck. The tarpaulin was let down; we rode in darkness. I laughed to myself. I was doubly underground, illegally a part of the illegal immigration.

There was a stop, a check post. All the others had been provided by the underground organization with false visa cards. I had none. We were entering the French occupation zone, and I was told to stand aside. But then one of the leaders of the group pulled up my sleeve, exactly as the German officer had done that night in Laaka. My numbers were exposed. "Isn't that passport enough?"

[ 306 ]

he demanded. The French officer motioned to me to climb back onto the truck.

The journey continued. We stopped at another D.P. camp, where the Haganah smuggled us in among the regular residents. We stayed a week. The coast was clear; we went on, and at last we reached a place in the Alps, an abandoned hotel, from which we started on our all-night trek across the mountains into Italy. On the Italian side we were again met by Haganah trucks and taken to a camp near Milan. And there, just as we arrived, I met Ari.

Whenever a new group came into the camp the single men would gather to look over the newcomers, for girls. Ari picked me out at once, he told me later, after we had started walking together.

It was as though we had had some agreement, some arrangement, to meet here. And this was as I had always imagined it would be. We were so familiar to each other, and we kept discovering each other.

He had a sensitive face, and was gentle, yet he could lead me, and he was, I saw at once, listened to and respected among the men. Ari was from Tarnopol. When the Germans came, he and his father had fled to join a partisan brigade, but his father had been killed on the way. Then Ari had fought as a partisan until the Russians came; he had joined the Soviet army, been wounded, hospitalized, had returned to the front, and fought to the end.

And so we waited for our place on an illegal vessel. We were moved from one camp to another for almost a year—to Ostia, to Castel Gandolfo, to Tradate, to Metapunto. Though the food was meager and monotonous, though there were often no lights in our primitive camps, and no toilets, the time was like a honeymoon. We studied Hebrew, we walked in the fields, Ari trained with the rest of the men, and in the evenings we sat among friends, trading rumors about coming ships.

Then finally our turn came. Again the blacked-out trucks, a ride to a secret beach, and rubber embarkation boats, and a freighter, waiting offshore. We mounted and were hurried to the hold, and there a surprise awaited us. We saw shelves, exactly as in Auschwitz. Only, instead of being three high, they were in layers of four! We even joked about this. Only the survivors of the concentration camps, we said, could have found this way to crowd five hundred people onto such a tiny vessel.

And so we lay retching for an entire week, layer on layer of us, as the vessel rolled in a heavy sea. The engine kept failing. We had to go back. We waited another month and embarked again, on a Swedish vessel that was somewhat cleaner. This time there were eight hundred of us. Ari and I had our places on the bottom layer of shelves, and there in the welter of voices I heard a familiar, raucous tone. I wormed my way out into the aisle. "Eva, what's the matter?" Ari asked.

"It's the first Room Eldest I had," I said. "It's Elsa, from Birkenau."

"Eva, wait." He squirmed out after me.

But I had already seen her, even in the dim light of the hold. There she sat among a group of men, telling tales, laughing. I approached and stood over her. "Elsa," I said, "do you remember me?"

She looked up and quietly said, "No."

"Take a good look."

All had become silent. "No, I don't know you," she said.

"Do you remember Block 9, in Auschwitz-Birkenau?"

"No."

"Do you remember The Lady?" I asked.

She looked directly at me. "No," she said.

"But I remember you!" I cried. And I shrieked out, "Look! One of them—from Auschwitz!" The same fury came over me as in

Katowitz, and I leaped on her. "I owe you something!" I kicked, tore at her.

But Ari and the rest of the men seized me and held me. A young Palestinian, the Haganah man for the boat, stepped in to quiet me. "If you have serious charges against her you can make them when we get home," he said. "But here you must control yourself or you'll put us all in danger." Then he took me aside and added, "She is a Jew too. No matter what they made of her, we'll make something else of her."

And somehow I felt it was enough. We had met. She was known.

For two weeks we sailed, and then the ship was spotted by a British cruiser. The men had their plan ready; they had sticks, bits of iron, empty bottles. On our ship, as on a score of others, battle had to be given so the world would know.

And so we waited for the fight. We were no longer bitter at our fate; this was our way, by our own choice. Where we were going, there was no peace. Palestine was wracked by bombings, terror, hangings, battle. And yet we felt whole in our hearts because the decision was our own—to face our fate.

The warship loomed over us, British soldiers leaped on deck, there were curses, blows, there was blood, and then the haze of the tear-gas bombs enveloped us all. In a few hours we were in Cyprus, again in a camp behind barbed wire. Yet we were somehow not depressed. We had taken our chance and made our fight.

And in that camp in Cyprus I made, in a way, our first home. Ari and I managed to secure a tiny hut to ourselves. Within a few days my brother had received word from me, and he began sending me all sorts of things: kitchen utensils, food. Groups of friends would gather in our hut for tea and potato pancakes. And each month, slowly, our names climbed on the list for entry permits.

My baby was coming. Ami was born in the military hospital in Cyprus, at the end of 1947, and when I opened my eyes and saw the nurse who brought him in, I stared at her and laughed. For the nurse was the girl who had worked in the kitchen in Bindermichel —Liza. It had been whispered that she looked Jewish and I had always avoided her out of fear. So she too had lived.

A few months later, our turn came. It was April 1948 when we mounted the British warship *Dolores*, with our permits in our hands. We were even given a cabin for the overnight trip. And, lying in my bunk, I heard a voice I knew, down the corridor. "Ari—" I said.

"Not another Room Eldest!"

I slipped out of the bunk and went into the corridor. At the far end stood a young woman, one of the Palestinian helpers on board. She was small, redheaded. "Rita?" I said.

Rita Mayer, from Hrebenko!


In the morning, we landed. My brother was there, a man, a man with a family!

Ari went at once into the army. We were just in time for the declaration of the state—and the war. There came two years of hardship. I knew my brother was having a real struggle to become established at last as a lawyer, and so I would not let him help me. I took bundles of sewing and worked at home. But my brother insisted to Ari, and at last we accepted a loan, so that I could learn Hebrew and qualify for work in the law courts. I studied at home, copying out whole newspapers to learn the language, and after almost a year I was ready for the test. Everybody helped me in the first few months, and there I was, working in the Ministry of Justice—almost a lawyer, as I had dreamed!

At last Ari came out of the army. He found work as an administrator in a co-operative. We had been living in a provisional shelter; at long last we were ready to find a home.

On the outskirts of Tel Aviv, in Ramat Gan, new apartments were going up. One day we found our flat, on a little street only a few stops from the bus. Three rooms, on the third floor. We borrowed for years ahead, to pay for our furniture. For three entire years we paid for our electric icebox.

And our second boy, Tsvi, was born.

They're full of life, our little boys, real bandits! They've broken the arms off our two easy chairs. Little Tsvi is so active and strong, he can't be confined to a crib; we've had to make him a bed on the floor.

"Cossacks!" my mother would have said.

Now and again in the streets of Tel Aviv I meet a survivor of Hrebenko. It may be Esther, Rita, Alla. And sometimes I meet the partner of my days in Auschwitz, Lola, for she too has come to Israel. Sometimes a number of us have a visit together on a Sabbath, with our husbands and our children.

But I like it best when I just catch a glimpse of one of my friends going about her life, perhaps going into a shop somewhere. And I say to myself, Why, she looks like an everyday housewife living her ordinary life. You'd never imagine what she's been through. And then I find myself thinking, You, too, Eva! That's what you must look like, too! And I feel content.

I do my shopping after work, and as I come to the house my boys often come tumbling down the stairs, calling "Mama!" to me in Hebrew. "*Ima! Ima!*" Sometimes my husband comes from work ahead of me, and as I open the door he speaks my name. "Eva?"

And I answer, "Eva. I'm home."

# About the Author

MEYER LEVIN *is perhaps most famous today for his novel* Compulsion, *based on the Leopold-Loeb case.* Compulsion *was published in 1956 and became one of the great critical and popular successes of the decade.*

*Of Mr. Levin's earlier books, the best known are* The Old Bunch, *published in 1937, a book considered the classic story of American-Jewish life, and* Citizens, *which won wide critical acclaim in 1942.*

*In 1930, he wrote a novel of modern Jewish life in Palestine,* Yehuda, *and after the war he returned to that land to write* My Father's House, *both as a novel and as a film. He has written for many magazines, including* The Saturday Evening Post, Collier's, The Reporter, Commentary *and* The New Yorker, *was an associate editor of* Esquire, *and worked in Hollywood until the war, when he became a war correspondent. He has spent a number of years in Israel and Europe writing and filming the story of the Jewish survivors, and now lives in Israel with his wife (who writes under the name Tereska Torres) and their children.*